Wooden Boatbuilding

Sydney
WOODEN BOAT
School
www:sydneywoodenboatschool.com.au

Ranger class gaff sloop with all ribs steam-bent in, ready to start carvel planking.

Wooden Boatbuilding

The Sydney Wooden Boat School Manuals

Ian Hugh Smith

Sydney
WOODEN BOAT
School

Also by the author:
The Open Boat: The Australian 18-Footer, Origin, Evolution and Construction

This consolidated edition comprises the previous Sydney Wooden Boat School Manuals:
- Traditional Clinker Construction
- WEST System Strip Planking
- Plywood Clinker Construction
- Building the Whiting Skiff

Published by Sydney Wooden Boat School
www.sydneywoodenboatschool.com.au

Copyright Ian Hugh Smith 2019

ISBN: 978-0-6481386-1-7

Design and layout by Tricia Smith

Illustrations and photos not attributed to others are by the author.

All reasonable efforts were taken to obtain permission to use copyright material reproduced in this book,
but in some cases copyright could not be traced. The author welcomes information in this regard.

Printed by Ingram Spark

Cover images
Front, Clockwise from top left:
Sayer 40 before strip-planking, Iain Oughtred strip-planked 11'6" *Egret*, Carvel planked Huon Pine 24' Ranger class, 13'9" Cedar Fisher Skiff (photo Tricia Smith), Cedar and Ash *Pee Wee* snub dinghy.

Back: Top : Atkin flattie.
Middle: Huon Pine *Pee Wee* snub dinghy.
Bottom: David Payne 14' clinker plywood putt-putt launch.

Contents

Introduction

Welcome to the combined edition of the Sydney Wooden Boat School manuals. The manuals evolved out of my years of experience teaching first-timers to build a boat, ranging from adults who were paying to learn, to at-risk kids and unemployed young and not-so-young people who needed to be persuaded. They have been available up to now in individual black and white photocopied spiral-bound editions, but printing technology has evolved considerably since the mid-90's and the images in particular needed updating.

I have a large collection of boatbuilding literature and a common feature is that some of the complex processes are glossed over and the first-timer will really struggle with some aspects. The authors generally know their subject well but have never had to explain it to a raw beginner. I believe my experience at the School developed my ability to explain complex procedures and this shows in the manuals. But you still have to concentrate!

I also published a catalogue of plans called *Designs for Wooden Boats* (our third catalogue 1996, long out of print) which contained the information repeated here on choosing a design and method for your wooden boat. We no longer carry the wide range of designs we dealt with years ago, just a few that are available through our website www.sydneywoodenboatschool.com.au.

I have included a totally new section on Carvel-Planked Construction which complements the older manuals. There is also an article on restoring a clinker launch that was first published in *Australian Amateur Boatbuilder* magazine some years ago, plus some other bits and pieces and a lot more colour photos than appeared in the original manuals. Some of the manuals also appeared in abbreviated form in the same magazine during the 1990's.

There are other boatbuilding methods mentioned that I have not covered including conventional plywood construction, cold-moulding and stitch-and-tape, and things like interior joinery and the fitting of systems, but these are covered well elsewhere by other authors. The manuals concentrated on the woodworking involved in the hulls and decks for three popular methods of hull building. I do not pretend that this volume contains everything that needs to be said about wooden boatbuilding. Batten-seam carvel construction is covered thoroughly in my other book *The Open Boat* as is wooden mast and spar making. The Building a Traditional Clinker Dinghy manual included is centred around the construction of a particular small type of clinker pram dinghy. A volume with a more thorough coverage of traditional clinker construction is currently in preparation.

I have chosen not to republish our fifth manual on Building a Stitch and Glue Dinghy which we called the *Poddy* dinghy, because although a large number were built and it served as a great introduction to simple boatbuilding and working with epoxy, especially in a class situation, there are much better-behaved and more attractive dinghy designs available. I did not hesitate to include the Whiting Skiff manual as that boat proved to be an ideal introduction to boatbuilding as well as being a versatile boat in the water.

There is a degree of repetition in that things like lofting and setting up are covered in each of the manuals, but as each method of building entails some variation in these matters I have left them as they first appeared, and besides, repetition helps learning.

Most measurements are in the metric system to which Australia converted decades ago. However many boaters still think in feet and inches, and most of the plans available for the more traditional boats are in feet and inches, so if you have trouble either way, buy a tape measure with both systems on it.

Tools and methods haven't changed much in the last few decades with the notable exception of laser levels which are now cheap and readily available and make setting up a lot quicker and easier, so some of my setup suggestions are redundant. And chipboard for moulds has almost been replaced by MDF.
Enjoy your project!

Ian Smith, December 2018.

There's something about boats that makes a lot of people want to build one for themselves, and I am not sure what it is. Some people may build their boat because they think it is the cheapest way to get a boat: First myth to explode, it usually isn't the cheapest way to get a boat. A second-hand boat is the cheapest way (though not always as cheap as it first looks as most second-hand boats will need money spent on them from Day 1). Materials of some smaller boats will cost about as much as the full cost of a production fibreglass boat. But for many people the attraction is that they can space out the cost of their boat over the period of construction without going into debt.

Some people want to build a boat because they see it as something feasible that they can do, and they're right! If you think you can, but you're not sure, you can. But if you think you can't, you're probably right. Boatbuilding with any of the modern methods in wood means that anyone that's just a little bit handy can produce a fine job.

But there must be some other reason and my nearest guess is that it is the same reason that drives more and more people to take up general woodwork or any other craft as a hobby, that is, our modern society is organised in such a way that it separates us from using our hands to create something that we can use, or something that we can admire, and boats are the perfect outlet as they can be both useful and beautiful, and the use to which they are put is mostly highly enjoyable. And building from wood means that you are using material that has a natural beauty of its own. But the sense of personal satisfaction and achievement or the quest for it is what I guess most people want to do it for, that feeling of having an empty space and turning it into something of beauty and something that will give you a lot of pleasure in use, of being able to say "I made it!" Try it, its a buzz.

The Three Ians!: Builder Ian Ritchie splashes champagne at the launch of his Iain Oughtred designed Egret while Ian Smith holds the bobstay.

I made it!

Choosing a Design

Whether building or buying a boat, many people make the wrong decision about the kind of boat they want. You need to ask yourself how do you expect to use the boat? Do you want to cross oceans, or cruise just on weekends? Many people select the kind of boat that will cross oceans and sleep six, but spend their boating time day-sailing, or not using the boat at all because it is too much of an effort. Or they have a sailing boat with respectable performance but are found motoring most of the time. Or the boat is selected by Dad to cater for the kind of boating that only he out of the family enjoys, and the boat ends up not being used because no-one wants to go out with him. So ask yourself honestly what kind of boat will fit into your lifestyle.

You might choose a traditional design like our Lyle Hess Seraffyn/ Renegade cutter SERENITY.....

Money

Any boat costs money, and you need to ask yourself what your realistic expenditure can be. If you have no figures from someone else who has built a similar boat, you will need to sit down and work out a detailed list of costings. You can spread the cost over the proposed building period, but you may have to draw up a budget to see if your proposed income covers your proposed expenditure during that period, adding in a percentage for inevitable cost overruns.

Space

You need to have somewhere to build it. At home is probably the most desirable, as you can work on it whenever you please, and it costs nothing. But there can be drawbacks: there is always something else to do at home. At least if you are building away from home you can generally spend productive time while you are there because there are not the same distractions as there are at home. If you are paying rent on a place to build, it can add up to quite a sum of money over the period of construction. But the corollary of this is that because you are paying, you are forced to disciple yourself to working more regularly and the boat will probably be finished earlier.

Skill Level

You should also realistically assess your skill level but this is less of a problem than it used to be as several methods of wooden boat construction have greatly simplified the process, and anyone who is slightly handy should be able to build a boat.

Or a more modern design like Ray Beale's 45-footer.

Time

Time is the most important factor. In this busy modern world many people find their leisure hours have actually decreased recently, and you need to work out how many hours you realistically will be able to bring to bear each week. Divide this into an estimate of the number of hours to complete the job, and you have the number of weeks to completion. Add in a percentage fudge factor because it will inevitably take longer than you think, and you will not always be able to work your quota of hours in many of the weeks, and you have a completion date.

Or a smaller boat like this Chamberlain rowing dory, but make sure you can get it out!

Choose a Method

As you will see on the following pages there is more than one way to build a wooden boat these days. So select a method that is suitable for the type of boat you require, and commensurate with your skill level.

Choose a Reputable Plan

You are going to invest a lot of time and money in your boat, so trying to save money on a plan is a false economy. Do not begrudge the designer their fee, they have put a lot of hours into their design, and none of the ones I know drives a BMW. Copyright laws and moral obligation stipulate that only one boat is to be built from each set of plans. Please do not use second-hand plans, you are stealing from honest toilers.

The Most Common Mistakes

You may be brilliant in your own field, but the world is full of brilliant people who mistakenly believe they know all about boats and racehorses. Do not be tempted to design your boat yourself, as with very few lucky exceptions, such boats turn out to be disasters. If you have the money and time to burn you may see it as an experiment and see the money and time as expendable. Do not be tempted to alter the design by beefing up the specifications or moving bulkheads or major weights around. If you want a heavier or stronger boat, buy a heavier or stronger plan, there are plenty to choose from.

The best idea is to select the boat according to all the above criteria, then purchase plans for a boat one size smaller.

Or perhaps you'd like a motor boat like Geoff Roberts' Hacker runabout.

Choosing a Building Method

There's more than one way to build a wooden boat these days.

Only a few decades ago, working and pleasure boats in countries with a European tradition were either built carvel-planked or clinker-planked, and though there had been a slow evolution, these methods had not changed substantially for hundreds of years, and the basics of both go back thousands of years. Variations did exist, including diagonal planking, used extensively in New Zealand for over one hundred years.

It's all changed since the advent of waterproof glues in the last 70 years. First came plywood, then moulded boats (diagonally planked and glued), then strip planking. All of these methods had their roots even before the development of waterproof glues, but the glues improved them and they would have become far more popular if fibreglass reinforced plastic boats hadn't started their quick rise to market dominance in the 1960's.

Epoxies were just one of the glues available to boatbuilders, and the next revolution came when the Gougeon brothers of Michigan, USA began to publicise the concept of using epoxy's moisture resistance to encapsulate every component of the structure of the vessel with epoxy to seal out moisture. They called their system Wood Epoxy Saturation Technique (W.E.S.T System TM), and though techniques have evolved since the late 1960's, this concept still dominates the field today, as the use of epoxies to encapsulate the wood has influenced all of the methods which use glue.

While there are now many different methods, there are only two main divisions which are of vital importance: the traditional versus the modern. All traditional systems are based on the concept of a group of individual pieces of wood held together with metal fastenings, while all modern systems are based on the concept of a continuously laminated vessel of monocoque construction. There is nothing wrong with either concept when done properly, but when the two methods become mixed, it usually spells trouble. For example, gluing traditional planking together will usually end badly; and puncturing the surface of a laminated boat with metal fastenings will generally allow water in and cause problems.

So there is quite a choice of methods available, but some methods suit particular types of boats more than others, and the table below might help you select the method that most suits you, and the following pages contain more detailed information about each method. The division into seven different categories is not exhaustive: and there are many variations within these categories, and indeed many combinations of these systems can be used on the same vessel.

Traditional clinker rowing boats built in the School.

Using the Table

The ratings are based on my own assessments of the suitability of certain construction methods for particular hull shapes, weight requirements of certain types of boats built in traditional methods are certain to dry out and leak, so any of the modern methods is preferable. There is also I must admit a degree of my own personal preferences involved here.

A is ideal
B is fine but you would have to have a reason for it
C is possible but you'd have to have a bloody good reason
X is not suitable

	Carvel	Clinker	Conventional Plywood	Cold-Moulded	Stitch & Tape	Strip Planking	Ply Clinker
Canoes	X	C	C	B	A	A	A
Dinghies	X	A	C	B	A	A	A
Rowing Skiffs	X	A	C	B	A	A	A
Day Sailers	C	A	B	B	A	A	A
Trailer Sailers	C	C	A	A	A	A	A
Yachts	A	B	A	A	B	A	B
Launches	A	A	A	A	B	A	A
Planing Power Boats	C	B	A	B	A	B	A
Multi-hulls	X	X	C	B	B	A	X

Some boats like the School's Pippy dinghy can be built diagonally planked, ply clinker and strip-planked or even traditionally planked.

Carvel Planking

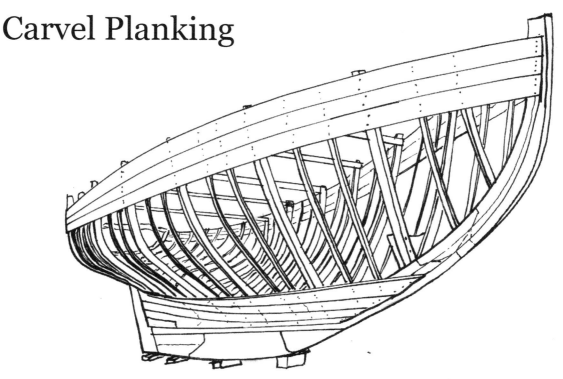

Carvel-planked boats are built by erecting permanent frames or temporary moulds on the keel structure, and if steam-bent frames are to be used they are bent to fit battens or ribbands wrapped around the moulds. The planks are individually shaped to fit and are fastened with copper nails and roves and/or screws to the frames. The planks are fitted with a small V-joint outboard, into which caulking cotton or oakum is hammered and payed or puttied over. Carvel-planked boats are generally built right way up. Variations include batten-seam carvel construction, used where the thickness of the planking is too light to hold caulking cotton (usually ½ inch or 12mm). Each seam has a batten behind it, and each plank is fastened to the batten as well as to the frame.

History

Carvel planking evolved from a Mediterranean tradition with roots back in the Bronze Age. The last big change was when the Industrial Revolution allowed cheaper production of stronger metal fastenings and carvel-planked boats began to get lighter. Except for some classes of fishing vessel, very few carvel-planked vessels have been built since the 1960's. In spite of rumours to the contrary, materials to build carvel-planked boats are still available, and there are still professionals available who can do it, but it is also possible for a determined amateur.

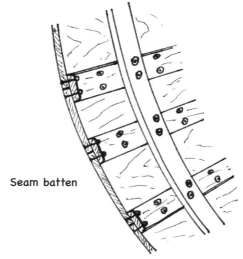

Seam batten

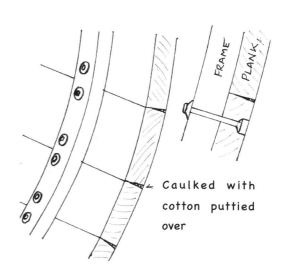

FRAME PLANK

Caulked with cotton puttied over

Sydney's historic racing skiffs like the 10 footer replica Republic were generally batten-seam carvel planked.

Types of Boats

Yachts, fishing and commercial vessels and launches over around 20 feet long were almost exclusively carvel-planked until the 1950's. It is still more suitable for yachts and launches of more traditional style. Because the timber will expand and contract when wet and dry it is most suitable for boats that are moored in the water. Boats that have been designed for more recently developed constructions systems will often not adapt because of the greater weight of carvel construction. Batten-seam carvel boats have been built down to around 6 foot in length. Sydney's racing skiffs from 6-footers to 18-footers and even larger 22 and 24-footers were generally batten-seam Cedar-planked, as were many launches of 16-20 feet.

Advantages

- With such a history it is definitely a proven system.
- When executed properly it is a strong way to build a boat.
- As a carvel-planked boat is a collection of individual pieces of wood held together with metal fastenings, every part is replaceable.
- The work of constructing the vessel is interesting and challenging and this is very important when you consider that if you are not looking forward to the process of building a boat you should not attempt it. Working on a carvel-planked boat also has that intangible feeling of being in touch with tradition: you are using techniques that have been used by thousands of people in the past.

Disadvantages

- The main disadvantage is that it will take longer and cost more than several of the more modern alternative methods that could build the same hull.
- A greater level of skill is necessary than for most more recently developed methods.
- Maintenance is necessary, otherwise the boat will deteriorate. Of course this is true for any boat, including fibreglass ones: it does not take much more effort to keep a new carvel-planked boat looking good than it does a fibreglass one.....the difference is, if allowed to deteriorate the fibreglass boat will come good with less effort and expense than the carvel-planked one.

In short with a carvel-planked boat, you have to want to <u>do it</u>, and you have to want to <u>have it</u>. There are stronger, quicker and cheaper ways to build a boat, but for those who like it, nothing else is as good.

Clinker Planking

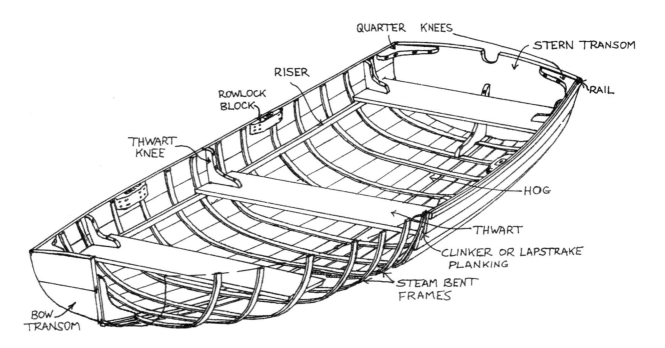

Clinker planks are individually shaped, fitted around temporary moulds and fastened to each other and to a permanent keel, stem and transom, each plank overlapping that previously fitted. Good wood-to-wood fits plus a little bedding compound of some sort are all that keeps the hull watertight. The planks are fastened to each other with copper nails and roves, and steam-bent ribs are added after completion of planking, and are also fastened with copper nails and roves or sometimes sometimes simply copper nails clenched or bent over. All but the smallest dinghies are more often built right way up.

History

Also referred to as lapstrake planking, clinker planking has its origins in a northern European tradition which also goes back to the Bronze Age. The Viking ships for example were clinker planked. Its more recent evolution resulted in lighter boats. The small dinghies we most often associate with clinker planking only really developed with the growth of yachting in the last 170 years.

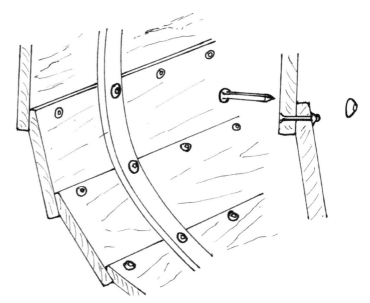

Traditional clinker Robin 10 foot dinghy.

Types of Boats

Clinker construction is suitable for dinghies, rowing skiffs, day sailers and launches and small yachts to around 25 feet, such as the common *Stella* class. Some Scandinavian vessels of 30' plus are still built this way. It is most commonly known in Australia from the large number of clinker putt-putt hire launches that were everywhere on our waterways until recent years (but are now making a comeback).

Advantages
- Clinker planking is light compared to carvel, but lighter systems are now available.
- It is also a well-proven system, and as it is a collection of individual pieces of wood, any part can be replaced.
- It is interesting and challenging woodwork and this is probably the main reason why people choose to build a boat this way today, plus that intangible feeling of the link with tradition.
- It also <u>looks</u> good, the sweep of the overlapping planks and even the structure of the ribs and knees is aesthetically pleasing.

Disadvantages
- It is far more expensive to build small boats this way than any of the more modern methods. For example, you can buy a brand new fibreglass dinghy (though of doubtful quality) for around half of the materials cost of a similar-sized clinker dinghy.
- Traditional clinker construction also requires a higher skill level and will take you longer than any of the modern methods, though not significantly more in small sizes.
- Maintenance is also necessary, and boats left out of the water for long periods will dry out, shrink and leak next time. They will generally take up enough to stop or reduce this leakage, but over many years it will usually worsen. Trailing the boat will greatly increase this problem.

Like carvel planking, with clinker planking you have to want to do it and to have it.

Conventional Plywood Construction

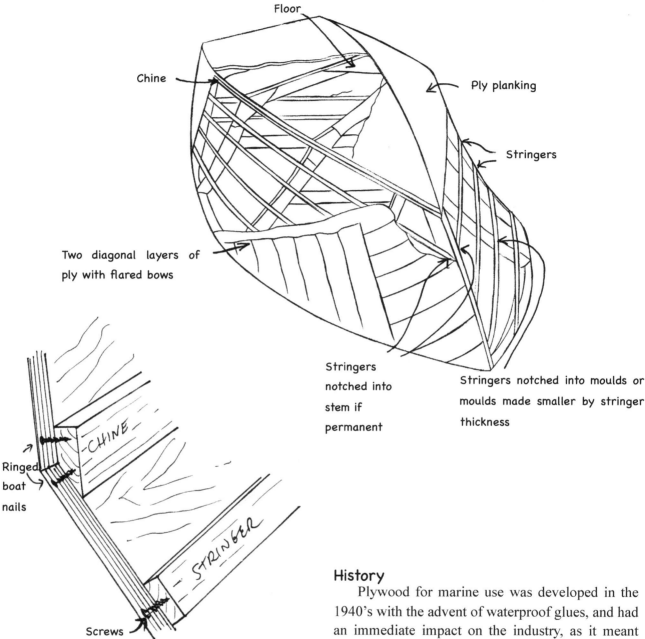

Floor

Chine

Ply planking

Stringers

Two diagonal layers of
ply with flared bows

Stringers
notched into
stem if
permanent

Stringers notched into moulds or
moulds made smaller by stringer
thickness

Ringed
boat
nails

CHINE

STRINGER

Screws

Permanent frames and stringers are set up with a permanent keel, stem and transom, and clad with sheet plywood, generally glued and fastened with nails or screws. In sheet form plywood can only bend one way so the design of the boat must allow for this: the curves of the hull must be either cylindrical or conical. If compound curves occur, they must be planked in multiple layers of thinner plywood in narrow strips. Boats are usually built upside down.

History

Plywood for marine use was developed in the 1940's with the advent of waterproof glues, and had an immediate impact on the industry, as it meant that amateurs could build a boat with lower levels of skill than for traditional carvel and clinker construction. More recent developments have decreased this former dominance of amateur construction, but there are still some types of boats which the method suits. Since the WEST System concept of encapsulating all timber in a laminated boat with epoxy has come come to dominate laminated-boat thinking, plywood has actually raised its profile. For many years it suffered the stigma of susceptibility to rot, which is no longer the case given properly sealed and maintained plywood boats.

Framing for 18 foot Hacker - designed runabout.

Types of Boats

Because of the limited ability of sheet plywood to take compound curves, boats built with conventional plywood construction have to have their hulls built up from flat sections, the simplest of which is a flat bottom and flat sides, or a V-bottom and flat sides (single chine). Multi-chine boats can approximate round-bilged hulls by narrowing each flat panel. Seeing that many planing hulled power boats have flat sections and a single chine as part of their design, these are the most obvious candidates for conventional plywood construction, but any vessels from dinghies to large yachts and cruisers can be built this way. Stitch-and-tape plywood construction (see later under own section) is a simpler way of building many of these same hull types, but there is still a role for conventional construction, especially when combined with diagonal laminations in a boat where the design calls for some compound curve.

Advantages

• Conventional plywood construction is reasonably cheap, quite quick and comparatively easy.

Disadvantages

• It is limited to certain hull types, and hard-chine construction and is generally, although not always, quite unattractive.

• Because plywood hulls were mostly amateur built and were usually suspect in terms of rot, resale value is usually low, though this should change as the market begins to realise that soundly built epoxy-sealed plywood boats need not have the same problems as their forbears.

Cold Moulded or Diagonally Planked Construction

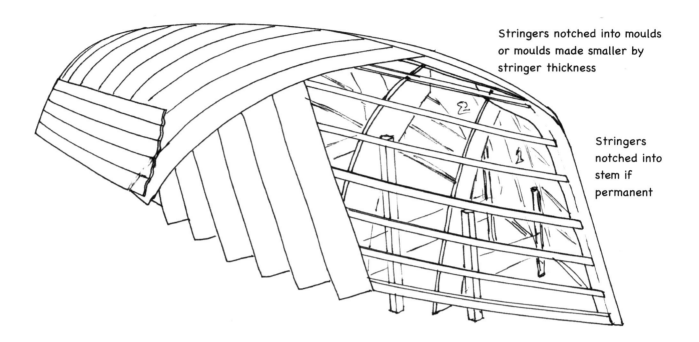

Stringers notched into moulds or moulds made smaller by stringer thickness

Stringers notched into stem if permanent

Two or more layers (most commonly three) of timber veneers or thin plywood are laminated together over permanent or temporary longitudinal stringers. Each layer is usually diagonally laid, though often the outer layer is laid fore and aft especially if the surface is to be varnished. The planks are held together with staples or temporary screws until the glue sets. Boats are built upside down.

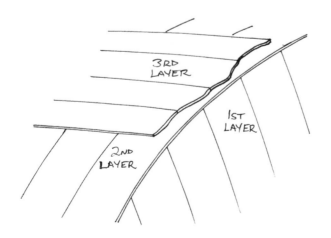

History

Diagonal planking was used long before the advent of waterproof glues, and was especially popular in New Zealand more than a century ago with extensive use in the famous yachts of the yards of the Logan and Bailey families. Three layers of planking (two diagonal, one fore and aft) were copper fastened to each other, with calico in white lead or shellac as a bedding compound between layers. Elsewhere in the world, the method only became popular with the development of waterproof glues in the 1940's. The first glues would only cure under applied heat and were called hot-moulded boats. It was only when glues that set at room temperature were developed within just a few years that the term cold-moulding began to be used, and is therefore really a relict feature, and we prefer to simply refer to it as diagonal planking. Its inherent strength enabled boats to be built lighter at a time when competitive sailors were calling for this, and it would have had far more impact if fibreglass boats hadn't come on the scene.

Roger Deerness' Wright 10 metre cold-moulded in Kauri.

Types of Boats

Just about every type of hull has been built with diagonal planking, from the smallest dinghies to large (over 100 foot) yachts. It particularly suits rounded hull types with easy curves. Tight radius curves can be difficult. Its use as a method has declined for most types of boats, particularly in Australia and New Zealand because the same hull can be better, quicker and cheaper built with epoxy strip planking. It is still dominant in very large (over 60 foot) wooden yacht construction, particularly with a variation that starts off by strip-planking the hull and laying 2 or more diagonal layers over that, as pioneered by the Gougeon brothers.

Advantages

- For its weight it has immense strength, so lighter boats can be built than with traditional methods, or heavy boats can be built stronger.
- If the outer layer is not sheathed, it can be finished bright (varnished) if desired even on quite large vessels.
- Skill level needed is less than for traditional construction.

Disadvantages

- Diagonal planking is slow and expensive.
- Fitting the stringers alone takes almost as long as it takes to plank up a strip-planked hull, and you still have three or more layers to go.

Epoxy Strip Planking

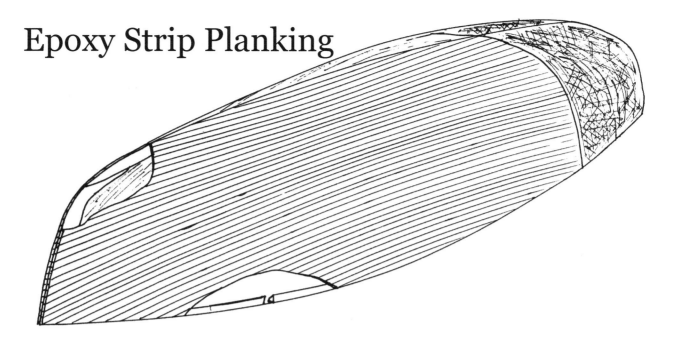

Thin strips of wood are edge-glued to each other over temporary moulds, then sheathed with glass cloth in epoxy resin, then turned over, cleaned up and sheathed inside also. This results in a sandwich construction that has immense strength and stiffness for its weight. The core timber can be solid timber such as Western Red Cedar or a manufactured product such as Durakore, which is end-grain balsa sandwiched between veneers and cut into strips which are joined end-to-end to make up planks which are then fitted to the moulds just like solid timber planks. Durakore allows the construction of extremely lightweight vessels. The boats are always built upside down.

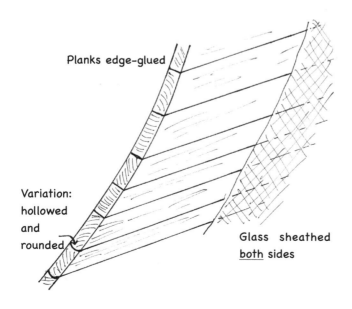

Planks edge-glued

Variation: hollowed and rounded

Glass sheathed both sides

History

Strip planking was used earlier this century even before the invention of waterproof glues, but the planks were nailed both to frames and the rest of a backbone similar to a carvel-planked hull, and a variety of bedding compounds were used to keep the water out. Each plank had to be bevelled to fit against the previous one, and the whole process was extremely slow. The same system remained essentially unchanged even when waterproof glues came into use. Small canoes were built with narrow edge-glued strips in the USA from the 1960's, sheathed both sides with fibreglass cloth in polyester resin, and therefore needing no internal framing, but the Yanks never made the connection to using the system with larger craft. In the late 1970's Arnie Duckworth of ATL Composites, the WEST System agents in Australia and New Zealand began building larger boats this way using WEST epoxy resins for both gluing and sheathing and within a few years the method came to dominate one-off wooden boat construction in this part of the world. Arnie's invention of Durakore in the early 1980's meant that ultra-lightweight boats could be built that rivalled those built from foam cores, but much cheaper for one-off construction.

First planks on racing yacht designed by John Sayer.

Types of Boat

Any type of hull of any shape can be built using epoxy strip planking. There are ways around even the most difficult of hull shapes. Dinghies and canoes, yachts, launches and powerboats, ultra-light racers and heavy displacement traditional designs can all be built. Boats with large flat panels can more easily be planked with sheet plywood, but any one-off round-bilged hull can be built quicker strip-planked than with any other method.

Advantages

- As above, its main advantage is its versatility - any type of hull can be built.
- The other main advantage is its speed. It is a faster method than any of the other except perhaps for some simple stitch-and-tape and some conventional plywood designs.
- A relatively low skill level is needed.
- And compared with many slab-sided designs which were promoted with amateur builders, the round-bilged designs which can be produced easily with strip planking are attractive.

Disadvantages

- It is a reasonably expensive method compared with designs for plywood, particularly the smaller the boat. In larger boats at least, the difference may be offset by higher resale value.

Salvo Class yacht planked up.

21

Stitch and Tape

Plywood panels are cut to pre-determined shapes and stitched together, usually with wire ties or plastic cable ties spaced as necessary, and the joints filled with thickened epoxy glue. Both sides are smoothed and taped with fibreglass tape in epoxy resin. The pre-determined panel shapes and careful setting up result in the hull shape coming together vey quickly.

History

The method was first used in the 1950's with polyester resin and glass tape for a number of small classes of boat including the *Mirror* dinghy. The greater strength and ease of use of epoxy resins meant that they took over in the 1970's.

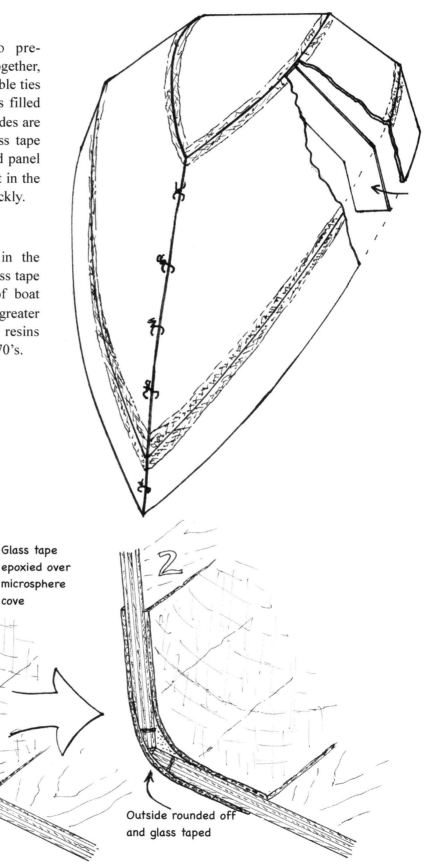

1

Glass tape epoxied over microsphere cove

Epoxy and Microfibres

Wire ties spaced as necessary

Epoxy and microspheres cove on inside

2

Outside rounded off and glass taped

David Payne-designed Kayak.

Types of Boats

There is a wide variety of designs available for stitch-and-tape construction for canoes, kayaks, dinghies, day sailers, trailer sailers, multihulls, launches, power boats and small yachts. U.S designer Sam Devlin has designs for even large motor yachts. The plans must already be drawn up for this method.

Advantages

- Stitch-and-tape is the quickest method to put a simple hull together, is probably the cheapest method, and requires the least skill.
- But this is not to say the builder can be sloppy. It is very easy to get a very ugly boat if care is not taken when aligning the panels to ensure all curves are fair without humps and hollows and that both sides of the boat are symmetrical.

Disadvantages

- You are limited to certain hull shapes, namely those with chines and flat panel sections. Many of the designs available are downright ugly but this is not always the case. The boats will usually have a low resale value.

Murray Isles-designed Nesting dinghy.

Plywood Clinker Construction

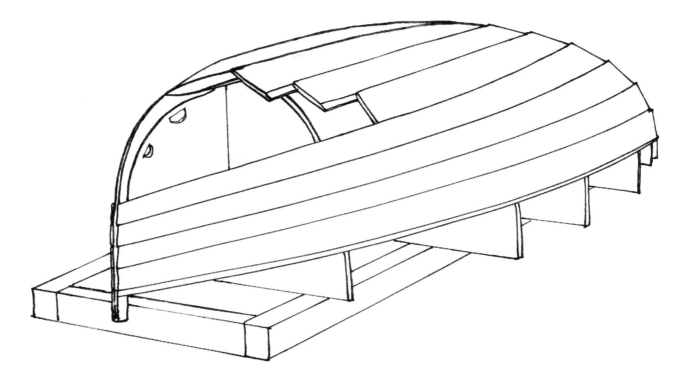

Like traditional clinker construction, plywood clinker has individually shaped planks fitted over temporary moulds, but in this case the planks are cut from sheet plywood and are epoxy-glued to each other along the laps. The hull needs very little internal framing, perhaps just in stressed areas such as supporting the rig or the engine beds.

History

Plywood clinker construction as outlined here is the most recent development of all the methods mentioned here. Plywood was used for some clinker boats from its inception, but they were generally still ribbed and roved traditionally. Some designers and builders left out the frames in the 1960's but ran permanent stringers along the laps. It was only in the 1980's that designer Iain Oughtred showed that the glued laps were self-supporting and the boats needed very little internal framing, and the method began to grow in popularity.

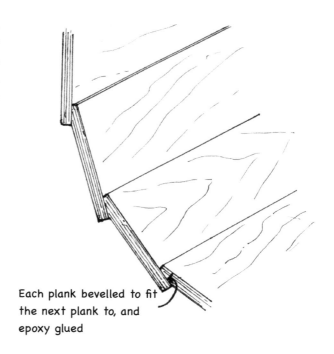

Each plank bevelled to fit the next plank to, and epoxy glued

Types of Boats

Any hull shape and type of boat that was built in traditional clinker construction suits the new method. These range from dinghies and canoes to launches, power boats and small yachts. It particularly suits boats that were once built traditionally, where the style of boat still demands clinker planks but need to be built stronger and more leakproof. For example, the clinker speedboats built in Australia in the 1950's and 60's were built traditionally, but increasing engine sizes and loads caused problems for the traditional hulls, problems that now disappear with a properly engineered ply clinker hull with laminated support where it is needed.

Advantages

- The main advantage is that you can get the attractive looks of a clinker plank lineout with none of the traditional disadvantages, that is, the hull is a glued structure and should never leak, and by sealing out the water, the hull can never dry out and shrink, and the hull will be stronger for a given weight, or lighter for equivalent weight. This fact means that the method is particularly suitable for boats that will be trailed or car-topped, either of which is hard on a traditionally planked boat.
- The method is easier for several reasons: the traditional rabbet along the keel and stem is no longer necessary, it is far simpler and quicker to run the planks past the keel and stem, cut them off after the glue cures, plane a flat landing and glue on an outer keel and stem cap. Light-tight fits are also not as important to keep the water out, as epoxy will fill the gaps with no compromise with strength. And without much internal framing the hull surface inside is clearer and easier to keep clean and to sand and repaint when necessary.
- Ply clinker is also cheaper in a small boat than either traditional or strip-planked construction.

Disadvantages

- Ply clinker is slower and involves slightly more woodworking skill than strip planking, but not by much, and I cannot think of any other disadvantage.

Iain Oughtred's Robin design shows clean interior of ply clinker boats.

Clinker ply ski boat designed by David Payne.

Mistakes to Avoid - worth repeating!

➡ Don't alter the plans! Don't design your own boat unless you are quite happy to throw away your money. Don't beef up the specifications! If you want a beefier boat, select a beefier plan. I could fill a book with sad stories from the waterfront, but here are two short illustrations:

A first-time builder wanted a trimaran to go off cruising, but felt that he needed to use thicker plywood in case he hit the Barrier Reef. In the rush to launch he hadn't got around to sealing the holes around where the large tangs that anchored the stays to the amas (floats) emerged from the main hull about 200mm above the waterline. Unfortunately the additional weight he had built into the boat meant that his new waterline was 300mm above the old and in front of the celebratory crowd his life's dream began to sink. Modifications recommended by the original designer to add more flotation were not successful and the builder sold the boat for a tenth of the material costs.

Another guy whose success in business led him to feel that this meant he knew everything about boats designed his own racing yacht which behaved so badly downwind that he terrified the crew so nobody would sail with him and he could neither race it or sell it. If you persist in ignoring these rules you are a fool.

➡ Don't mix old and new methods of building. A traditional boat is a bunch of wooden parts held together by metal fastenings. A modern laminated boat is a monocoque construction of wood from which all water must be sealed out. A traditional boat with planks glued to frames and to each other will generally cause later problems, as will a laminated boat which allows water penetration through metal fastenings.

➡ Don't try to display too many varieties of wood on exteriors and interiors. This is, I admit, largely down to my personal tastes. We all love timber, but to show off 16 varieties of rare timbers in your boat is a sign of the recent convert. Even the finest yacht interiors were limited in the number of timbers used. There is a similar mistake in trying to dress up a simple workboat with things like laid decks and varnished cover boards etc that they never would have had. There is enough charm in simple functional beauty.

Safety in the Workshop

Working on wooden boats means you will be regularly coming into contact with sharp tools and nasty chemicals. I strongly advise you to take all necessary precautions to protect yourself from problems arising from these.

The chemicals thing is fairly easy....follow the manufacturer's recommendations. This will almost certainly involve gloves and mostly masks of some sort.

Sharp tools and machinery are another matter. The secret of staying safe is to have a good imagination. If you know what could go wrong and think of the consequences of that, you can take steps to avoid it. For example, when you are cutting a piece of wood on a bandsaw, think about what could go wrong....for a start, your hands could go into the blade! But how could this happen? Well, the wood could split, and because you were leaning your weight into it, you fall forward. The answer is to make sure that if you do fall forward your hands are nowhere near in line with the blade, so they will safely pass each side of the blade. And even better, if you think you might fall forward, push with one leg behind and balance with another foot well in front which can catch you if you fall forward.

Even with hand tools the same rule applies. Don't hold a piece of work in your left hand in a manner that will be in the road if the chisel in your right hand slips.

Get the picture? Suss out what could go wrong, even with hand tools and work out the safe way to do it.

Mind you, more people have been injured by ladders in boatyards than by tools or machinery.

The Sydney Wooden Boat School Manuals

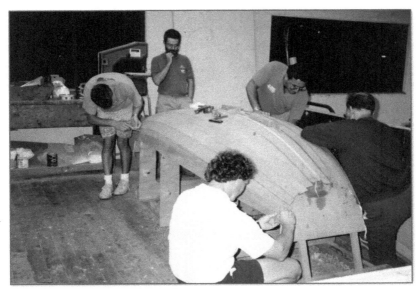

A School class builds one of the first traditional clinker Petrels.

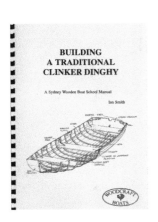

Building a Traditional Clinker Dinghy

This manual was developed over years of teaching traditional clinker construction to people who mostly had no experience of boatbuilding at all, and focuses on two similar dinghies whose features have been proven to be effective in conveying the concepts of traditional clinker construction to first-timers. It is not meant to be a complete guide to everything involved in clinker boatbuilding, but a guide to building a type of small boat that is an excellent introduction to the subject.

The methods used and the sequence of events in some procedures have been developed with this in mind, and in several instances differ from the way things were done around Sydney in years gone by. This is especially true of the sequence of events when planking. The way I have explained it here is the way I have found to be most effective for showing first-timers how to cut accurate jerralds or matching rebates in the ends of planks. Every sequence we tried resulted in expensive planks being ruined until I hit on this sequence which when followed with care enables first-timers to cut accurate jerralds from the first plank.

The fact that these boats are built from plans is the major difference from the traditional method. Clinker dinghies around Sydney were generally built right way up over a midships mould only, plus the stem knee and transom, and usually a forward mould which did not exactly represent the shape of the boat but was used to tom off, or shore out the forward planking to the desired shape. The shape of the boat in between these widely-spaced guides was a matter for the experience and skill of the builder. Building from detailed plans is the only way that most people in this day and age will ever get to build a traditional clinker dinghy.

I trust the manual will make interesting reading even if you do not build a boat yourself, but reading it alone will not teach you how to do it, you have to get out there and get your hands dirty doing it before you can say that you know how. Try it, I can think of almost nothing else I'd rather be doing.

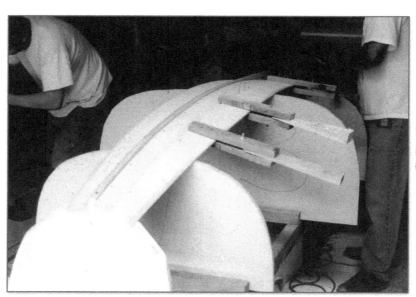

Early stages of planking on a Huon Pine Pee Wee.

Building a Traditional Clinker Dinghy

Not too many years ago most dinghies and skiffs were built in a similar fashion to what I'll describe here, and had been built this way for may hundred of years (at least back to the Vikings). Plywood and fibreglass changed all this. Now anyone who wants a purely utilitarian dinghy can get a fibreglass and polyester resin boat popped out of a mould for a few hundred dollars.

No-one in their right mind would want a traditional labour-intensive clinker-planked wooden dinghy. Or would they? A small number of people are prepared to pay high prices for a well-crafted boat built for them by professionals, but a larger number are interested in building one for themselves, thus keeping the cost down and involving them in an activity that is itself a satisfying and rewarding experience.

This manual takes you step-by-step through the construction of a small snub-nosed or pram dinghy (a pram dinghy has a blunt squared-off bow; a stem dinghy has a pointed bow). The illustrations and photos are of two similar dinghies that we generally used as the focus for our course on Traditional Clinker Construction at the Sydney Wooden Boat School. *Petrel* (2.3m, 7'6") was designed by Nigel Shannon to provided an introduction to the art of clinker construction while resulting in a dinghy which is extremely attractive and well-behaved on the water.

Petrel, 7'6" (2.3m) snub dinghy designed by Nigel Shannon, built at the Sydney Wooden Boat School 1991. Huon Pine planking on Silver Ash frames, Queensland Maple thwarts, White Beech floorboards.

Pee Wee (2.1m; 6'11") was designed by myself originally as a tender to a small yawl I once built. Either dinghy makes an ideal yacht tender or small fishing boat. They both row well, and can take a small (2hp) outboard motor, or could be rigged for sailing. We chose a pram design because stem dinghies generally involve several more difficult procedures, including a severe twist to some planks. But both boats are an excellent introduction to the craft of clinker boat-building.

To build either boat will require the full large scale plan available through the Sydney Wooden Boat School website. This manual contains enough information for a first-timer to build from the plans. Or the information herein can also be used with minor variations to build dinghies to other plans.

As I said, it's a labour-intensive operation. A first-timer can expect to spend no less than 100-120 hours on this dinghy, but they'll be enjoyable hours.

Pee-Wee, 6'11" snub dinghy designed by Ian Smith, built by Eoin Carragher 1993. White Beech planking on Silver Ash frames, Mahogany thwarts.

Construction Plan
Pee-Wee

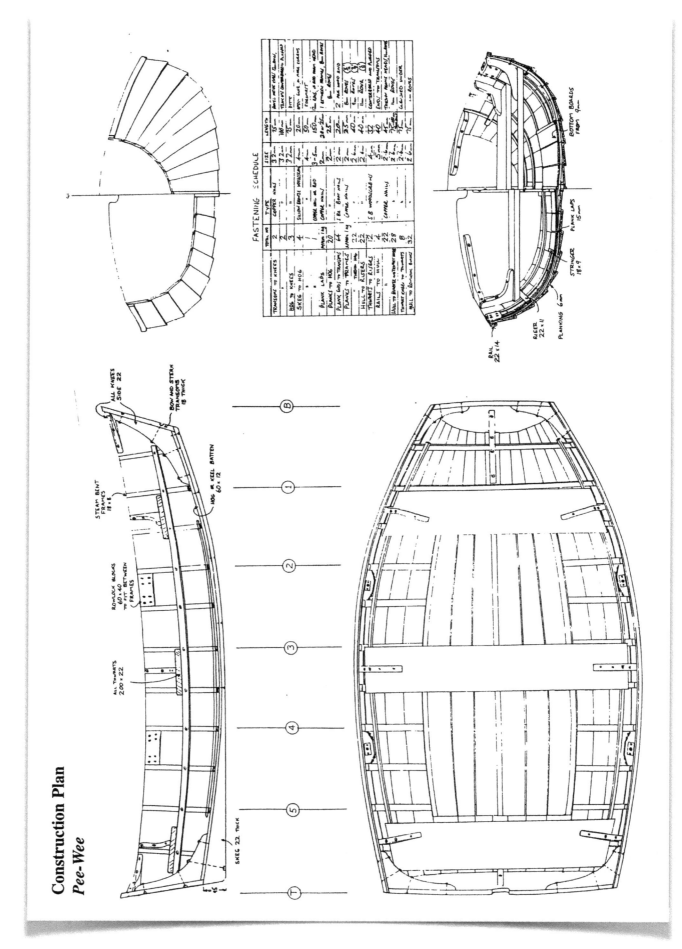

Materials

Around Sydney, traditional dinghies were generally planked with Australian Red Cedar with frames and backbone of Silver Ash. Silver Ash is commonly chosen for frames because it steam bends easily yet its relatively strong and resilient. Most other Australian bending timbers such as Spotted Gum are heavier but Spotted Gum was also commonly used in dinghies and was the general rule for larger craft.

Other planking timbers are Huon Pine, Hoop Pine, White Beech, King William Pine and Queensland Maple. Amongst imported timbers, Mahogany, Kauri, Brazil Cedar and Kalantas and Surian have been used. Many clinker putt-putts in hire fleets around the coast were planked in Meranti/Pacific Maple.

In the School for the first few courses we planked with marine plywood, mostly for economy (we saved on initial cost and machining time) and you could certainly do the same, but you may well prefer the greater cost of fine timber for the increased pleasure of working with it. We have also used Surian Cedar, White Beech and Huon Pine for planking.

The thwarts or seats can be Huon Pine, Silver Ash, Silky Oak, Queensland Maple or Mahogany or Kauri. The knees which reinforce the corners of the transom to the hog and keel were traditionally cut from Melaleuca (Tea-tree) crooks where the grain curved to follow the angle necessary. In this dinghy where the angles are relatively obtuse, straight grained timber will suffice, from the same list of timber species as for the thwarts.

Fastenings

This dinghy is fastened with different sizes of square cut copper boat nails riveted over cupped copper washers called roves which are still available from traditional boat suppliers.

Tools and Equipment

A basic woodworking kit will suffice for most parts of construction but among the hand tools you will need will be a block plane, and at least one rabbet plane. A rabbet plane like the Stanley No. 78 with adjustable fence is very handy along with a small shoulder plane such as the Stanley No. 93. If you have to choose between the two, go for the shoulder type, it can handle all the necessary work. A spokeshave or two will enable you to clean saw marks from curves on knees etc. but a power drum sander would be quicker. A sliding bevel is a necessity, as is a set of long series drills.

A bandsaw would be nice, but a jigsaw will do. A power drill is the only necessary power tool (although they did quite well without them for may hundreds of years), but a belt sander would speed up operations.

Several necessary tools are not generally commercially available. For fastening the copper nails and roves used, you will need a rove punch and a bucking iron or dolly (see Fig 1). These can be made up from bright steel or even mild steel on a metal-working lathe. Unless you have three hands or an apprentice, you will need a knee dolly for riveting alone. I have successfully used several different types of panel-beaters' dollies for this purpose.

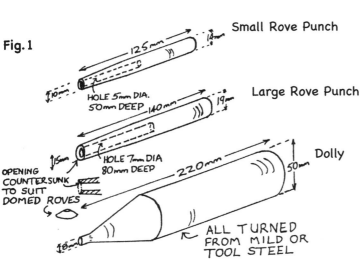

Fig. 1

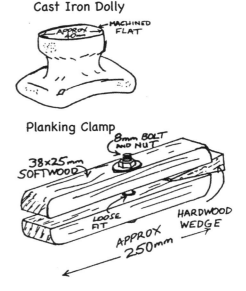

Fig. 2 Drawing Perpendiculars

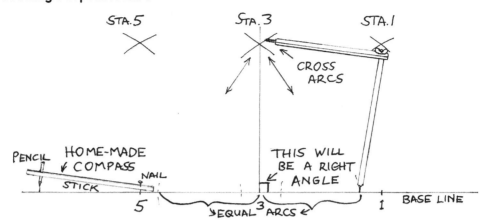

Roving will also require a pair of end cutters, preferably double-action, and the smallest size ball pein hammer.

You will also need to make up several planking clamps from scrap timber, and some sort of set-up for steaming timbers, which can be as simple as a section of 100mm downpipe (we will go into this in depth later).

Lofting

The plans for these two boats come with full-size patterns for the mould shapes, so lofting is not necessary, but I will briefly describe lofting in case you have plans which have no patterns, and because an understanding of lofting will help anyway. Full-size patterns are in fact tracings of someone's lofting anyway. Any boatbuilding project without full-size patterns must start with lofting, which is drawing the plans out full-size to determine the shape of the moulds or forms over which you will build the boat. Lofting checks the

designer's accuracy, at the small scale to which he or she works, the thickness of a pencil line may represent 5 or 6mm at true size.

On a sheet of plywood or chipboard painted flat white, draw out the grid as measured off the plans. Use a stretched string line and straight edge to mark the straight lines and school geometry as in **Fig. 2** to draw to the perpendiculars.

The sheer line is the first bit of boat to draw. The offset table is a list of distances you use to locate the boat lines on the grid as in **Fig. 3.** Connect the marked points with a batten bent around the nails, and view it from all angles to see if the line is fair, that is, without bumps or flat spots. Adjust the nail positions until it looks fair, then ink it in. Do the same for the bottom of the boat in the side view.

To save the room, the three views of the boat are drawn super-imposed, so that the base line becomes the centreline for the plan view, and Station 3 becomes the centreline for the end

Fig. 3 Using the Offset Table

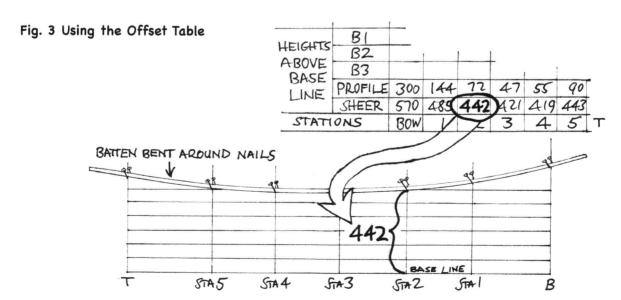

Fig. 4 Establishing the Body Plan

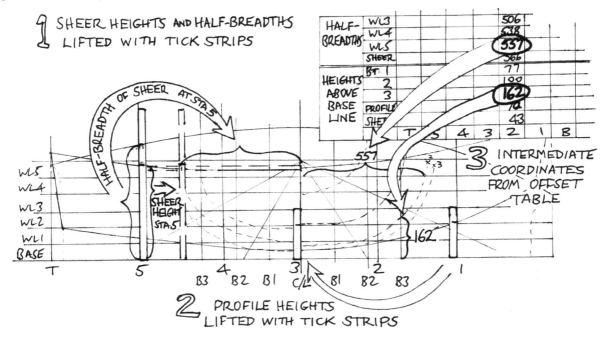

elevation, referred to as the body plan. The whole point of lofting is to get the lines in the body plan accurate so that the temporary frames or moulds can be cut to these shapes, so that when the planks are bent over the moulds they will lie fairly, without bumps or flat spots.

Draw in the plan view of the sheer with nails and batten, then establish the position of the sheer in the body plan and the bottom at the centreline directly from the three lines you have already drawn in, and mark the other points for each station from the offset table as in **Fig. 4.** Join the dots with nails and batten, and expect to find errors. Average out these errors, drawing in a line of best fit.

Fairing the Lines

You could make your moulds from these shapes, but if you did, you could expect to find bumps and hollows when planking. You need to fair the lines longitudinally, that is, you ignore the offset table and plot the lines out from your pencilled lines in the body plan as in **Fig. 5.** Fair the diagonals first, then the waterlines in the topsides (WL3-5) and the buttocks in the bottom (Buttocks 1 & 2). Transfer any errors (unfairness) back to the body plan as you go, and when diagonals, waterlines and buttocks are drawn, redraw the station lines in the body plan to take in all the corrections. If there are still errors of greater than 2mm, draw in new lines of best fit and refair these. Keep going until everything agrees.

Fig. 5 Fairing Waterline 3

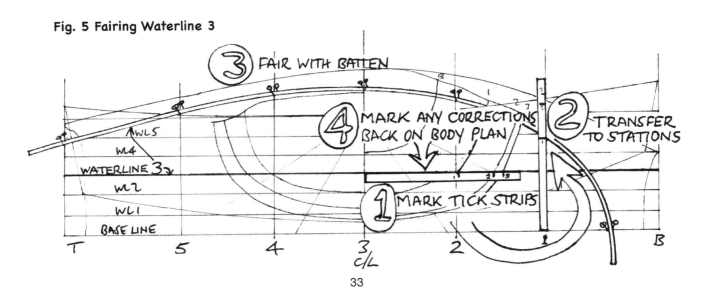

Planking Thickness Deduction

The lines you now have are drawn to the outside of the planking. To get the line to the inside, simply draw a line 6mm inside Station lines 1, 3 and 5, and both transoms. It is not necessary to fit Station 2 and 4, though if you are willing to do the extra work it might make some aspects of planking easier.

True Shape of the Transom

The transom outlines on the lofting are not true shapes because they both slope, so their true shape must be found by squaring out from the intersection of each waterline with the transom slope line and transferring the waterline half-breadths as in **Fig. 6**.

Fig. 6 Finding the True Shape of the Transom

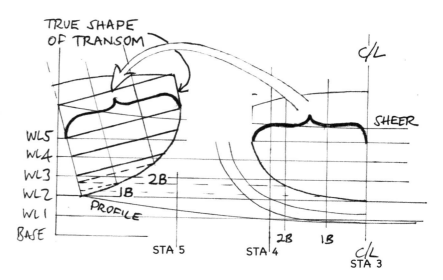

Construction Plan

The last thing to do before making the moulds is to draw in the construction plan to show any timber parts that we need to shape. On this boat, we need only draw the hog, the skeg, the thickness of the transoms and the knees at bow and stern. Some clinker boats have much more complicated backbone structures and these must all be drawn, including the position of all backbone fastenings.

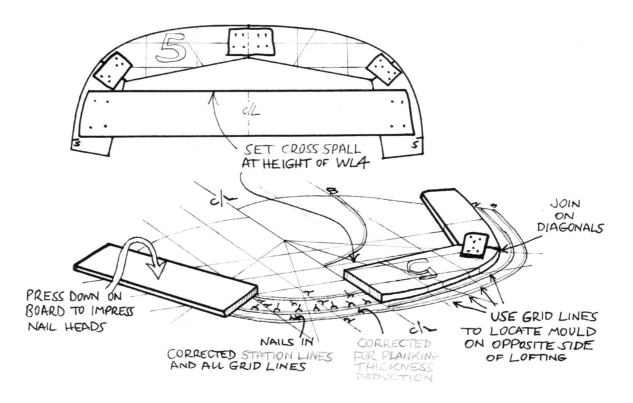

Fig. 7 Marking Out and Assembling Moulds

34

Finally we're ready to cut timber. Moulds can be made from chipboard, low-grade plywood or cheap Radiata Pine boards. The shapes can be obtained either by tracing and marking through onto the mould stock, or by placing rows of flat-headed nails on their sides with heads pressed into the lines, pressing the boards onto them (see **Fig. 7**). Join up the nail-head impressions and cut with jigsaw or bandsaw. Cut square, and trim fair and square with plane and spokeshave. Make sure you trace or nail-impress the lines of the grid for each mould, as each is only half-drawn, you need to repeat the procedure for the second side, and the grid lines are necessary to locate the side opposite the drawn section line for assembling the moulds. You need to choose and mark at least one of the horizontal lines as a means of lining up the heights of the moulds when setting them up. You can either draw in an arbitrary floor line beyond the sheer line at a height which will enable the moulds to stand on the floor while having the boat at a good working height as we did or you can choose to set the moulds on a low bench or jig, and line them up either with a base line of arbitrary height, or by setting the horizontal cross-spalls on each mould at a height of say, waterline 4 and lining these up level both ways. Make sure you mark the height of the sheer on each mould.

The transoms and their attached knees are the first parts of the actual boat you will cut. Edge-join 18-20mm thick boards with splines (loose 4mm plywood tongues) with epoxy glue. Remember that the true shape of the transom as drawn, less the planking

thickness, is still the line of the outside of each transom. Because of the angle of arrival of the planking, the inner face of each transom is larger. It is possible to plot the true shape of the inside face (we have done it for the full-size patterns) but unless you thoroughly enjoy lofting, the process can be laborious and frustrating. I would advise leaving the transoms 25mm bigger all round, and as each plank is fitted, remove the excess at the correct receiving angle until the plank sits on the line.

The knees can be grown tea-tree, or laminated, or simply cut from straight stock with the grain running as a hypotenuse to the triangle to avoid weak short grain. Round over or chamfer the non-joining edges and sand before fitting. They are fastened to the transoms with two 3mm square-cut copper nails (see **Fig. 8**), making sure they are square to the transom, and are bedded on white lead, old thick varnish, or a soaking coat of 50/50 linseed oil and turps or a product such as Watsonia Decking Oil. A modern flexible bedding compound such as polyurethane like Sikaflex is also acceptable.

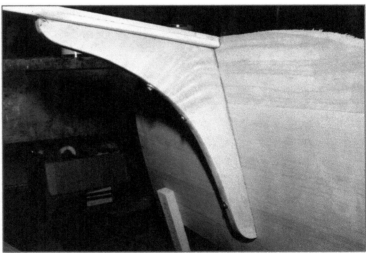

Tea-tree stern knee connects hog and transom.

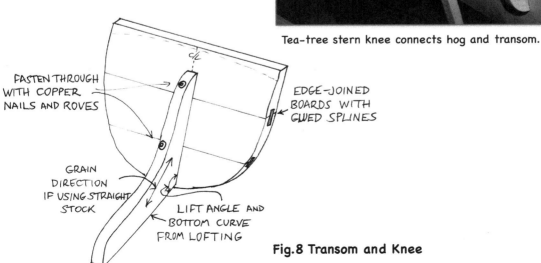

Fig.8 Transom and Knee

Marking From Full Size Patterns

Of course if you're building this particular boat, there are full size patterns and full lofting will be unnecessary. The patterns are drawn as half-hull shapes on drafting paper. It is a simple matter to lay the paper on plywood or chipboard and prick through the lines with a nail or awl, then join up the dots with nails and batten. Transfer all grid lines also, including the centrelines, and simply flip the sheet over, align the centrelines, and mark back through the same holes to establish the other side. Cut out with a jigsaw and plane to the line. You do this for Stations 1,3,5, both transoms, and the transom knees at both ends.

Patterns from lofting or full-size paper patterns are used to mark out the knees.

Setting Up

You now have a larger pile of pieces on the floor. On a strongback of say two 100 x 50's of Oregon, either fixed to the floor or with legs depending on how you laid out the moulds, fit cross-pieces of at least 50 x 50 checking that they are square to the strong back, in positions such that moulds 1 and 3 are aft of the line representing the station, and mould 5 is forward of the line (see **Fig 9**). Fix the moulds to the cross-pieces with nails or screws and brace them so they are vertical. Erect mould 3 first, then 1 and 5, checking that the waterlines marked on them are level athwartships (across the boat) and with respect to the other moulds. Double-check everything. Fit angled

bracing taken from the lofting, and at the correct height and correct distance from the nearest station, remembering that the inside of the transom will be against these supports.

Put adequate bracing to keep the whole set-up rigid, it will have a hard life. Before fitting the transoms, it is best to laminate the hog, the 60 x 14mm centreline piece of the boat. As you see in the photo, it has quite a curve to it in a small pram dinghy like this. Traditionally it would have been steamed to shape from 14mm stock, but in the School we liked to expose the students to more than one boatbuilding method, and seeing they'll get all the steaming they like when the frames go in, we've always glued this piece up with epoxy from two 7mm laminations. Always cut stock for laminations slightly overwidth to allow for misalignment of the parts, and glue to a clean sawn surface if your saw is good enough, or scour a

Fig. 9 Alternate Mould Set-Ups

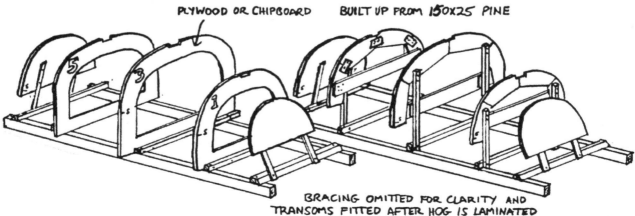

PLYWOOD OR CHIPBOARD   BUILT UP FROM 150x25 PINE

BRACING OMITTED FOR CLARITY AND
TRANSOMS FITTED AFTER HOG IS LAMINATED

planed surface with rough sandpaper to improve the penetration of the epoxy. You can use either the gel-type epoxies or the liquid type with microfibres or powder added.

All are two-pot, with resin and hardener added to different ratios according to brands. Apply to both mating surfaces and fit to the jig. Use lots of clamps and cleanup as much squeezed-out glue as possible with a metal putty knife (not fingers and not a rag).

You could fit the transoms with their knees and laminate the hog over these. It would be necessary to cut the hog laminations to length first (before applying the glue) and to protect the knees and transoms from glue seepage with plastic sheeting or tape. We have generally found it easier to laminate the hog overlength to a temporary board clamped at transom height and cut it to length when dry, usually at least overnight, longer in winter. Use lots of clamps, but don't squeeze them up too tight, epoxies work by leaving some glue within the joint and too much local pressure can result in glue-starved joints.

The hog is laminated across the moulds. See text regarding fitting of the transoms.

When dry, cleanup the glue dags and plane the sides. Round over or chamfer those edges which will be visible inside the boat and sand the whole thing. Fit the bow end first and then the stern, not finally fixing the stern transom on its holding supports until you're happy that the fit of this hog is good. Use the marked waterlines and centreline to locate the transom accurately. Some builders let the hog in to the transoms, but we simply butt it up. The hog is fastened to the knees with long copper nails, rivetted over roves on the knee. One of the stern fastenings should be left out until the skeg is fitted so that the fastening (probably a 3 or 4mm

Fig. 10 Scribing and Fitting the Skeg

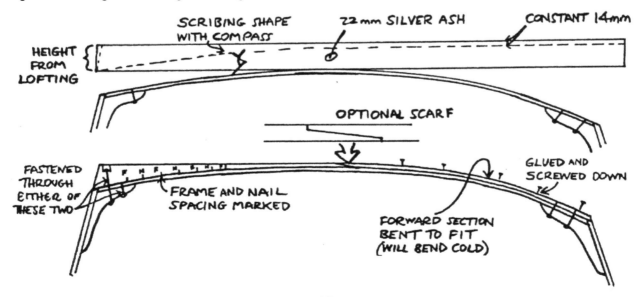

copper rod with a peened-over head if a long enough nail cannot be found) can support the skeg as well as tie the skeg, hog and knee together. The skeg and keel strip can either be cut from one piece, or scarfed in the centre as in **Fig. 10**. The forward section can be bent cold, the after section scribed as illustrated and cut to fit. A solid, close, square fit is needed. To assist in strengthening this important area, and to reduce the number of fastenings needed, we generally epoxy glue it down. If not glued it should be bedded in white lead or black jack or possibly one of the modern polyurethanes or polysulphides. Cleanup the wet glue well, it is much more difficult to remove when dry, and it is very hard on plane blades.

Bow Transom fitted.

The skeg is glued down to the hog.

Roving Copper Nails

A roved nail is in effect a rivet, and is a very strong form of fastening, much stronger than screws in comparable sizes. All of the knees in these dinghies are fastened with large copper nails and roves, and the plank laps are fastened with smaller gauge nails and roves, as are the ribs to the planks. The hole for a square-cut copper nail should always be drilled, generally at the same size as the distance across the flats on the square nail. This allows the corners of the nail to dig in to the wood fibres and prevent the nail from turning. Occasionally, like through thick dense hardwood, you should drill the hole out one drill size bigger in order to make it possible to drive the nail, and to help prevent splitting. This is especially the case with tea-tree knees.

The nail should be driven through the hole with a dolly held just alongside where the nail will emerge on the other side. The dolly should then be held over the head of the nail while a rove is forced down over the point and onto the timber surface with a rove punch hit with a hammer. The part of the nail protruding is now cut off close to the rove, in fact as close to the rove as the jaws on the cutters will let it. Peen over the nail by hitting it dead centre with multiple light blows the ball of a small pein hammer. When the copper has spread out as a rivet over the rove, strike the nail with several blows around the perimeter of the rivet to turn down the edges. The small gauge nails used in planking should require only 15-20 blows to rivet, the larger nails in knees and hog will require many more.

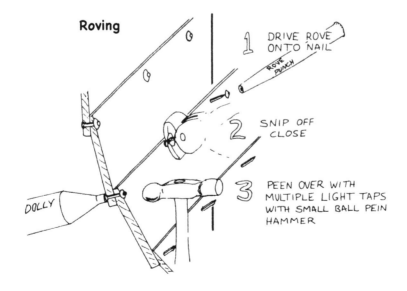

Roving

1 DRIVE ROVE ONTO NAIL

ROVE PUNCH

2 SNIP OFF CLOSE

3 PEEN OVER WITH MULTIPLE LIGHT TAPS WITH SMALL BALL PEIN HAMMER

DOLLY

The Planking Process

Planking any boat in any material is a fascinating part of boat building. Every plank you fit adds to the emerging shape of the boat, it's a bit like reading an exciting book when you have to keep turning the pages to see how it comes out.

Lining Out

The first step is to decide exactly where the plank lines are to go. The simplest way is to measure the girth from the skeg and keel strip around each mould to the sheer, including both transoms, and divide each by the number of planks you propose to use, so that all taper evenly. We chose to use eight planks a side, based on familiarity with other dinghies of this size. Using more planks makes some aspects of planking easier but increases the amount of work.

The overriding concern is that it looks right, and this is affected by the following factors:

1. On some dinghies, particularly stem dinghies, if the garboard (the first plank next to the keel) is not wide enough forward, the succeeding planks tend to dip when viewed from the side. This is not a concern on this dinghy due to the strong sheer and pronounced upward curve of the hog forward. Sometimes if the garboard is carried too wide the remaining planks are made so narrow at the forward end as to be difficult to fasten.

2. If a boat is relatively flat-bottomed, there will be a relatively hard turn to the bilge on each side.

This affects the planking in two ways: firstly, one plank will have to run along the crest of the tight turn on each mould; it would be too difficult for a plank to start on one side of the turn and twist over a short distance to finish on the other side. Laying a batten or some plank stock over the moulds will help you to judge this. If the best position is a little skewed, planks above this plank will have to be treated differently from planks below it.

The second effect of the hard turn is that if the planks are too wide, the required bevel where they overlap will result in either a feather edge inboard, a gap outboard, too narrow a landing, or all three (see **Fig. 11**). The general rule therefore is the tighter the turn, the narrower the plank. This does not necessarily mean increasing the number of planks; the first few planks on the flattish bottom can generally be quite wide to make up for the narrow bilge strakes. They are called the broad strakes or broads for this reason. On a new boat it is generally advisable to draw the proposed plank layout in section on the lofting on at least one station to check that the chosen plank width will not lead to any of these problems.

3. If a rub rail is fitted to the sheer, the sheer plank needs to be wider all the way along by the width of the rail so that the exposed part of the plank is visually as wide as the previous plank; but more specifically, seeing that all other planks are wider than the visible part by the width of the land (the bevelled overlapping area), in our case 16mm, rarely more than 19mm, the actual width of the sheer plank is greater than the previous plank by only the difference between the land (16mm) and the rub rail (25mm) i.e. 9mm.

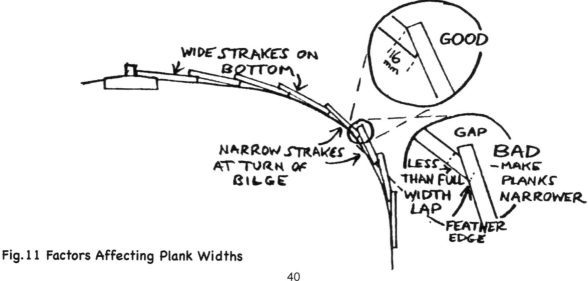

Fig.11 Factors Affecting Plank Widths

40

Table of Plank Widths for Petrel

		Stern	Sta 5	Sta 3	Sta 1	Bow
1	Garboard	84	90	99	82	57
2	Broad	84	90	99	82	57
3	2nd Broad	84	90	99	82	57
4	3rd Broad	84	90	99	82	57
5		74	80	87	72	50
6		74	80	87	72	50
7		81	87	95	78	55
8	Sheer Strake	81	87	95	78	55

Note:

Figures in tables are visible plank widths

True plank widths are therefore plus 16mm (15mm for Pee-Wee).

Sheer plank is wider to allow for gunwale rail.

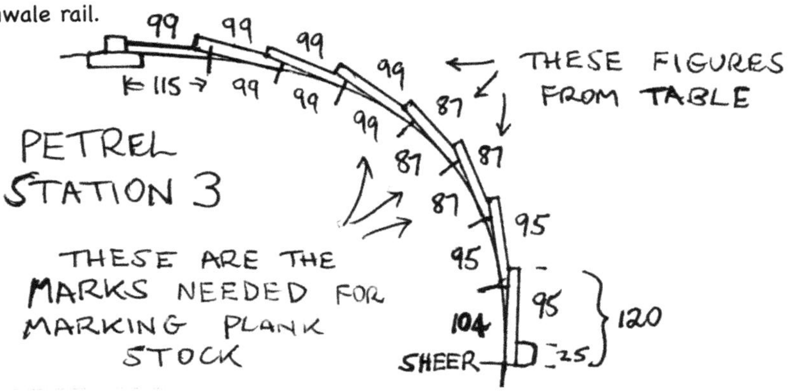

PETREL STATION 3

THESE ARE THE MARKS NEEDED FOR MARKING PLANK STOCK

THESE FIGURES FROM TABLE

Note:

If building from our plans, these marks are already drawn on the full-size patterns. This diagram is presented to explain how we arrived at these positions.

Table of Plank Widths for Pee-Wee

		Stern	Sta 5	Sta 3	Sta 1	Bow
1	Garboard	86	94	102	77	57
2	Broad	86	94	102	77	57
3	2nd Broad	86	94	102	77	57
4	3rd Broad	86	94	102	77	57
5		71	79	86	65	49
6		71	79	86	65	49
7		83	87	96	72	56
8	Sheer Strake	83	87	96	72	56

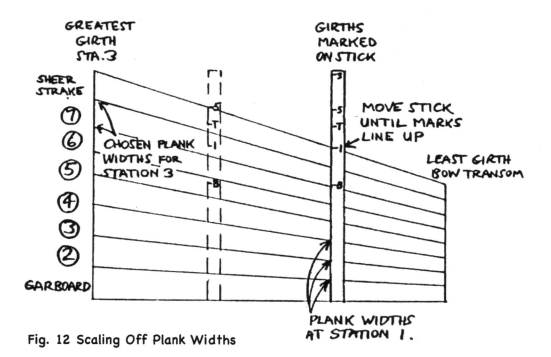

GREATEST GIRTH STA.3

GIRTHS MARKED ON STICK

SHEER STRAKE

⑦
⑥
⑤ — CHOSEN PLANK WIDTHS FOR STATION 3
④
③
②

GARBOARD

MOVE STICK UNTIL MARKS LINE UP

LEAST GIRTH BOW TRANSOM

PLANK WIDTHS AT STATION 1.

Fig. 12 Scaling Off Plank Widths

Taking all these into consideration we divided *Petrel's* girth at Station 3, took off this 9mm, and divided it by eight planks to get an average width of plank of 95mm. We decided to narrow down two planks nearest the turn of the bilge (planks 5 and 6) by 8mm each, and add this amount to the garboard and three broad strakes at the original figure. Scaling this by percentages with a calculator, we arrived at the table on the previous page. A similar table applies to *Pee-Wee*. Remember that these are the visible widths, viewed from outside the hull. The first seven planks are actually 16mm wider, and the sheer strake is 25mm wider. Prior to calculators, the method would have been as in **Fig 12**.

The best method for checking the look of the lining out process is to fix battens of equal width to the plank lands (in our case 16mm) to the moulds (tack them with temporary steel nails) exactly on the proposed land areas, giving you the visual impact of the planking (only one side of the boat is necessary). On this boat, the strong sheer curve at Sta 5 tended to repeat itself on each succeeding plank toward the keel, and it was found necessary to move two of the battens very slightly for the best line viewed from different angles. You may come to a different conclusion if you line out using our table. Once any adjustments are completed, the width of the batten automatically gives you the position of the top of each plank where it bears on the mould, which is the mark we need for each plank, pencilled in on the forward or aft face of the

mould where it will be visible from inside the boat once the planking is on. Next you must decide the frame positions on the boat though they are not fitted until later, their exact positions decide where the plank fastenings are to go. It is easiest if a frame is located at each mould position, and the spaces between divided evenly. In a boat of this size, a frame spacing of 125mm would be

Skeg and keel fitted to hog, ready for browing off for planking.

considered close, and a spacing of 225mm would be considered wide- if we put three frames between each pair of moulds, the spacing will be about 180mm which is about right. Mark this spacing along the keel where it will be visible after the first planks are fitted. You now have to decide the nail spacings. Clinker lap nails are generally between 50 and 75mm apart along each plank. on this boat, fitting two nails between each pair of frames will give a spacing of 60mm. Mark these spacings clearly on the keel/skeg.

Browing Off

The hog and transom must now be shaped to receive the garboard plank. At each mould , a short straight edge or rule (or the side of a block plane if straight) is laid as in **Fig. 13**, and wood removed by plane until the plank will bear across the full 20mm of landing. This is referred to as browing off. Between moulds, you have to estimate the amount to remove, but of course it will never exceed the amount removed at the nearest moulds. If in doubt, leave a bit extra there until the plank is ready to fit and checkout with the plank in position. Because this type of boat was usually built with very few moulds, in the classes we generally left out moulds 2 and 4, but if you wish it certainly does make it easier to bevel the plank landings as there are more moulds at which to get the exact angle.

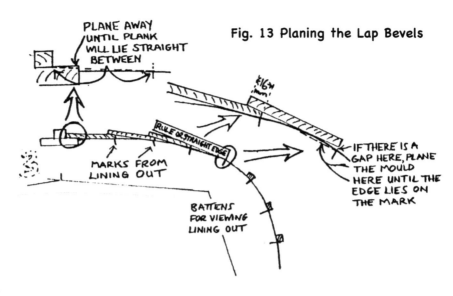

Fig. 13 Planing the Lap Bevels

At the transoms, there will be considerable bevel needed to ensure the plank lands fairly. Chisel and plane a flat at the correct bevel to receive the plank, judging this with a batten (see **Fig. 14)**, and keep removing material (constantly checking your bevel angle with a batten) until your flat touches where the plank width mark crosses the lofted line of the transom, whether this is marked on the outside or inside of the transom. Be cautious! It is very easy to go too far; constant checking is the only insurance.

It is easiest to bevel the transom at least for the plank after the one you are going to fit, because a fitted plank hinders the plane's access to the next plank landing. It is possible to bevel all at one go using battens, but it is safer to stay just two plank widths in front. It is sometimes easier to bevel the second plank landing out from the skeg first to improve the plane's access to the landing for the garboard strake.

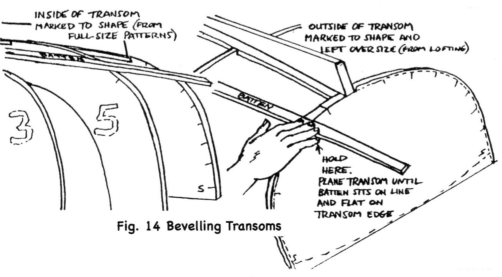

Fig. 14 Bevelling Transoms

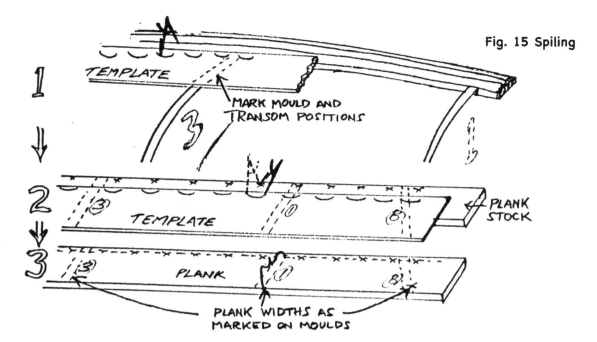

Fig. 15 Spiling

TEMPLATE

MARK MOULD AND TRANSOM POSITIONS

1

2   TEMPLATE   PLANK STOCK

3   PLANK

PLANK WIDTHS AS MARKED ON MOULDS

Spiling

The shape of the inner edge of the garboard is determined by spiling. A spiling batten or template of say 3mm plywood at least as long as the garboard and about as wide is clamped or tacked onto the moulds and transom so that its inner edge is between about 5mm and 30mm from the keel/skeg. Accuracy will benefit from having the template lie fairly, touching the hog all the way along. With a pencil compass, mark a series of arcs along the template with the compass point tight against the hog/skeg junction (see **Fig. 15**). Mark all mould and transom positions. Take the template to the plank stock carefully positioning it to get the best use from the plank, and reverse mark the plank by drawing two intersecting arcs each with the compass point at opposite ends of each arc on the template. The point where the arcs intersect is of course the point position from which each of the original arcs on the template were drawn. Extend the mould and transom marks onto the plank stock. Remove the template, connect the intersecting arcs with nails and batten, the transfer the desired plank width at each mould. Join these marks with a fairly stiff batten, and cut out your plank.

Cut slightly outside both lines because sometimes the timber will change shape slightly after cutting. Always leave at least 10mm extra on the outside in case the inside fit needs adjusting. Check the fit to see if there are any major problems (there shouldn't be), then plane to the line on the inner edge and check the exact fit. The plank should be held with nippers and/or clamps so that it

bears on all moulds. Do not edge-set the plank to get it to fit, it must lie naturally. If you edge-set such thin planks, another part of it will lift up.

When happy with it (it should be a very tight fit) unless you were lucky enough to get a perfect fit to your spiled line you will need to re-mark, the outside of the plank. With the plank in position against the keel and keg, transfer the marks on the moulds to the underside of the plank, remove the plank and connect these with a line drawn around a tackled batten, and cut and plane to the line. It is more important that the outside line be fair than that it be exactly on the pencilled line.

Offer the plank reverse side up on the other side of the boat. If it fits within a couple of millimetres, use it as a template to mark out a plank for that side. It is most likely that minor variations will be found, but if planing wood from the inside edge, be careful not to narrow the plank so much that it is shy of its outboard marks on the moulds. It is best again, to leave a little extra wood on the outside edge at first for this reason, fit the inside edge first, and then mark the outside edge from the mould marks underneath.

Browing Off the Lap and Cutting Jerralds

Before fitting each plank for good the plank should be bevelled all the way along the lap for the next plank to lie fairly. This is done exactly as it was when bevelling the hog for the garboard, as in **Fig. 13**. You can get the angle exactly right at each mould, and fair in between by eye. You may find it easier to fair in between mould positions by taking the plank to the bench where there is more support. <u>Bevel at the transoms at both ends as if they were moulds</u>. There will be rebates cut here so that at both ends the plank edges are flush, or nearly so. If this were not done, either there would be a triangular gap at the transoms under each plank lap, or the transoms would have to be notched to eliminate this. Either would be harder to seal against water than the traditional rebates, called gains by the Americans , and Jerralds by shipwrights in Sydney.

The rebates are exactly as wide as the plank laps (on this boat 16mm), and commence anywhere from 150mm to 375mm from the plank ends on different boats. The longer they are, the more likely they are to fair in. Choose a figure and stick to it for all rebates one one boat; in our case we normally choose around 200mm. The depth of the rebate at the end and the angle of the bottom of the rebate depends on the angle at which the two planks meet in section. By bevelling the plank lap all the way to the ends of the boat and treating the transoms as if they were moulds all you have to do to get the angle of the jerrald right is to <u>cut the jerrald at the exact same angle as the bevel that has already been planed at the plank end</u>. **Fig. 16** shows the angle and depth at plank end-of-rebates for different

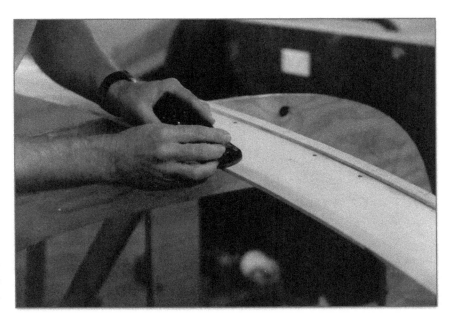

Top:
Browing-Off (bevelling) the plank lap as a fair landing for the next plank.

Middle and Bottom:
Bevel the plank at the transom as if it were another mould, then deepen it into a rebate.

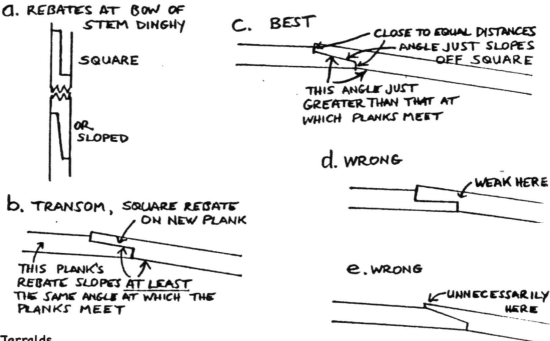

a. REBATES AT BOW OF STEM DINGHY

SQUARE

OR SLOPED

b. TRANSOM, SQUARE REBATE ON NEW PLANK

THIS PLANK'S REBATE SLOPES AT LEAST THE SAME ANGLE AT WHICH THE PLANKS MEET

c. BEST

CLOSE TO EQUAL DISTANCES
ANGLE JUST SLOPES OFF SQUARE

THIS ANGLE JUST GREATER THAN THAT AT WHICH PLANKS MEET

d. WRONG

WEAK HERE

e. WRONG

UNNECESSARILY HERE

Fig. 16 Jerralds

plank angles. On stem dinghies (**Fig. 16a**) at the stem, and on very flat-bottomed dinghies where the planks meet virtually straight, the rebates can be cut almost square, and to half the depth on each plank. As soon as some angle between planks comes into it (**Fig. 16b**) both rebates can no longer be square. If the rebate on the new plank is square, the rebate on the previous plank must be cut at the angle at which the planks meet. The neatest look is achieved when the angle of both rebates is the same on both planks as in **Fig. 16c**. The underneath plank's rebate cannot be made square, or the rebate on the new plank will be undercut as in **Fig. 16d**, leaving

a weak spot. By the same token, don't increase the angle too much, otherwise the new plank will be too thin and liable to damage on its outer edge, as in **Fig. 16e**. By cutting the jerrald at the same angle as the bevel planed on the plank end, you ensure that the angle is on the safe side of the angle at which the planks meet in section. Cut it just deeper than halfway through the plank, as the outside plank to be rebated and fitted against it needs to be thicker so as to resist being damaged. Plane it so that it grades into the full depth in a fair curve with no hard spots as in **Fig. 17**.

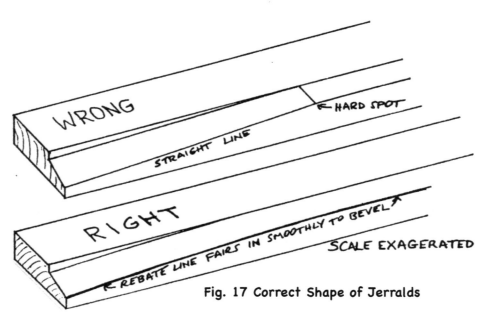

WRONG

HARD SPOT

STRAIGHT LINE

RIGHT

REBATE LINE FAIRS IN SMOOTHLY TO BEVEL

SCALE EXAGERATED

Fig. 17 Correct Shape of Jerralds

46

Fitting the Garboard

With the jerralds cut, the garboard is ready for fitting. Clamp it in place and drill the nail holes at the spacing previously marked, in the centre of the laps (i.e. 8mm in). Use a drill bit the same size as the square size of the nail used, in this case 2mm. Hold the drill square to the surface of the plank. Countersink so the heads will be flush. Drill only for the nails between the frames. Fastenings into the transom (and/or stem) can be screws, bronze-ringed boat nails, or copper nails twisted with two pairs of pliers. On this boat we generally use bronze boat nails. Drill for these also. Remove the plank, brush away the drilling swarf, then brush oil (linseed or decking-type oil) or thick old varnish onto both mating surfaces if you are doing it completely traditionally, and lay a strand of caulking cotton along the transom edges and the

hog and wet it out with the oil or varnish. If you are allowing some modern advances, lay a bead of Sikaflex or some other polyurethane sealant along the lap and the transoms.

Clamp the plank on and drive the nails, holding the dolly underneath to take the shock of the hammer blows. Start in the middle and work towards one end, then the other. You may tack the plank at Station 3 because the frame will eventually sit exactly where the station is and the tack hole can become the nail hole for the frame, but this is not the case at Stations 1 and 5.

Unless you are a masochist or are building the boat right way up, don't attempt to rove over the nails yet. The nails themselves have enough holding power to hold the planks together.

Other Planks

All the other planks can also be spiled onto templates, but if your plank stock is narrow enough to offer up to the boat close to its fitted position, it is generally quicker to clamp it into position with a minimal overlap, and run a pencil underneath along the outer edge of the previous plank thereby marking the required shape on the underside of the new plank. Ensure that the plank material covers the outer plank lineout marks by at least 16mm, because once the plank is cut to the drawn line the plank will be fitted over the previous plank's lap and will therefore be 16mm closer to the centreline. Before moving the plank, mark the mould and transom positions then take it to the bench and cut to the scribed line and to the required width not forgetting the safety margin. Plane the inside line until you are happy with the fit, remembering not to edge-set the plank but let it wrap naturally around the moulds. The plank should fit very closely into the jerralds at both ends, but along the plank lap it is more important that the plank edges be fair than it be exactly on the line 16mm in. Variations of up to about 1.5mm are acceptable. Clamp it in place and mark the outside plank lineout marks from the moulds underneath, join these marks with batten and pencil and cut and plane to the line.

A bead of low-modulus polyurethane is laid just prior to final fit of the next plank.

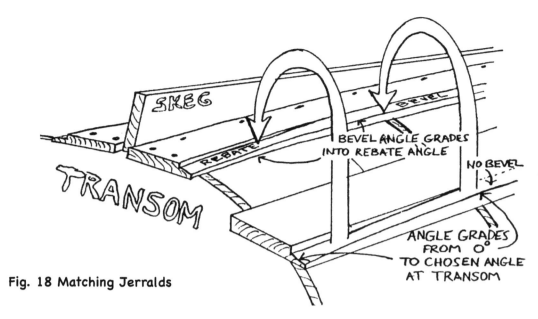

Fig. 18 Matching Jerralds

SKEG

REBATE

TRANSOM

BEVEL

BEVEL ANGLE GRADES INTO REBATE ANGLE

NO BEVEL

ANGLE GRADES FROM 0° TO CHOSEN ANGLE AT TRANSOM

There has to be a jerrald underneath each succeeding plank at each end to match the jerrald on the previous plank, as in **Fig. 18**. There is no short cut to getting these accurate. There is always less to remove than you think. Offer up the plank and sight the jerrald you have to fit the plank to, estimating the angle and depth you will have to cut to get them to fit together. Cut with a rebate plane to your estimated angle, but plane only a few strokes, and I mean literally that, a few strokes only before offering the plank up to check that the angle you chose is accurate. If it is, estimate the depth

you will need to cut and cut only half that amount at the same angle. If it is not, estimate how much you need to correct it and plane only a few strokes again before checking again. I cannot stress too much that there is always much less to remove than it looks, and that the only way to be accurate is to do only a few strokes at a time between checking your progress.

The sequence of events from here on is the same as for fitting the garboard. At the turn of the bilge where the planks lap at a greater angle, the jerralds at the transoms get steeper and their inboard edge shallower. It could even be that no rebate will be possible, as in **Fig. 19**, but it is more important to avoid a feather edge than it is to insist on a rebate. If you have both a feather edge and no rebate, your planks at this point are too wide, but you're stuck with it unless you line out the topside planks again. Mark for fastenings in each succeeding plank by squaring out from the previous nail, along a line 8mm (half the lap width) in from the plank edge, as in **Fig. 20**.

The Sheer Strake

Mark the gun'l edge of the sheer strake from the marks on the moulds, but cut about 3mm clear of the line. Final adjustment of the sheer line waits until the rub rail is fitted.

NO REBATE

16mm

FEATHER EDGE NOT BEST

THESE ARE WORST CASE: ANY GREATER ANGLE MEANS PLANKS IN THIS AREA SHOULD BE NARROWER

16mm

DON'T REDUCE WIDTH OF LAP

BETTER

Fig. 19 Extreme Angles

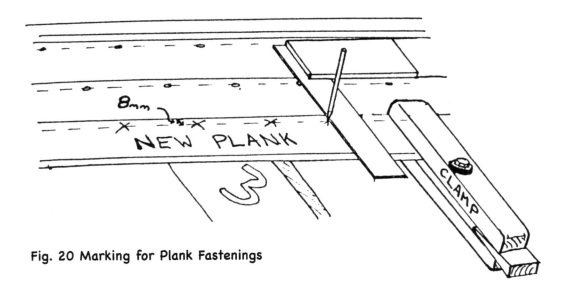

Fig. 20 Marking for Plank Fastenings

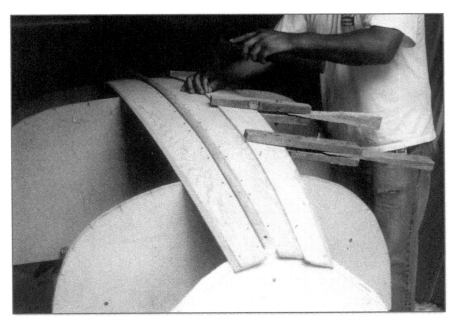

Second plank on starboard side being fastened on. Temporary steel nails are used to locate the pre-drilled holes.

Summary of Planking Sequence

1.   Spile the plank, or offer up the plank stock, ensuring that it lies naturally around the moulds with no edge-set and mark the outer edge of the previous plank onto the plank stock from underneath with a pencil, mark mould and transom positions.

2.   Plane to the line, adjust fit if necessary. Once edge fits well, clamp in place and mark the outer plank edge from the plank lineout marks on the mould underneath. Cut and plane this line fair.

3.   Decide angle and depth of jerralds underneath to match those on the previous plank. Be careful to cut them on the correct side of the plank; don't laugh, its been done. Cut conservatively, check often.

4.   Mark the 16mm plank lap and clamp the plank in place and brow off (bevel) the lap using the angles at each mould as the control points and fairing the bevel in between moulds either on the boat or on the bench. Bevel at both transoms as if they were moulds.

5.   Deepen the bevel into a jerrald (rebate) at each end over the last 200mm.

6.   Clamp and drill for fastenings. Mark for holes square from previous plank as in **Fig. 20**. This will ensure comfortable lines for the frames.

7.   Apply oil, varnish or chosen bedding compound to mating surfaces.

8.   Fasten plank.

Note on Planking Timber

If you have the machinery, careful cutting and planing will enable you to get a pair of 6mm planks from a 25mm sawn board. If using our lining out measurements for either boat, planks 1-4 and 6 can be cut from 150mm wide boards; plank no. 5 from a 125mm board; plank 7 from a 200mm board or two 150mm boards scarfed; and the sheer strake from one 250mm or scarfed from two 175mm boards. **Fig. 21** illustrates scarfing details.

There's just one more thing to do before taking the boat off the moulds and turning it over. Mark the frame positions with a flexible batten (from gun'l to gun'l), exactly half way between the nearest nails. Average out any errors, but be sure the marks for the frames fastenings are in line. Drill these holes and countersink. Take out the temporary screws holding the transom and hog to the jig, then you can turn the boat over and admire it until you're ready to rove the nails and steam bend in the frames.

Planking completed, ready to lift off moulds.

Roving

You've turned the boat over, and have it resting on trestles at a comfortable height to lean into to work. The hull will still be quite floppy at this stage. It will probably need to be pushed out at the sides to reach its true beam, and a notched stick or two should be fitted to hold the sides to the correct beam. The inside of the boat looks like an echidna inside out, with about two hundred nails sticking through. By the time you get through this lot you'll be a dab hand at riveting copper nails over roves. The technique is as illustrated before. Back up the head of the chosen nail either by a partner holding a dolly, or by yourself with a knee dolly or panel beaters' dolly pressed against the hull with your thigh or whatever part of your body can reach. Unless you have extremely long arms and legs you will need a partner for the first two or three rows from the centre. Drive the rove down over the nail with the rove punch. A couple of extra taps once it reaches the bottom will help pull the nail head in

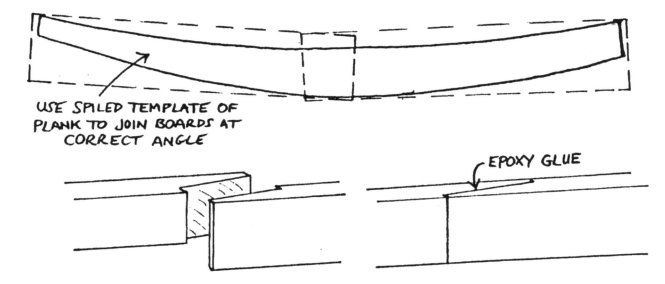

USE SPILED TEMPLATE OF PLANK TO JOIN BOARDS AT CORRECT ANGLE

EPOXY GLUE

Fig. 21 Scarfing for Very Curved Planks

tight. Clip it off with end nippers as close to the rove as the nippers will allow you to get. I've seen it written that you should leave an amount of nail showing equal to the square diameter of the nail, but this leaves far more copper to peen over than is necessary and makes for bulky and unsightly roves.

Still backing up the nail head, peen the nail over by lots of light tapping blows with the ball head of a small ball pein hammer aiming the apps dead centre and in line with the direction of the nail. You will

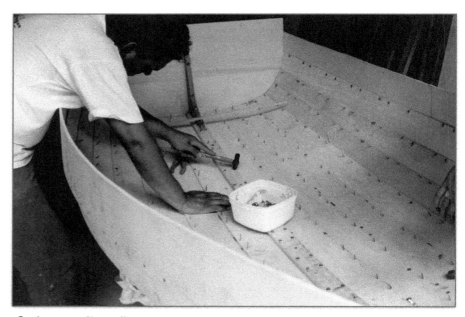

Roving over the nails.

see the copper start to spread out over the hole through the rove. Hit just hard enough to spread the copper slowly; too hard and you may bend the nail inside the wood. Stop when the edges of the spread copper are touching the rove most of the way around. Don't flatten the rove; if you do, grind it off, drive out the nail and start again. Tap around the edges of the peened area to bend them down they won't catch on clothing etc; and move on to the next one. Several hours work will see the job finished and the boat ready to steam in the frames. The last thing to do before getting ready for bending in the frames is to mark 9-10mm either side of each nail hole drilled so the frames can locate accurately over the holes.

Steam Bending

In different parts of the world boatbuilders have used various combinations of heat and water to bend timber, from soaking and holding over a fire, to boiling and steaming. With our British traditions we will steam them.

Selection of Timber

We normally use Queensland Silver Ash in these dinghies, but Spotted Gum is also a favourite if you don't mind the extra weight. Most, though not all, eucalypts will bend fairly well, but Silver Ash and Spotted Gum have had the NSW and Queensland market sewn up for yonks.

No matter what species you select it must be the absolute top grade, and for this you will have to personally select each piece. The grain must be straight, without knots, grain runout, cranky grain or shakes or it will definitely break. It is easier to bend green timber, but seasoned timber will also bend if steamed long enough, and preferably soaked (usually in salt water) for 24 hours or so prior to steaming.

You should machine the timber so that the rings lie across the flat of the frame, that is, in line with the wider dimensions, see **Fig. 22**, though some builders have contrary views. Boatbuilders like many other tradesmen often hold strong views on certain subjects, often conflicting, and almost as often, not mattering a great deal. Especially for these frames which are quite thin at 19 x 8mm and bend very easily, the issues of seasoned/green and flat sawn/quarter sawn and possible additives to the boiling water are not of vital importance.

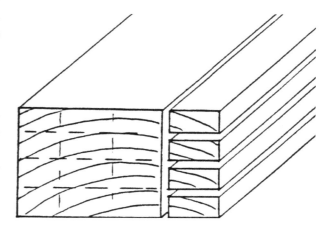

Fig. 22 Cutting Flat-Sawn Timber for Frames

Steaming Equipment

The setup for steaming need not be very sophisticated. The simplest method is to get a 100mm steel downpipe (not plastic or all you will bend will be the pipe), seal one end (preferably by welding), one-quarter fill it with hot water, lean it against a trestle and light a fire or gas burner underneath the lower end. The only drawback with this simple system is that the ends of the timbers left in boiling water are usually considerably darkened.

A more sophisticated setup is the one we use. A gas burner heats a boiler made from an out-of-date gas cylinder and the steam is led through a 38mm car radiator hose to the bottom end of a welded steel box with opening lid and a built-in-rack to allow the steam to circulate under the timber. Any condensation is drained via a 12mm fuel hose to the boiler. Blankets or carpet underlay are usually thrown over the box to slow heat loss.

Steaming the Timber

The frames should be sanded to remove machining marks and all four corners eased. They should be cut at least 400mm over length for handling, and enough frames to do the boat plus a third again for wastage placed in the steam box. The rule of thumb is to steam timber for an hour per inch of thickness. We generally leave our 8mm frames in for at least half an hour once steam is up. As the job takes an hour or two, the last frames will have been in there much longer but it does not seem to affect them either way. The box or tube should be kept shut and steam retained as much as possible, but it is not necessary to have it airtight, we are trying to steam them not pressure-cook them.

Bending in the Frames

The whole process for each frame must take place very quickly. The high heat is lost very rapidly and the frame is really flexible for only 30 seconds or so. So the steam box must be near the boat, at least one helper (and preferably two) primed and ready, and all materials to hand. This includes gloves for handling hot timber, lots of clamps (two per frame for at least several frames) within reach, and a reasonably heavy mallet. W h e n all is ready, one person pulls one frame out of the box (and slams the lid shut again), hands one end to a helper on the opposite side of the boat, and each holding one end with one hand, they push the middle down with the other into the boat in the required position (see **Fig. 23**), normally fitting a central frame first and working towards each end.

The first place to exert force is on both sides just out-board of the hog where there is a slight reverse curve needed in the frame, then with one hand holding the top end, push the frame out to the hull with the other bending the top end inboard a little to overbend the frame slightly.

Be careful in bending not to apply too sharp a force to too local an area. A hot timber does not bend fairly under strong local pressure but will try to fold around the point of pressure. You must bend it small amounts each time, moving your hand around constantly to even out the bend. Expect to break some. The first few frames in the middle of the boat should have no real twist, so clamp the frame to the sheer strake (with plywood pads under the clamp) fairly tightly, and when both clamps are on, grab the mallet and hit the top of the frame on

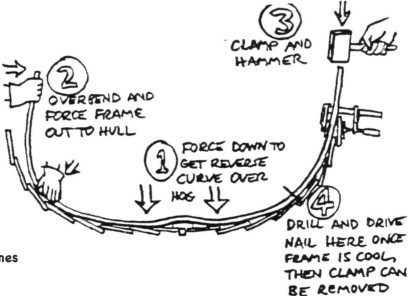

Fig. 23 Bending in the Frames

each side. This will force the frame out hard to the planking. Make sure the frame is very close to its marks. The whole process should have taken less time than it took to read about it. Get more clamps ready for the next frame and go again.

As you get further towards the ends of the boat, particularly the bow, the frames tend to require some twist. For these light frames it is generally sufficient to put in the twist by hand. On larger frames a plywood pad with a hole cut to fit the frame tightly

Steam bent ribs (frames) are held by clamps until cool.

and a handle can be used to twist the frame, or simply tighten a clamp on the end and twist that.

Sooner or later you will run out of clamps, so you will have to drive nails in some frames. Do the frame you put in first so it will have had a chance to cool (10-15 minutes is ample). Make sure the frame is seated as close to the hull as possible and is on the pencil marks which show it is evenly over the drilled hole, then drill through the plank hole right through the frame on just one of the planks on each side at the turn of the bilge; this means the frame is held at its point of maximum bend. It will not be necessary to rivet these nails for the moment unless the frame tries to lift off when you remove the clamps.

NOTE: Some authorities suggest driving the nails through the hot frame as soon as it is fitted, without drilling. While it is possible to do this, you will occasionally split a frame while driving the nail, and the fibres of the timber are so distorted the frame will almost always split there sooner or later in the boat's life. It is cheaper to buy a few extra clamps and drill each hole when the frame has cooled.

Once you have a free bunch of clamps, start bending in more frames. The last two frames at both ends must be fitted in two separated halves because of the transom knees. These frames also have the greatest twist. As soon as the half-frame is out of the steamboat, pre-bend by hand a slight reverse curve into the lowest 100-120mm to allow for the hog, then quickly fit the frame to the boat. If

it doesn't go right, it is probably small enough to fit back in the steambox. Pick another frame to try, and come back to the problem one 10-15 minutes later when it has heated up again.

Don't drill and nail these end frames yet. The ends were cut square, but because of the slight cant (slope) of the frames because they are set nearly square to the lines of the planking, the bottom ends should be trimmed to slight bevel to fit snug against the knee. Once the frames are down to room temperature (usually 15-20 minutes), they can be removed from the boat without danger of them springing back excessively. They will straighten out slightly, but they will easily be bent back to the hull by hand once the ends are bevelled.

Fastening Off

Before you let your helpers go home, you might as well drill for the rest of the nails and drive them home. The most important thing to remember is to keep the frame as close to the hull as possible at the point where the nails will come through. Expect that at the hardest turn of the bilge, the frame will touch the centre of one or two planks but will not touch where the nails come through (see **Fig. 24**). If this occurs at just a few spots it can be ignored apart from remembering not to over-rivet these nails because you may split the plank or pull the head through. It is possible of course to fit small timber wedges behind the frame when this occurs. The same applies to the reverse curve over the hog. If the frames are not very close to the lap at the nail position, fit packing wedges underneath the frame, as in **Fig. 24** otherwise the roving will distort the

Fig. 24 Fitting Wedges to Gaps Behind Frames

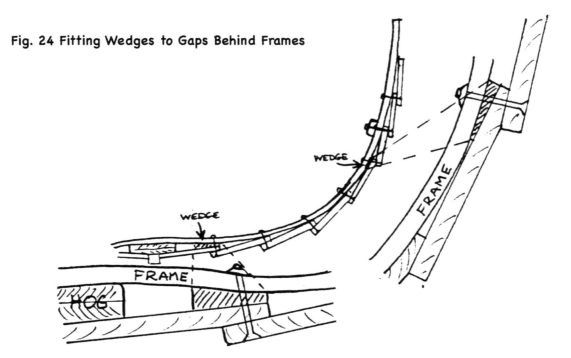

plank lap upward rather than bringing the frame down.

Don't drill or drive nails through the lap at the bottom of the second plank from the sheer. This is the position where the riser or seat support will live, and the nails for it will be put through the plank laps, frame and riser in one.

Don't rove the nails over today, have a break. Though the frames are cool, they are still wet, and they will shrink a little on drying, which will take several days. So it is better to rove them later. If time considerations mean you must rove them sooner, or if you had to rove some to prevent a frame lifting, check a few days later that none of them have loosened. They can easily be tightened with a few more backed blows of the ball pein hammer at any stage before some are made more difficult to get at once the risers, thwarts and knees are installed.

Risers

To fit the thwarts (seats) we need to fit the seat risers to support them. You remember that we left out the nails from the frames along the bottom lap of the second plank down from the sheer because this happens to be a good height at which to support the thwarts. It is not necessary on all boats for the seat risers to follow the sweep of the planking as it does on this boat. You can choose an arbitrary height to suit your desired thwart height and fasten it through the frames. You may need to

pack between the frames and planking if there are gaps where you plan to put nails.

Drill through the pre-drilled plank hole from outside through the frame with a 3mm bit aiming the drill to be square with the frame inside. Pencil mark 11mm above these holes as a guide to locating the risers. These are again of Queensland Ash, 22mm by 11mm with their inner edges chamfered or rounded before fitting.

They need be just long enough to reach the last frame at each end of the boat. They should bend in cold. Drill right through planking, frame and riser right in the centre at Station 3. Drive a 75mm by 3mm nail from outside. Drill and drive nails every third frame or so in both directions from the centre. This helps the riser to fair to the required curve. Drill and drive the intermediate nails and rove them all over with 9mm roves.

Thwarts

The thwarts are cut from 200 x 25mm boards of Damar Minyak, Mahogany, Hoop Pine, Queensland Maple or Silky Oak. They should be machined and sanded before fitting. Both ends are to be cut so as to be parallel with the planking fore and aft, and bevelled to fit hard up against whatever frame the touch. The thwart does not actually touch the planking. It is possible, but entirely unnecessary to notch the thwarts for the frames and have the thwarts hard up against the planking.

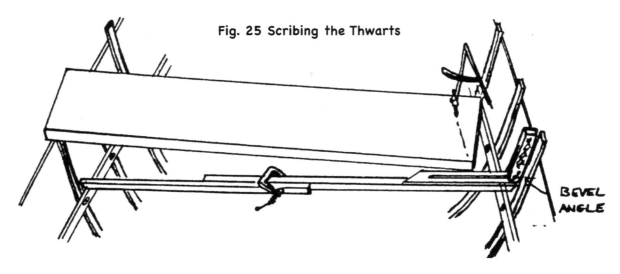

Fig. 25 Scribing the Thwarts

BEVEL
ANGLE

The ends are trimmed in several stages by scribing as in **Fig. 25**. The board is placed in position on one side of the boat with the other side protruding past the gun'l. Compasses are used to scribe a line parallel with the planking. Two sticks are used as an expanding rule to measure the greatest distance the thwart will span, then the scribed side is lifted onto its gun'l, and the other side is dropped into the boat and scribed parallel to the planking picking up the measurement taken from the expanding rule. Cut with a bandsaw or jigsaw and trim to the correct bevel angle (found with a sliding bevel gauge). Cut conservatively. The first marks will likely be quite inaccurate, so cut well clear of the line, and re-scribe with the thwart close to its final position which allows more

accuracy. As with any close fits, constant checking is the safeguard as you remove material. Final trimming should be with a sharp, fine-set block plane.

Fit the centre thwart first (that way you can use it for one of the shorter ones if you muck it up), then the aft thwart, then the forward one. Screw them down to the risers with two 8g by 30mm silicon bronze woodscrews each side, counterbored and plugged.

Rails

Many small dinghies, particularly British ones, have a complicated system protecting the gun'ls comprising of multiple rails on both sides of the sheer plank (inwales and outwales) and sometimes full capping on the plank frame ends. These are mostly difficult and time-consuming to build, and generally unnecessary. The traditional Australian system which we follow with these dinghies is simply to fit a rub rail to the outside, level with the top of the sheer strake. The rails are pieces of Silver Ash 25mm x 14mm. They are clamped on and viewed from all angles, one side at a time to check that the sheer line we agonised so much over during lofting still looks fair and sweet. If you took my advice and left about 3mm above the line at the sheerstrake, you must remember to set the rail

A Traditional Edge Moulding

The edges of the thwarts and sometimes stringers and inwales often had an edge moulding of a cut "V" a few millimetres in from each edge. It was made by a very simple tool: a slotted screw driven into a block of wood. Rub the block gently along the edge of the timber until the screw slot as a cutter begins to make an impression. Press harder taking care that the cutter does not run out through the side. The groove can only be as deep as the size of the screw head. Round over the edge slightly. Stop the groove an inch (25mm) from each end of each piece.

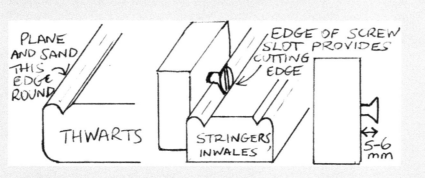

PLANE AND SAND THIS EDGE ROUND

THWARTS

EDGE OF SCREW SLOT PROVIDES CUTTING EDGE

STRINGERS INWALES

5-6 mm

to the line rather than the edge of the plank, and plane it down once the rail is fastened off. Once you are happy with the rail's clamped position, drill and fasten it with 3mm nails through the head of each frame, riveted over 9mm roves, and with a 12g x 38mm silicon bronze woodscrew into the transoms at both ends. These screws into end grain might not be strong enough by themselves in the long run, but the knees will be fastened through the risers and tie it all together.

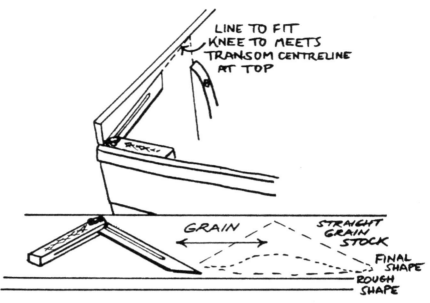

Fig. 26 Measuring Knee Angles

The Knees

There are four quarter knees (one in each corner) and six thwart knees to fit to this boat. Pick up the required angles with a sliding bevel. At this point extreme accuracy is not required, see **Fig. 26**.

Fig. 27 Laminating Knees

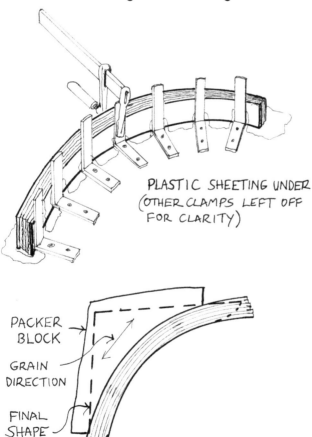

PLASTIC SHEETING UNDER
(OTHER CLAMPS LEFT OFF FOR CLARITY)

PACKER BLOCK

GRAIN DIRECTION

FINAL SHAPE OF KNEE

Grown Knees

Traditionally boat knees were cut from grown tea-tree (melaleuca) crooks, where the grain follows a curve such as where a branch or root joins the trunk. It is possible but difficult to get these today. The rough knee needs to be planed to the correct thickness, in our case 22mm before fitting.

Laminated Knees

Laminated knees can be made with equal or greater strength than grown knees (see **Fig. 27**). They can be cut from any reasonably strong gluing timber such as Mahogany, Silver Ash or Silky Oak. To reduce wastage, use the thickest timber that will take the required bend with excessive force.

Cut the laminations at least 6mm overwidth so they will clean up to the required thickness without containing pockets of glue where one veneer has slipped below the level of the others. In fact, seeing all knees are in matching pairs, it is better to laminate them more than twice the width and, split them on the saw to form two identical knees. Assemble the pieces and bend them dry around a jig of angle brackets or blocks of wood on a board of plywood. If all is okay, release them, apply epoxy glue to both sides of each piece and clamp them on the jig with plastic sheeting under to stop them becoming part of the jig. Cleanup as much of the glue as possible while wet. Leave them in the jig for at least 36 hours because of the stress, and then cleanup both sides preferably with a tungsten-tipped power plane. Glue an oversize corner packer block of the same timber on the knee.

Knees from Straight Stock

None of the knees on this dinghy are at particularly acute angles nor are they usually under a great deal of stress, so we find it possible to fit knees cut from straight stock. The chosen timber (usually Mahogany or Silky Oak) is planed to 22mm thickness, and the angle lifted from the boat with the sliding bevel is placed on the timber so the grain runs evenly across the angle of the knee for greatest strength. You should decide on the length of the arms of the knees (can I say that? or are they legs?): in most cases these can be scaled off the plans. Cut these 4-6mm over length, and leave the timber as a rough triangle; final cutting of the elegant shape of the knee should wait until after checking the final fit.

Fitting the Knees

So you have the knees planed to thickness and cut slightly oversize no matter whether they are grown, laminated or cut from straight stock, with the angle at the back of the arms close to the correct angle.

Fig. 28 Fitting Knees

The Quarter Knees

All four quarter knees (one in each corner) on this boat have one straight edge and one edge fitted to a curved surface. The basic principle of knee fitting is to get the straight side correct first, that is, dead straight and dead flat with the bevel cut exactly to hold it in its exact position. This is one point at which extreme accuracy is essential. The knee gets its strength from a solid bearing on both surfaces to which it is attached. To get the correct bevel angle for the straight side, hold the rough knee as close as possible to its final position and pick up the angle with the famous (and indispensable) sliding bevel (see **Fig. 28**). Because the top of the transoms eventually curves up in an arc, the knees must also angle up a little because if they were dead level they would appear to angle down. The best angle is found by drawing a line from the corner up to where the centreline meets the top of the transom (see **Fig. 26**). If you have a bandsaw with a tilting table you will have no trouble setting the table to the angle measured with the bevel and cutting close enough to the line so that a few plane strokes will finish the surface. Failing that a jigsaw will do a less accurate job resulting in a bit more planing. As you plane (again I favour a No. 60 block plane for this work), constantly check the fit to ensure you have the bevel angle right. Once it is damn near perfect (that is, a light-tight fit with no wobbling or rocking possible on the bearing surface), you are ready to cut the curved side.

Place the knee with the flat side on the transom and the rough curved side close to its final position, and scribe the curve of the sheer plank with the compass as in **Fig. 28**. Eyeball the gap see what sort of bevel is required. On these boats it is so close to square that a few plane strokes will make the bevel, constantly checking that you are on the right track. For all this work place the boat next to the vice on your workbench to save time; you'll walk from one side to the other a lot of times.

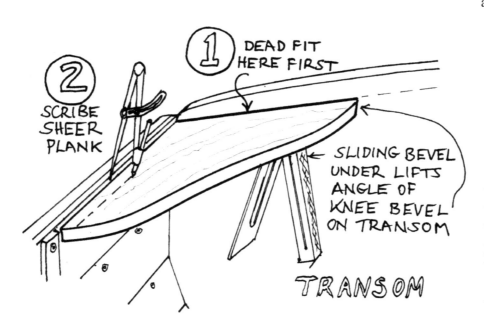

① DEAD FIT HERE FIRST

② SCRIBE SHEER PLANK

SLIDING BEVEL UNDER LIFTS ANGLE OF KNEE BEVEL ON TRANSOM

TRANSOM

When you're happy with the fit, draw the desired shape on the knee; every knee has to be a compromise between elegance (narrow throat and arms) and strength (leaving it chunky). Sometimes even things like the length of the nails available will have a bearing on the shape of the knee. Quarter knees generally look better if one arm is longer than the other; at the stern the transom arm will be longer, at the bow the gun'l arm will be longer. Round or chamfer the visible edges and finish sand the knee.

Thwart knees ready to fit.

Pencil the fastening positions on the top of the knee angling them as in **Fig. 29** to draw the knee tighter into position when the nails are roved over. The outer fastenings should not be too close to the end of the arm to avoid splitting. For the same reason, the holes should be drilled one size over the square shank size of the nail. Drill these holes on the bench, starting from the visible side of the knee. Move the knee to its correct position on the boat and continue to drill through the gun'l and transom.

Bed the joining surfaces (oil, varnish or white lead or Sikaflex) and drive 3.5 or 4mm nails through from the outside, roving them over on the inside with 9 or 11mm roves.

NOTE: Don't measure for or fit the knees until after the rails are on, as sometimes the corner angles will change slightly after fitting the rails.

Thwart Knees

Vertical thwart knees are fitted to each side of all thwarts to support the gun'ls against the strain of rowing and to generally stiffen the boat. With no inwale fitted (a rail inside the frames at the gun'l), these knees are easier to fit than the quarter knees, because there is hardly any bevelling.

All are fitted by planing the underside dead square and flat so as to sit snug on the thwart, then sliding it out to the hull to scribe the shape of the planks on the other arm. It is possible to notch the knee over the plank lap, but it is more normal and quite acceptable to continue the line of the lower plank upward to intersect with the other line, leaving a triangular gap just above the plank lap as in **Fig. 29**.

On the central thwart the knees are set in the middle with the lower arm parallel with the thwart. The planks are almost square to the thwart here, so very little bevelling is required, and can be judged by eye and the careful use of the block plane. On the forward and aft thwarts, the knees are set square to the line of the planking, so that the arms on the aft thwart are

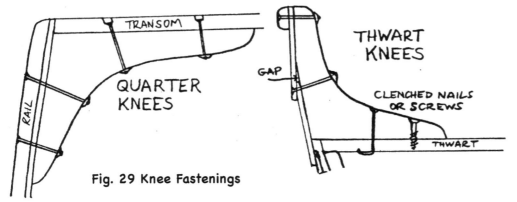

Fig. 29 Knee Fastenings

Fig. 30 Rowlock blocks

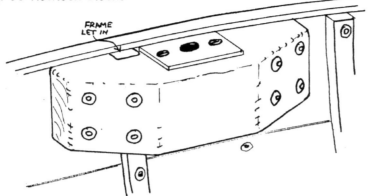

skewed forward, and those on the forward thwart are skewed aft. Thus no bevelling is required here either. Once you're happy with the fit, cut the required shape, which in the case of thwart knees generally means arms of approximately equal length with the vertical arm flush with the top of the gun'l. Chamfer or round the edges, sand the knee, then drill, bed and fasten with a roved nail through the rail, one through the plank lap, and two nails clenched over (bent) underneath the thwart, or two large screws into the thwart. The forward thwart knees are quite small and can have just one nail through each arm. We generally fit the thwart knees simply against the planking. Sometimes knees will be seen fitted alongside a frame, and often sitting on top of the frame and fastened through it. This would be marginally stronger, but requires more forethought in the placement of the frames. Once all knees are in and fastened, give the boat a shake and you'll see how much it has stiffened up.

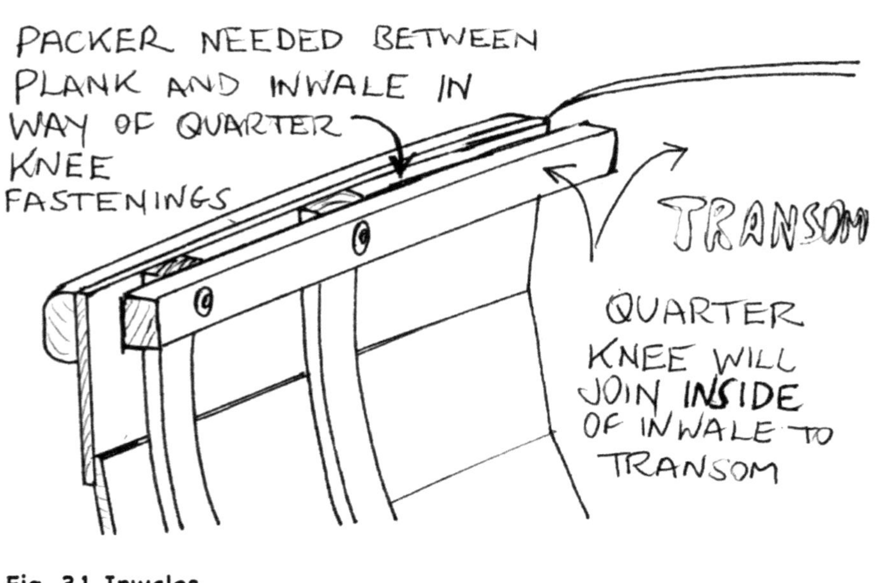

Rowlock Blocks

The simplest rowlock installation is to bolt a proprietary metal rowlock holder to the gun'l. However it is more traditional to fit a block of hardwood of around 200-225mm length, 60mm depth and 40mm thickness to the gun'l for each rowlock position, drill a vertical hole through it (parallel with the sheer plank to which it is fitted), and fit a brass or galvanised rowlock plate to it. The hole can be drilled oversize and fitted with a copper tube to take the wear of the rowlock.

The rowlock position is generally between 175 and 250mm behind the aft edge of the central thwart, with another pair the same distance from the forward thwart. Two hundred millimetres is a good compromise for different sized rowers. When rowing alone or with two passengers (one forward and one aft) the rower will sit on the central thwart, with one passenger in the stern, the rower should row from the forward thwart.

The blocks should be scribed and planed to fit the slight curve of the gun'l where they are going to live, shaped something like **Fig. 30**, and each fastened with eight copper nails and roves as in the diagram. The back may have to be notched for a frame. The metal rowlock plates can be let in flush, but as this is a likely place for rot, we generally screw them down on top after painting or varnishing.

Inwales

Several boats to these designs have been built with inwales, that is, rails along the sheer inside the frames. They add strength to the gunwales and look quite attractive. As I mentioned before, they were not often fitted in Sydney Harbour boats because they are time consuming. They have to be fitted in conjunction with fitting the outer gun'l rail.

The tricky part is getting the length exactly right. Fit one end first trimmed to fit hard up against the transom at one

PACKER NEEDED BETWEEN PLANK AND INWALE IN WAY OF QUARTER KNEE FASTENINGS

TRANSOM

QUARTER KNEE WILL JOIN INSIDE OF INWALE TO TRANSOM

Fig. 31 Inwales

Pee-Wee with optional inwales fitted.

frame thickness inboard of the planking. Take a short piece of the same stock and shape its end to fit the transom at the other end of the boat as if it were that end of the inwale. Clamp both the inwale and the outer rail together on each successive frame head. Screw the outer rail to the transoms at both ends. Clamp at every frame head because if the inwale is not exactly where it will live when the end is cut, it may shorten up when fastened off. At the unfinished end, the long inwale will have to hang out over the transom. Hold the trimmed short piece in position up against the underside of the untrimmed inwale, and put a pencil witness mark across both pieces. Remove the lot from the boat. Place the short piece against the inwale with the

witness mark lining up and mark the inwale at the same distance and angle as your short trimmed piece. Cut just beyond your mark to be safe. Fit the pieces back to the boat and shave the inwale end down until it fits, loosening just enough clamps to be able to trim it on the boat, rather than removing the whole lot every time. Remove the clamps one at a time and drill and fasten off with roved copper nails driven from outside through both rails at each frame head.

The quarter knees will be fitted to the inside of the inwale, with a packer fitted between the inwale and the plank to take the knee fastenings. It is best if the packer extends from the transom to the nearest frame.

The inside of this Huon Pine Pee-Wee gets a coat of oil.

Painting and Varnishing

We generally oil the inside of the hull, with either a linseed/turpentine 50/50 mix, or a proprietary decking oil such as that made by Feast Watson. Several applications over one or two days are advisable. Painting or varnishing is possible, but can you imagine the labour required sanding all those frames and plank edges between coats! We often pick out the thwarts, knees and rowlock blocks in varnish. Choose a marine varnish with U-V inhibitors.

The outside also can be varnished,

but if you want to use the dinghy I suggest you paint it. A painted hull can be easily brought back to top looks after scratching the bottom on a rocky shore by filling, sanding and painting; a varnished hull cannot.

You could varnish the sheer strake and the transoms if you have fine timber and workmanship to show off, or you could pick out the sheer strake in a different colour.

For the rest of the hull, as a famous boatbuilder once said "There are only two colours to paint a boat: one is white and the other is black, and only a fool would paint it black!"

The outside of this Cedar Petrel gets a coat of varnish.

White or at least light colours tend to reflect the heat and limit wood movement. Use only oil-based paints, starting with a primer such as red lead or a metallic primer, then as many coats of sanding undercoat as you need to get the finish you require, and finish with two coats of gloss enamel. Neither the undercoats nor the enamels need to be specifically a marine paint, as long as they are oil-based.

There are other items you can add to your boat to give it a more finished look. You'll need a painter (a rope to tie it or tow it with) which can be attached to an eyebolt on the bow, or you can simply drill two holes in the bow either side of the knee and splice a rope through these.

If you want to use an outboard, you will need to glue a piece of 18mm marine plywood to the outside of the transom a little larger than the landing area of the outboard, before painting.

Floorboards

Floorboards (bottom boards, sole boards) are a good idea to protect the frames and the plank edges in the bottom of the boat from the feet.

The best way is to fit a bottom stringer of Ash, or whatever timber you used for the risers, 20 x 11mm to the line of the third plank outer lap, replacing the frame nails with ones going right through the stringer as well. The stringer (and floorboards) should extend from the frame nearest the forward edge of the aft seat to the frame nearest the aft edge of the forward seat.

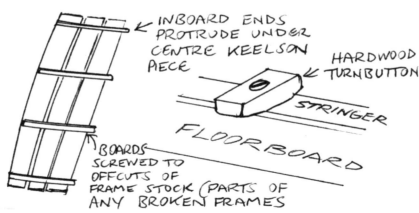

Fig. 32 Floorboards

Fit another piece of wood 60 x 11mm over the frames along the hog, screwing it down. The boards of 8mm thick White Beech, or Kauri or even clear Oregon should evenly taper in the area between the stringer and the keelson. Measure the distance at each relevant frame, and divide it into 3 (after subtracting 4 x 6mm = 24mm for gaps between floorboards), to get the width of the board at each frame. Pencil these marks on the frames and spile for the floorboards as for the planking. Screw the floorboards with 6mm gaps between each to cleats from offcuts of frame stock, preferably parts of broken frames with a slight curve. Use brass or bronze screws with heads set flush and slots lined up at right angles to the centreline.

As in **Fig. 32**, the floor boards are held down by putting the inboard end's protruding cleats under the centreline keelson piece, and two or three hardwood turn buttons mounted on the stringer.

See also *Pee-Wee* drawing on page 30. The boards should be oiled not varnished.

Now all you need to take her rowing is a pair of metal rowlocks with shafts to fit the holes you drilled (usually available in 3/8" 7/16" and 1'2") and a pair of six foot oars which you can buy off the shelf or make yourself from some clear Oregon, but that's another story.

Launching Day for first Petrel, River Quays Marina, 1990.

Strip Planking

Introduction

When first printed this manual was called WEST System Strip Planking. Arnie Duckworth of Adhesive technologies, the agents for WEST System epoxies in Australia and New Zealand was basically the inventor, or at least the developer of the method outlined here and it was Arnie who first proposed that we run classes on the method. Prior to setting up the School I had spent several years during the 1980's working casually for Adhesive Technologies as a travelling trouble-shooter for the large number of home builders at the time and it was this experience that led me to believe I could run classes. I still use and recommend WEST System epoxies, but in the thirty or so years that have elapsed the focus of their business has changed and other players have become dominant in the home builder market and I have dropped WEST System from the title to reflect this. Sometimes in this volume I will refer to the method as Epoxy Strip Planking, or just Strip Planking. Whichever brand you choose be sure it is an established company and not a backyarder who will lure you with cheap prices, I bet you will regret it. And whichever brand you choose make sure you **read the instructions on the container** as most manufacturers use different ratios. If I ever build another strip-planked boat it will be with WEST System epoxies.

Important Note

The boat used as a focus for the information is a 9 metre yacht, but the method can be used for any type of boat of any size, from small dinghies and canoes to large yachts, power boats and multi-hulls. If your project is a boat under 6 metres, keep the following points in mind:

1. Temporary moulds can be made from 12mm chipboard, especially if full-size paper patterns are available for the mould shapes, which is the case for many of the plans available.

2. If the boat is under 5 metres, the moulds are best set up on a simple ladder-frame jig, which is just the strong back as described in the manual set up on short legs.

3. Planking stock is sawn from 25mm boards, rather than the 50mm boards for larger boats, which means the planks will finish about 19-20mm wide, sawn to whatever thickness the designer suggests.

4. The glass cloth used for small boats is generally 330gsm or less, and is transparent when wetted-out with epoxy, so the hull can be varnished if desired for an attractive finish. It helps if the glue used for planking is coloured with a small amount of cement colouring. As bog cannot be used for fairing, the timber surface itself needs more careful fairing, and final sanding before glassing should involve a thorough woking down through the grades to around 180 grit, otherwise the scratches left from rougher paper will stand out as soon as the surface is wet-out.

Strip Planking

PART 1
Strip Planking - Getting Started

I'll start with a categorical statement: Strip planking is the best method for an amateur to build a boat for a variety of reasons:

1. It is the quickest method there is, rivalled only by chine plywood (and possibly chine steel).

2. Its material is relatively low and can be staggered over a period.

3. The skill level is low compared with other methods.

4. It nevertheless produces attractive round bilge hulls where attention to detail will result in high resale value.

5. A wide variety of hulls can be built, modern or traditional, light or heavy displacement, monohull or multi-hull.

To say that it is a quick and cheap method is relative; the quickest and cheapest method to get a boat is to buy one secondhand. There are plenty of sound boats available for less than the cost of the materials you will put into any home built boat.

A considerable effort in both time and money is necessary for you to build a boat. As a vague guide a 30 foot cruising yacht could not be built ready to sail in less than 3000 hours, and probably more. This represents at least 18 months full-time work at a 40 hour week. Working part-time, not many people could maintain 20 hours per week at which rate it would take three years. Don't let this dissuade you; for the most part it is pleasant work, and you will get a buzz out of seeing it come together. There are a lot of boats out there built by amateurs and professionals both proving the success of the method, but it does involve a commitment in time and money.

Design Selection

It is always best to buy plans from a reputable designer. They may cost more, but it will still be only a small percentage of the total cost of the boat.

Almost any design can be built to. It is possible to build a modern ultra-light racing machine, or a heavy displacement traditional yacht or anything in between. It is possible to build everything from a dinghy to 40 foot plus. It is not necessary that the plans be specifically designed for this method. Most plans can be converted to a strip plank construction plan, but please engage a professional to do this, either the original designer if he is experienced in this method, or another with the experience. Plans for a variety of lightweight craft specifically designed for this method are available, as also are plans for many multihulls.

Because of the size of the investment you will be making, you should consider resale value. This will be affected by many factors including interior and exterior finish, equipment etc, but at the design stage you can do a lot for resale value by selecting an attractive design.

Pretty boats sell a lot better than ugly ones, but for some reason there are a lot of ugly boats around. Beauty is in the eye of the beholder sure, but there are a lot of boats which by general consensus the boating community agrees are ugly, and these tend to appear regularly in for sale notices, getting progressively cheaper and more run down. Ugliness is often a product of trying to cram too much into too little. Also in considering the resale value, do not go to extremes. You may have a great theory of the performance of junk-rigged proas, and if so, good luck to you, we need experimenters, but do not expect any resale value from your boat.

Unless you are a very experienced sailor with a lot of money you are prepared to throw away, do not be tempted to design it yourself; therein lies heartbreak. If you want to be a designer, there's nothing wrong with that, but start with something small and work up, don't put your life savings into a large project which is bound to lead to disappointment.

Epoxy strip planking can be used to build hulls for all types of boats from heavy displacement traditional types like this Lyle Hess Seraffyn (top) to modern yachts like David Payne's Salvo class (middle) and his 14 foot putt-putt launch (bottom).

Smaller and lighter boats can also be built strip planked, like Iain Oughtred's Gannet and Egret designs (top), and elegant rowing skiffs like this Fisher skiff (middle), and even dinghies and canoes (bottom).

The most common error amateur boatbuilders make is to choose too big a craft. You don't need a 50 footer to live aboard and go cruising. Most long term cruisers have boats less than 35 feet. Anything larger is not only a big boat to handle at sea (and more especially manoeuvring in port), but is a huge investment in time and money.

The waterfront abounds in tales of disappointment and heartbreak due to the owner choosing too big a boat. Large incomplete boats are more common than they need to be.

Remember that the time taken to build the hull and deck is less than half what's required to finish the boat, and the cost is around one-third of the total. Do not be deceived by plan sellers who tell you how cheap the hull materials will be.

The second most common error is to change parts of the design, especially by shifting weights or beefing up specifications. If you feel the design you like should be stronger, then find a stronger design! There are enough to choose from. Major weights such as engines and fuel tanks should not be moved or increased in size. Please heed this; it is a sad fact that a majority of amateur built boats are beefed up or altered, and launching day is an embarrassment and a disappointment, but it need not be so.

Where to Build?

Having taken all this under your belt, you still intend to build, and you need a place to which to do it. Your own backyard is ideal: no rent, no travel. If you don't have a backyard, you have a problem. Paying rent at a location a distance from your home will soon become a strain. If you do have to pay rent your building program will have to be much better organised or the rent can amount to be a significant component of your boat's cost!

But no matter where it is it must be under cover. This need be no more elaborate than a weatherproof tent or awning over a timber frame. But for a project which is likely to last for years, it is generally better to erect a semi-permanent structure of timber and steel roofed with corrugated iron and/or fibreglass sheeting. In most Australian climates permanent walls are not necessary. Any time and money invested in a cover will be more than repaid in working time available on the boat.

Lofting

It appears I can't dissuade you, you've selected your plans and you're anxious to start. Your boat begins with lofting. Lofting need not be the great mystery it is often purported to be. It is simply drawing out the plans full size to check the shapes which the designer intended that you cut. The worst

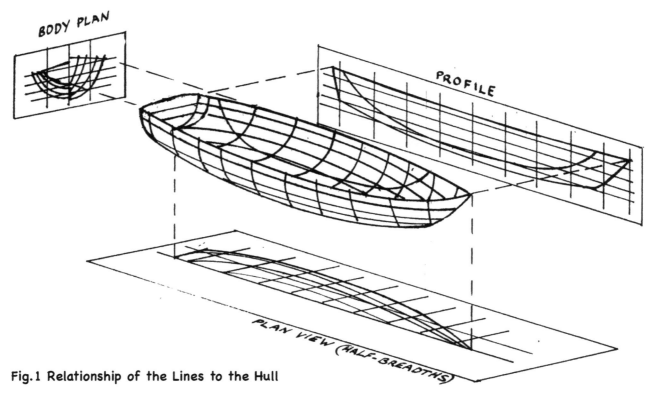

Fig. 1 Relationship of the Lines to the Hull

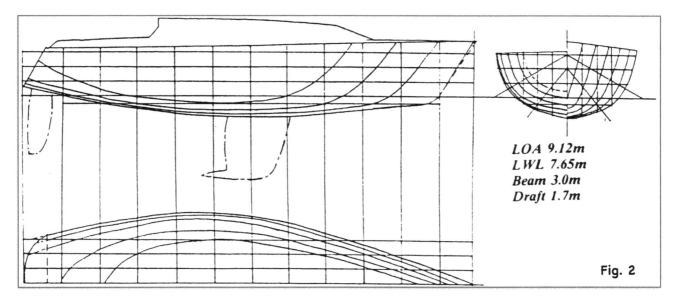

LOA 9.12m
LWL 7.65m
Beam 3.0m
Draft 1.7m

Fig. 2

that can be said of it is that it is laborious. There are even tragics like me who find it interesting! **Fig. 1** shows the relationship of the lines on paper to the lines on the hull.

The first question that usually comes up here is what about full size patterns? Many plans are available with these patterns, usually on sheets of drawing paper, which you transfer to your mould stock (temporary frames). They promise to save a great deal of time, but that is not always the case; due to dimensional changes in the paper and the ease of creating small errors in the transference, boats set up from paper patterns nearly always need a good deal of shimming and shaving of the moulds to get the set-up fair for planking.

The time involved can sometimes exceed the time it would have taken to loft the design fully. This also applies to those who wish to plot the body plan (the mould shapes) without fairing them longitudinally. There will inevitably be much shimming and shaving to get the set up fair. However, some people can relate to the set-ups in 3-D much better than they can to the loft floor in 2-D, and the end result can just be as good. Personally I believe any time spent on the loft floor will be more than saved on the hull, so I will describe the lofting process for those of a similar pedantic mind to myself.

But firstly computer lofting is now often touted as outmoding traditional lofting. This may in fact be the case, but a word of caution. In lofting two boats whose offsets were apparently computer lofted, I discovered errors in the full size lofting which had not been noticed on the scale plans. In one case a slight fish-tail had developed in the aft topsides which I was not prepared to build to: sure the lines were fair but full-size lofting showed that they were incorrect. Computer lofting programs available to yacht designers will obviously become more sophisticated, but I for one will use them cautiously for the moment.

The Grid and the Equipment

You will need to lay out a grid as detailed in the plans. The boat whose design we will follow here is a 9m sloop, designed by Glen Davis of Shiptech P/L as in **Fig. 2**.

You will need an area just bigger than the boat, in this case at least 11m x 2m. You should lay down a level surface of sheets of plywood or chipboard, painted flat white or melamine covered, at least ½" thick. Cleat them together so they can't move. If the surface is irregular you may have to level the boards with timber blocking.

You will need a whole bunch of battens, clear Oregon is best. For this boat:
- one of 11m x 38mm x 19mm
- one of 11m x 19mm x 12mm
- one of 3m x 19mm x 12mm
- and several (you may break some) of 2-3m x 3mm x 6mm

The longer ones will need to be scarfed. Fibreglass battens (if you can get them) are great. Buy a bag of 30mm x 2mm flat-head bright steel nails and some carpenters pencils, some HB drawing pencils and some coloured biros and marker pens, and a steel tape measure at least as long as the boat. You will need a straight edge 8' long (one machined side of a sheet of plywood is ideal), and a string line.

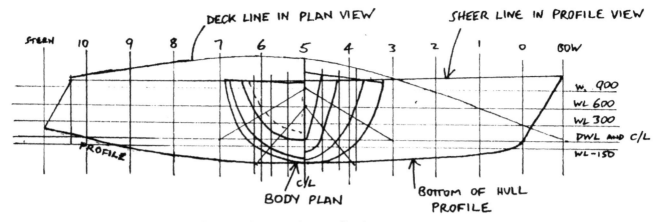

Fig. 3 The Three Views Superimposed as on the Loft Floor

The designer draws the three views separately but to save space it is normal to loft the three views superimposed on each other **(Fig. 3)**. Your first line is the designed waterline (DWL). Stretch the string line in the required position between two nails, mark very carefully underneath it every couple of feet, remove the string line and join up the dots! It is very important to take particular care to be accurate at this point; an inaccurate grid will make lofting difficult.

With either a set of trammel points or a homemade beam compass, establish a perpendicular which will become station 5 right in the middle of the lofting. **Fig. 4** shows the technique. Lay your tape along the baseline and mark the position of each station. Draw perpendiculars at 1 and 9, check your accuracy by ensuring that the distances between stations 9, 5 and 1 are the same at the top as well as the base of the board. Mark in the intermediate stations on the top as well, (make sure your tapeline is parallel with the DWL) and draw in the perpendiculars with the straight edge.

All the above lines should be inked permanently as soon as their accuracy is checked. Black ink is best. Each line should be labelled with a marker pen in several different places; it is all too easy to lose track of what is what. With the tape and straight edge, mark in all the grid waterlines, I would suggest in blue ink. The vertical buttocks (in green ink) and the diagonals (purple ink?) come next. Give it a final check by measuring across the grid diagonally both ways; the result should be within a millimetre or two.

Fig. 4 The Grid

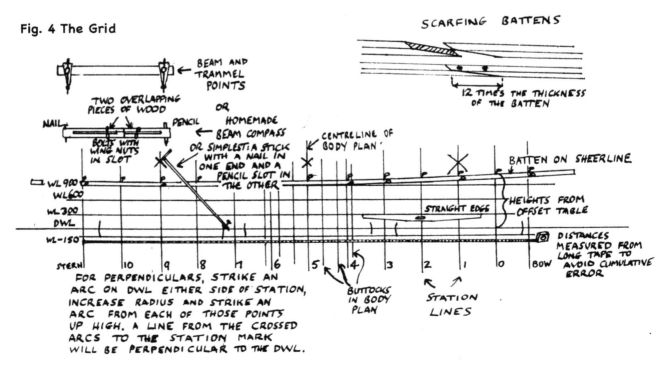

70

The Sheerline and Profile

The first line we draw that actually belongs to the boat is always the sheer line. From the table of offsets, read off the measurements of the heights of the sheer at each station. You simply mark each of these off, tack in nails at the marks, and bend your longest and stiffest batten around the line of the nails, holding it in place with other nails behind (not through) the batten.

Sight along it from both ends, and see if the curve is fair, that is, without bumps, hollows or flat spots, see **Fig. 5**. Move any nails which appear to be holding the batten in a bad position. Make the batten continue to bend past the last nail at either end of the batten in the direction it was tending just before the last nail, to avoid a flat spot in the ends. If no nails need moving, well that's friggin' unusual, but expect to adjust several nails by up to 6mm or so.

The general principle where several nails are out of line is to adjust all to an average line of best fit. When you're happy your line looks good from all angles, ink it in permanently, this line will no longer change; so you'd better be happy with it; it's the most noticeable line of all on the finished boat, and in the past the beauty of a yacht was often judged on the sweetness of her sheer.

The lofting floor.

The next line to draw in is the same line, only in plan view, generally referred to as the Deck Line to avoid confusion. The same principles apply; once you're happy with the fairness of this line, ink it in, it will not change.

The profile of the hull is the next line to ink in the same positions, followed by (on some boats) the line indicating the half-breadth of the stem and the half-siding of the keel. On this boat the boat lines are carried forward to an imaginary meeting point.

Fig. 5 Battens

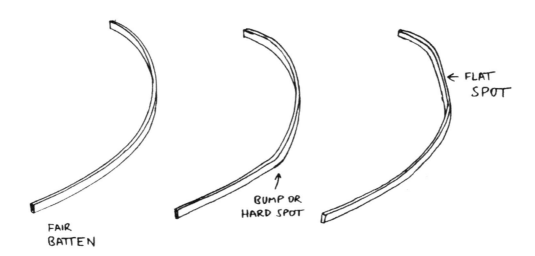

FAIR
BATTEN

← FLAT
SPOT

BUMP OR
HARD SPOT

71

The Body Plan

You now need several flat straight strips of wood, about 1½ - 2 metres x 20mm x 1.5mm or 2mm thick, known as tick strips or pick up sticks. As in **Fig. 6** you pick up the marks for the width of the deck line at each station and the height of the sheer at each station and realising that these are co-ordinates of the one point on the sheer, plot them onto the body plan. When each has been done, use the same technique to locate the intersection with the profile, and plot these points on the body plan.

Now turn to the table of offsets. At each station there is an offset given for the half-breadth of each waterline, for the height of each buttock, and for the distance along each diagonal, see **Fig. 6**. Plot out each of these points onto the body plan grid, then throw away the offset table, you won't need to again. With your most flexible battens, pencil in a line of best fit through the shotgun scatter of the designers intended points (**Fig. 7**). In some cases, most points will fit. In most cases most will not. Do not ink in this line, it is bound to be changed.

Fairing the Diagonals, Waterlines and Buttocks

With your new friends the tick strips, pick up all the distances along Diagonal A at each pencilled station line, and transfer these out from the base line at each station. A smattering of nails, a long batten, and we see how far out diagonals are - the diagonals more than any other line follow the line of the planking - by plotting out the diagonal in the manner described we are finding out if the planking would lie fairly if we cut our moulds to the shapes we pencilled in on the body plan, see **Fig. 8**.

Most likely, this first plotting will show one or more small corrections necessary to gain a fair curve. Note these, and mark them back on the body plan in red as a correction. Don't redraw the station lines in the body plan yet.

First do the same for the other diagonal(s), then do the same for all the waterlines, then each of the buttocks. When all corrections have been carefully marked on the body plan (mark them as soon as they are discovered), redraw the section lines in the body plan to the line of best fit.

Oh lucky you, if all the corrections agree and fit into the new line! It's much more likely that several points will not. So with your tick strips, pick up the points of any corrected section lines and again plot out the diagonals, waterlines and buttocks.

If these longitudinal lines are still fair with these changes, well and good, but if not, new corrections need to be marked on the body plan and the whole process double-backed over again. Each time should bring you closer. You can ink the line in when you feel no further correction need to be made.

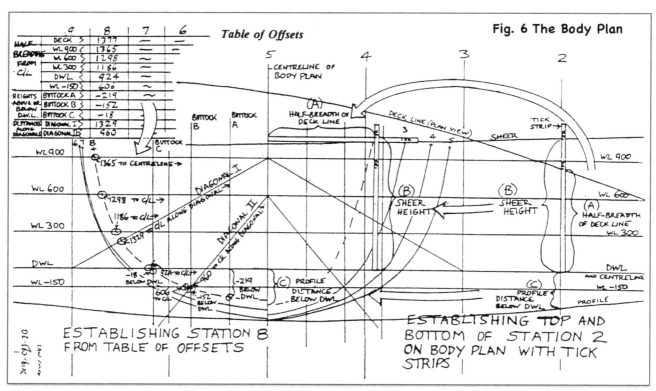

Fig. 6 The Body Plan

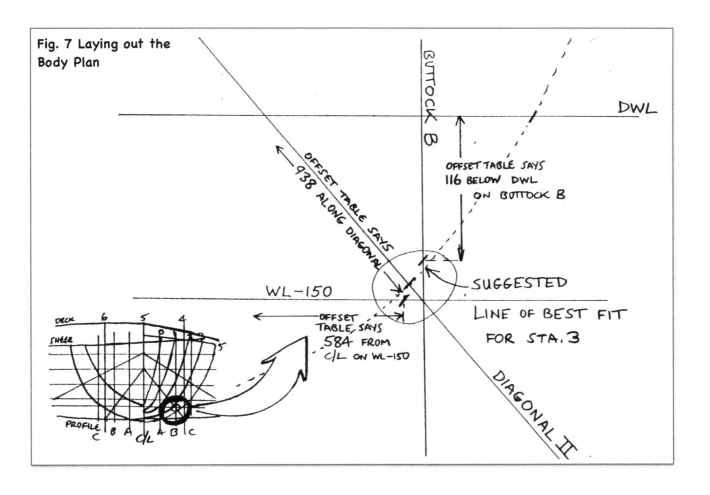

Fig. 7 Laying out the Body Plan

Fig. 8 Fairing Diagonals

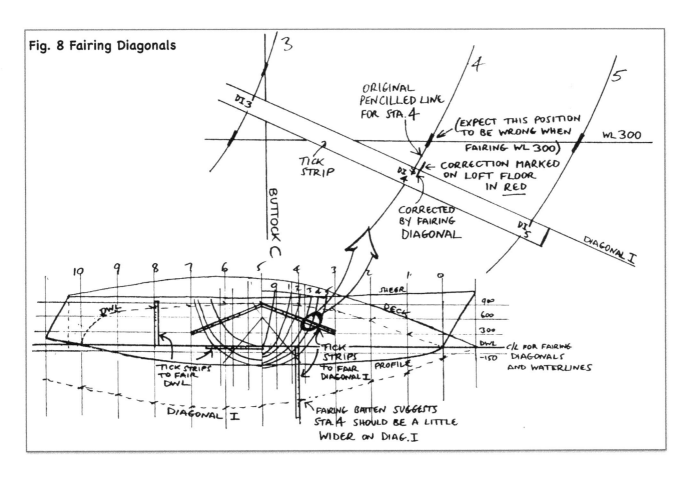

Lofting Agreement

Every line on the lofting is represented by a different view. For example, waterline 900 is a straight horizontal line in both body plan and profile, and a curved line in profile in plan view. Buttock A is a vertical line in the body plan, a horizontal line in profile, See **Fig. 9** - wherever two lines cross in one view, this position in space (relative to the grid) should agree with the position where these two lines cross on both other views. This the essence of lofting, but some points are easy to miss - being methodical is the only way.

Transom Expansion

Because the transom is sloped, if you were to include it in the setup you would have to geometrically develop its true shape, but the good news is you don't have to do it. When setting up the boat, make a vertical mould at the stern station and carry all the planking aft to it. When you turn the boat over and remove the moulds not having a transom will make it much easier to climb in and out of the boat while you complete the interior. Then it is a relatively easy matter to cut the planking at the correct angle and add a plywood transom.

Construction Plan

Once lofted to agreement, we can commence drawing in the construction plan, preferable in red ink. First the hog, as in **Fig. 10,** being careful to transfer the correct heights to the body plan. The stem should be drawn in profile (**Fig. 11**), and several sections through it drawn in to determine the bearding one (to which the sides of the stem are bevelled).

Of course the lines on the original lofting are to the outside of the planking, so we must reduce these, by the thickness of the planking. But remembering each station is a section through the boat, and well forward or well aft, the planking crosses these stations at some angle, the actual planking thickness deducted at the ends should be greater.

Fig.10 shows the method for picking this up. With the actual shapes to the inside of the planking marked on the body plan, you are now ready to cut the moulds, over which you will plank the boat.

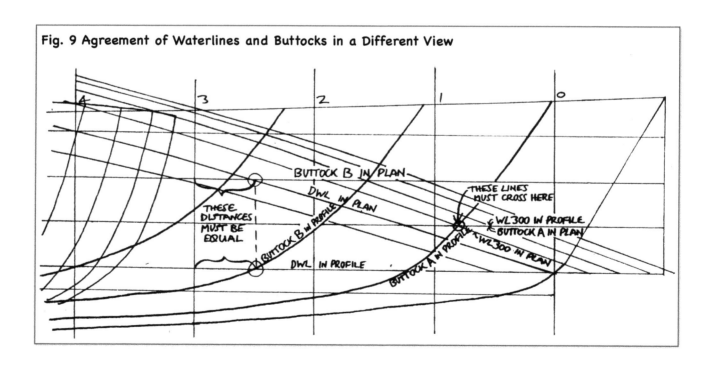

Fig. 9 Agreement of Waterlines and Buttocks in a Different View

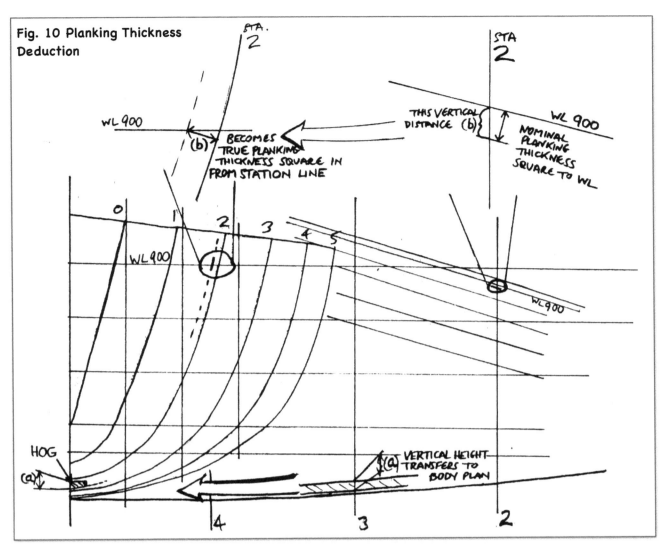

Fig. 10 Planking Thickness Deduction

STA. 2

STA 2

WL 900

THIS VERTICAL DISTANCE (b)

NOMINAL PLANKING THICKNESS SQUARE TO WL

WL 900

(b) BECOMES TRUE PLANKING THICKNESS SQUARE IN FROM STATION LINE

0   1   2   3   4   5

WL 900

WL 900

HOG

(a)

(a) VERTICAL HEIGHT TRANSFERS TO BODY PLAN

4   3   2

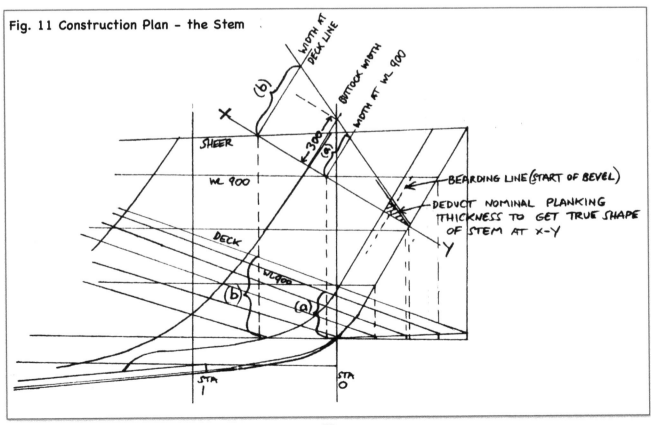

Fig. 11 Construction Plan – the Stem

WIDTH AT DECK LINE

BUTTOCK WIDTH

WIDTH AT WL 900

(b)

X

SHEER

←300→

(a)

BEARDING LINE (START OF BEVEL)

DEDUCT NOMINAL PLANKING THICKNESS TO GET TRUE SHAPE OF STEM AT X–Y

WL 900

DECK

WL 900

Y

(b)

(a)

STA 1

STA 0

PART 2
The Moulds and Setting Up

So you've got a set of lines on the loft floor you're happy with, with the correct planking thickness deduction marked, the position and the shape of the stem drawn in. Or maybe you have a set of full size patterns in which you have confidence. If you have, you can skip the next bit until we start talking about laminating the stem.

There are three things you must do, and another that you should do before taking up the loft floor:

1. The position of the sheer clamp or deck shelf where the deck joins the hull must be marked on the stations.

2. The station shapes must be marked on the mould stock and the mould assembled.

3. The stem must be laminated.

You should also mark in the position of as many bulkheads, partitions and shelves as you feel like.

Virtually every plywood component of the interior can be drawn on the loft floor, the shapes transferred to sheets of plywood which can be cut and stored until the boat is turned over and ready to receive them. This is a big advantage that you get from complete lofting, it will save you many hours during your interior fit-out. You can virtually make yourself a kit of parts of the interior! Every bulkhead can be drawn in on the three views as if it were an extra station. It will be a straight line athwartship (across the boat) in the plan view, and everywhere this line crosses a waterline, transfer its distance from the centreline plan, horizontally out along the relevant waterline from the centreline (see **Fig. 12**).

Do this for each waterline in plan view, for each buttock in profile view (and the diagonals if possible), join all the dots on the body plan, and after deducting the planking thickness you have the true shape of the bulkhead against the hull.

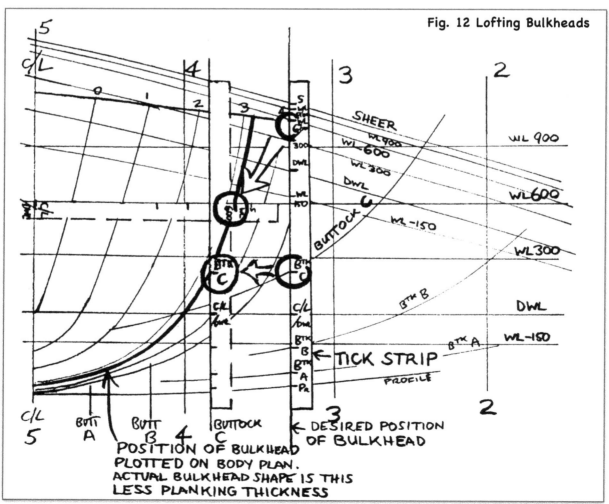

Fig. 12 Lofting Bulkheads

POSITION OF BULKHEAD PLOTTED ON BODY PLAN. ACTUAL BULKHEAD SHAPE IS THIS LESS PLANKING THICKNESS

Similarly, every horizontal plywood surface against the hull such as bunk tops and shelves can be traced as a new waterline, and every fore and aft partition (such as bunk fronts) can be treated as a new buttock.

Marking for the Sheer Clamp

The fairness and sweetness of the sheer is very important: a bad sheer is very obvious! The heights of the sheerline are marked on the station lines, but they must be transferred correctly to the moulds.

First you have to establish the camber or crown of the deck. Some boats, particularly more traditional designs will have all deck beams cut to the same curve, which makes it easier, but most modern designs, such as the 9m sloop by Glen Davis we are using as a example will have a different curve at each deck beam. This must be worked out from the sheer line at each station (**see Fig. 13**).

Draw a horizontal line from the sheer mark on the station in the body plan back to the centreline, and describe an arc with a radius equal to the height of the deck centreline over the sheer, with its centre where the horizontal sheer height line meets the centreline of the body plan. Divide the perimeter of the arc into four; divide the line under the arc into four, and join these with lines A, B and C, and join up the dots with a batten to get the shape of the camber of the deck at that station. Do the same for each foredeck station.

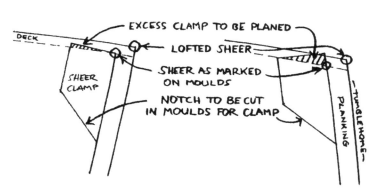

Fig. 14 Locating Sheer Clamp

The plans contain information on the slope of the side decks in the construction sections. You will eventually end up with the camber of the deck at the sheer marked on all stations of the body plan. Draw a parallel line representing the thickness of the deck, and thus at the hull/deck join you will have the shape of the top of the clamp and the planking on which the deck will sit. Draw in the sectional view of the sheer clamp at each station so you can set it at the correct height (**Fig. 14**). Forward of, say Station 4, don't forget the apparent thickness of the sheer clamp will be increased because of the angle it approaches the bow, in the same way that the apparent planking thickness increases here, and this can be calculated in the same manner for the deck line in plan view (see back in Part 1). There is no need to be pedantic about this, however, as the notches cut to receive the hog and sheer clamp can be cut deeper or packed out once everything is set up.

Marking out the Moulds

The moulds are best made from cheap Radiata Pine 19mm boards, for this boat 250mm boards are about right. Chipboard is also acceptable, at least 18mm thick. Start with the largest mould, Station 5. Lay a line of flat-head nails along the station line (the new line reduced for planking thickness), at about 40 to 50 mm spacing, and tap them to dig the heads in. Lay some also along the centreline and every straight line (waterlines, buttocks and diagonals) which the width of the board used will cover. Amidships here, each side of the mould will require separate pieces. It is sensible to pick diagonal A as the joining line between the two pieces.

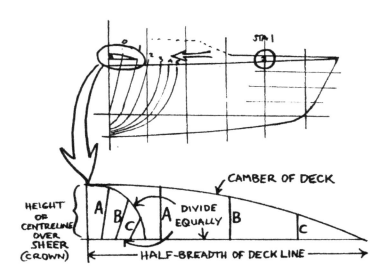

Fig. 13 Deck Camber

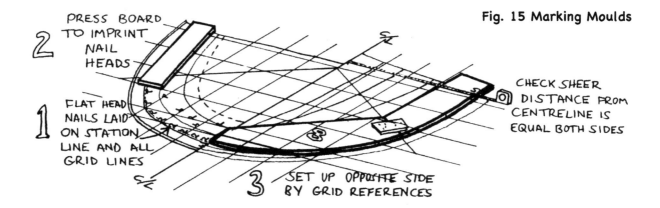

2 PRESS BOARD TO IMPRINT NAIL HEADS

1 FLAT HEAD NAILS LAID ON STATION LINE AND ALL GRID LINES

3 SET UP OPPOSITE SIDE BY GRID REFERENCES

CHECK SHEER DISTANCE FROM CENTRELINE IS EQUAL BOTH SIDES

Fig. 15 Marking Moulds

Place a pine board over the nails so that as little of it as possible is outside the line of nails, stand or kneel on it and tap it all around with a hammer to imprint the nail heads on the underside. Simply turn it over and join up the dots with nails and batten for the curved lines, and straight edges for the straight lines. Cut square with a jigsaw just clear of the line and plane down to the line, or if you have a bandsaw you may be able to cut accurately enough to reduce or avoid planing at all.

On the diagonals and centreline where the boards will join, cut under the line slightly; it is better to have a small gap between the sections than to not be able to line them up. Square the grid lines onto the board edges. If you have a bandsaw tack two boards together and cut them together, otherwise you will have to trace the first one onto the other and cut with a jigsaw. Remember to cut notches for the hog and sheer clamp.

Assembling the Moulds

One copy of each section can sit back exactly on the lofted line. To locate the other side where the section has not been drawn, we use the grid lines marked on the boards to line up with the grid pattern on the floor as in **Fig. 15**. Double check by measuring the distance back to the centreline along Waterline 900 on both sides. It is best to nail down through the mould into the loft floor to prevent movement. Glue (PVA is fine, but maybe you should practice with the epoxy here) and nail or screw plywood pads down across the joins at diagonal and centreline.

Straighten one edge of a 200 x 19mm board of pine with a power jointer or plane, and set it so that it follows exactly Waterline 600 with the board on the sheer line side of

the waterline. Nail and glue it in place. It is vital to be as accurate as possible, because this **cross spall** as it is called will be used to level up each mould athwartship and relative to the other moulds. Mark the centreline and buttocks accurately on the cross spall. Make a mould for every station, including the transom station lofted vertically.

Fitting Legs

Legs of 75 x 50 or maybe 50 x 50 for smaller boats are fitted to each mould so as to stand it up. The legs should be long enough so that when they are on the ground, the upside-down boat will be high enough to be at a good working height and so that the stem will easily clear the ground. Refer to the lofting for this. It would be worse than frustrating to forget this point.

The legs should be placed at regular width, so it is best to use one of the buttock spacings, in our case Buttock C, 900mm out from the centreline. Stations 0, 1, and 2 are too narrow for this and their legs will be set narrower. For moulds 3-10 and transom mould, set the legs 3-4mm inboard of the buttock line. They live on the side of the mould

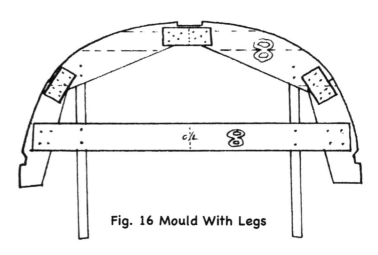

Fig. 16 Mould With Legs

78

facing down when you assembled the mould. This face will be the **control face** of the mould, that is, the face which will represent the station line when set up. By fitting the legs to this side, the joining face of the legs also represents the station line. Packers will be needed between the cross spall and the legs, of the same thickness as the mould stock. The joint face of each leg should be dead straight, and machining or planing may be necessary for this. The other sides may remain rough sawn.

Nail or screw each mould to its legs. Fast-drive chipboard screws are best when used with an electric screwdriver. You'll finish up with a stack of moulds like **Fig. 16**. You'll want to start setting them up, but before you move the loft floor you should laminate the stem.

The Stem

The stem is best laminated from clear Oregon. On most traditional designs, stems are curved and are best laminated from timber laminates bent around a jig of the shape required. On this boat and most modern designs, the stem is dead straight for most of it length, with a very sharp knuckle or turn just below the waterline. If it were laminated with thin enough veneers to bend around this tight curve, it would be very expensive. So we will laminate it with straight boards as in **Fig. 17**.

Three or four thicknesses of Oregon boards whose total thickness matches the designed width of the stem are laminated side by side with joints staggered. Use the stem shape drawn on the lofting to determine the angle at which the boards must

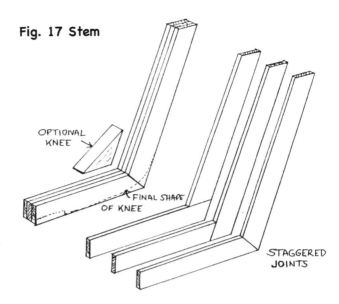

Fig. 17 Stem

OPTIONAL KNEE

FINAL SHAPE OF KNEE

STAGGERED JOINTS

meet. Apply epoxy to both surfaces and clamp together with as many clamps as you can. Small bronze nails can be used to stop the laminations sliding about under pressure, but make sure they are in parts of the stem that you will not cut into for shaping and bevelling.

Curved Laminations

If your boat's stem has a curve of radius wide enough to do it, you can laminate it directly on the picture of it that you drew on the loft floor. Machine the laminations to the greatest thickness that will easily take the bend, and to a width of at least 10mm wider than the designed finish size of the stem. Enough laminations must be cut to cover the area drawn on the floor. Screw metal right angle brackets to the floor along the line of the inside

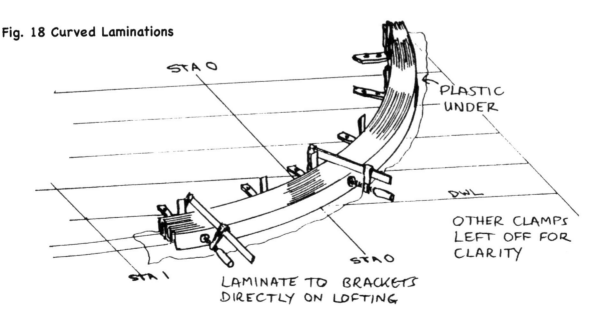

Fig. 18 Curved Laminations

STA 0

PLASTIC UNDER

DWL

OTHER CLAMPS LEFT OFF FOR CLARITY

STA 0

STA 1

LAMINATE TO BRACKETS DIRECTLY ON LOFTING

curve of the stem as in **Fig. 18**. Bend the laminations around dry to make sure they will do it. It is possible that you will have to laminate it in more than one go if the tension is too much for you to pull in, or too much for the screws holding the angle brackets down.

Assemble as many laminations as you can pull round and clamp them in place. Occasionally one or more will crack, especially if they contain knots or imperfections. Replace any cracked laminations as they will distort the others. Release the clamps and take the stack to a bench where you apply epoxy thickened with microfibres to all joining surfaces, and pile the stack together. Use plastic gloves from here on because the glue will get everywhere, but remove them when fitting the clamps or you'll cover them with glue.

It is best to have a helper without gloves, or possibly wear one glove only. Put plastic sheeting down on the floor so that the stem will not become permanently attached to it. Clamp whichever end of the stem has the greatest curve (usually the end below the waterline) to the correct bracket and slowly bend it around. Be careful not to pinch the plastic sheeting between laminations. As the timbers bear on each bracket, put a clamp there. Don't over tighten the clamps yet, just enough to hold the clamps in place. As you tighten each clamp, also tighten the previous one a little or it may fall.

If your stem is made oversize (as it should be) don't worry too much about pads under the clamps (unless the foot of the clamp is missing as some of mine are). If the laminations start to slide up, tap them back with a mallet and a block of wood to keep the glue off the mallet. You may have to temporarily loosen some clamps to do this. When all clamps are on, systematically tighten them, but don't strain your wrists, they should not be too tight.If you squeeze all the epoxy out, there will not be enough there to do the job. Scrape away as much glue as possible with a putty knife. Leave the clamps on for at least 24 hours, unless you have a heater on overnight. Clean the top surface up with a power plane with tungsten tipped blades, as the glue is extremely hard on steel blades. Hand planes could be used but will require constant sharpening, or a belt sander or grinder could be used to remove the glue, and then smooth the timber with a hand plane. Keep the surface dead flat, and stop when timber shows up on every lamination. Plane or belt

A dry fit for laminating the stem directly on the lofting.

sand the other side and then plane it to the desired thickness either by machine or by hand, then it's ready to mark to shape.

Shaping the Stem

No matter which method you used to laminate the stem, you now mark its outline by the same method as you used to mark the moulds, with flat-headed nails impressed on the outline and all grid lines (waterlines and station lines and the sheer line). The shape can then be cut on a bandsaw, or chiselled out Michelangelo style, including the landing for the hog. If you lofted the bearding line and the width of the stem at the bow (see Part 1) mark there also. You can then saw, chisel and plane as close as you dare to these lines. Be very conservative in the area of the sharp knuckle of the bow. It is better to leave fine tuning of this area until each plank is ready to fit there. If you didn't loft those lines, leave the stem square and proceed to setting up.

The Strongback

With a chalkline or a stringline, straight edge and pencil, make a line on the floor longer than the boat. Two Oregon 100 x 50's about 6.3m long are set on the floor reasonably straight, nearly but not necessarily level, and with each inner side 900mm from the line.

Fix them somehow to the floor. If the floor is cement, it will be sufficient to mix some epoxy and dab bits around the timbers where they meet and the floor as in **Fig. 19**. A short sharp hammer blow will break them off when dismantling. At one end put two 3m lengths of 100 x 50 Oregon angled in from the ends so they meet in the centre. Cleat these to the parallel pieces and to each other where they meet with plywood pads. Drive a nail into the forward cleat, dead centre on the line. Measure from this nail back along the centrelines about 4.5 metres, and place a 75 x 50mm piece of Oregon just spanning the two parallel timbers so that in the centre it is about that distance from the nail.

Measure from the nail to where this cross piece rests on both parallel timbers and adjust the cross piece until the measurement is equal. This ensures the cross piece is square with the centreline. Fasten it down with nails or screws. This piece becomes the base for Station 5, and the position of all other stations is taken from this. The actual line representing Station 5 is the **forward** side of the cross piece. Mark in the other stations and check

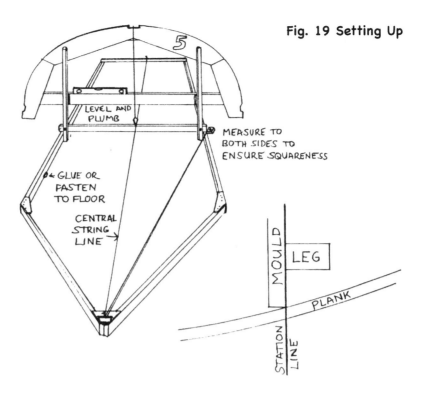

Fig. 19 Setting Up

that they are square to the centreline by measuring diagonally across both corners of the grid set up on the parallel timbers.

Fasten all the cross pieces forward of Station 5 aft of the station line, and all pieces **aft** of Station 5 **forward** of the station line. Thus the legs supporting the moulds will be forward of the line in the forward part of the boat, and aft of the line in the aft part of the boat.

You will remember that the face of the mould fastened to the legs is the control face of the mould, that is, the face which represents the actual station line, so the moulds will be aft of the line in the aft part, as in **Fig. 19**. The hull planks will just touch the corner of the mould representing the station line. It is not necessary to bevel all the moulds so that the planking will lie flat, it will sit quite well on the mould edge. If for some masochistic reason you wanted to bevel the moulds (or if you were building some permanent frames into the set-up), each of the moulds would have to be set to the opposite side of the station line for the control face to be on the station line.

Moulds set up for John Sayer racing yacht, stem laminated in place. This design also called for laminated frames on stations.

Setting Up

Straighten a string line from the nail at the bow to the centre of the aftermost crosspiece. Start by erecting mould 5, and work out in one direction, then the other. Estimate the amount of rise and fall of the floor, and using two of a bunch of small shallow wedges you've cut, stand mould 5 on these wedges and clamp the legs to the crosspiece. It can be done alone but a helper or two would be ideal.

You need to check the following:

1. The top of the cross spall must be dead level athwartship (across the boat). Use a spirit level and tap the wedges to adjust it.

2. The centreline on the mould must be plumb and exactly over the string line; use a plumb bob. Avoid confusion by ensuring that tools, power cords or feet are not distorting the string line. Tap wedges between the parallel floor timbers and the legs to adjust size to side.

3. The legs should be vertical fore and aft. Clamp diagonal braces of 50 x 25 mm Oregon to fix this position.

Double check all of these, and when happy they are correct, fasten the legs to the crosspieces (long screws or carriage bolts are best) and fasten the braces to the legs and crosspiece or floor with screws. Check again after fastening to see that nothing moved.

Each succeeding mould is set up in exactly the same fashion, with the further check that the cross spall is level with that on the previous mould.

When all are erected, there should be a continuous line of sight across spalls, all exactly level athwartships and with each other. Now it is getting exciting, you're starting to see the shape of the boat with each new mould erected.

Author's Note 2019

Since this was written laser levels have become easily available and cheap, so do yourself a favour and get one.

Setting Up the Stem

Use the grid lines on the stem to locate its position. Waterline 600 should be exactly in line with the top of the mould cross spalls; Station 0 should fit exactly on the control face (forward face) of mould 0. Viewed from inside the boat, the marked centreline on the back of the stem should be directly above the string line; and of course its sides should be plumb. Occasionally you will find minor discrepancies due to small errors in transferring marks, so it is best to average these out if you can't tell which ones are wrong. Fix the stem in place with temporary screws through mould 0,

Stem lamination and hog/keel batten fitted to moulds on the first of David Payne's Salvo Class.

angling them so that they will be able to be removed from inside once the planking is on. Fasten the extra length of the stem beyond the sheer to the strong back on the floor with cleats.

The Hog

The hog is the backbone of the boat, attached to the stem and running right through the centre of the transom and again should be Oregon. In this boat it is 195mm wide and 45mm thick , and can be bent over the moulds in one thickness. Many boats require more than one thickness to take the curve, and they are laminated in situ over the moulds. As you can imagine, lots of clamps are needed here. The hog is held down with temporary screws driven through the moulds from inside the boat; be careful to ensure the moulds are still exactly the correct distance apart here. It is glued and bolted to the stem. Two 10mm stainless steel bolts are well counterbored so as to be out of the range of plane blades when shaping. The nuts on the inside are counterbored and plugged or epoxy puttied up.

The Sheer Clamp.

The sheer clamp is fitted inside the notches already made in the moulds and fastened with temporary screws from inside, once again checking that the moulds are the correct distance apart. In most boats the clamp will need to be laminated from two thicknesses, and this is done in situ. Both the hog and sheer clamp may need to be scarfed to get the required length, and this is illustrated in **Fig. 20**. The scarfing can take place on the floor or on the moulds, with scarfs staggered so that each scarf joint can be clamped to the solid second part of the lamination. When fitting the sheer clamp, some notches in the moulds will need to be deepened and some will need to be packed out so that the surface of the sheer clamp is in line with the control face of the mould.

At the stem the sheer clamp is set into a notch so that the outside surface meets the bearding line. If you have no marked bearding line you will have to determine this by shaping the stem using a batten along the line of planking, but we will go into this later.

Fig. 20 Scarfing

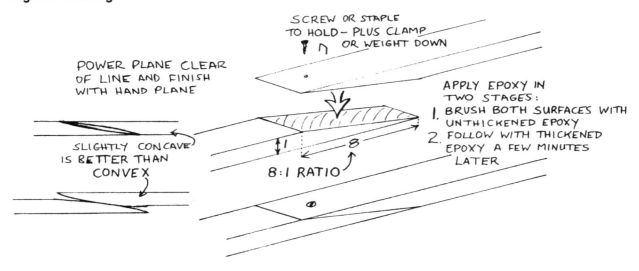

SCREW OR STAPLE TO HOLD - PLUS CLAMP OR WEIGHT DOWN

POWER PLANE CLEAR OF LINE AND FINISH WITH HAND PLANE

SLIGHTLY CONCAVE IS BETTER THAN CONVEX

8:1 RATIO

APPLY EPOXY IN TWO STAGES:
1. BRUSH BOTH SURFACES WITH UNTHICKENED EPOXY
2. FOLLOW WITH THICKENED EPOXY A FEW MINUTES LATER

Part 3 Planking

The backbone of your boat is set up; all the moulds are level and plumb, and the stem, hog and sheer clamp are all fitted. You have shaped your stem roughly to the bearding line, or it may still be square as is the hog.

Fairing the Setup

These parts have to be shaped for the planking to sit fairly, and the moulds themselves checked for the same reason. Along the top of the hog, we need to remove wood to continue the station line from the moulds. Make twin saw cuts as in **Fig. 21**, but be a little conservative. Mark a centreline on top of the hog, and keep just clear of it with the saw cuts from each side. The hog will eventually have a ridge along here where the planking from both sides meets. Chisel out the saw cuts, and you have guidelines to remove the stock in between the moulds.

Tack a light batten along the side of the hog resting on the moulds, and pencil a line under the batten. This will give the line below which no wood should be removed. Make simple saw cuts (every 50mm or so) along the hog staying above this line, and just clear of the centreline. Chisel out the chunks of wood in between, chiselling with the grain. When close to the bottom of the saw cuts, change to a power plane. Don't go too close to the line with the power plane either. Fine tune it with a No. 3 or No. 4 hand plane. Lay battens across the moulds parallel with where you expect the planking to lie, and keep removing wood from the hog until the batten lies fair.

Ray Beale 45 footer ready for planking.

The same system is used to shape the stem, except that there are no moulds from which to get a line, and it all must be done with battens. Constant checking as you remove wood is necessary so as not to remove too much. Pretend the batten is a plank, and remove wood until it lies fair.

With a helper or two, hold the batten over the moulds also to check their fairness. If your lofting was correct, and the boat was set up carefully, there may be no changes necessary. But it is possible some error has crept in, or perhaps you have used the designer's full size patterns or attempted to save time by not lofting fully, and if the batten refuses to sit on a particular mould without a flat spot being forced into it, or if a high spot holds the batten off the moulds either side of it, they must be corrected.

Removing the high spots is easy with a plane. Filling the hollows is done by gluing (PVA is fine) wood strips onto the offending areas, then planing them back until the batten sits fairly.

Fig. 21 Fairing the Set-Up

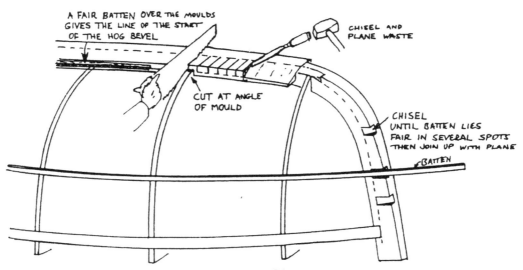

Materials for Planking

Western Red Cedar is the ideal material for planking. It is light, strong for its weight, easy to work, glues well, is reasonably cheap and readily available. And even if the planks you get are unseasoned, it seasons very quickly in thin planks. I have used New Zealand Kauri, Clear Oregon, King William Pine, Kalantas, Poplar and Mahogany successfully. Australian Red Cedar would also work well if you can afford it, but unless there is a specific reason, such as wanting to clear finish a particular timber, you can't really go past Western Red Cedar.

Stem and frames faired off ready for planking on Sayer 40.

Balsa cored panels such as Durakore are terrific if your design is ultra-light and the weight is critical. These panels are constructed as sheets of end-grain balsa blocks, sandwiched between veneers. The sheets are then cut to a useful planking width, usually 45mm, and joined into planks as long as the boat by finger jointing or by scarfing, and strip planked on the moulds in exactly the same manner as solid timber planks.

If using Durakore you must take the following into account: more care is needed to get the planks to lie fairly between the moulds, possibly even by setting your moulds closer together, and all the surface fairing must be done by adding bog as the veneers should not be planed at all. This makes it a little more expensive than solid timber, but for those boats for which lightness is critical, it is a superb way to go.

Machining Planking

There are boatbuilding supplies companies in most cities who custom machine boat grade planking, but for those who have access to a thickness planer and a reasonable saw bench, here are some details of how to machine your own planking.

Order it in standard sizes like 200 x 50 or 150 x 50; that way you can plane it to 45mm thickness and then saw the planks to your designed thickness as in **Fig. 22.**

Cut them 2mm over the designed finished thickness to allow for fairing. It is not necessary to thickness plane them because any reasonable saw bench will give a correct thickness and an adequate surface considering that both sides will have to be planed and/or sanded fair anyway. Align the grain as in **Fig. 22** so the planking is quarter sawn, that is, the tree rings meet the wider surfaces of the plank at more than 45 degrees, so that the surface will be more stable and easier to fair.

Hollowing the bottom and rounding the top of each plank tends, I say tends, to help them lie together better in the easy areas, but it actually makes things more difficult in the difficult areas. There is considerable wastage involved in machining this detail which far outweighs any small benefits. The planks are better off left square.

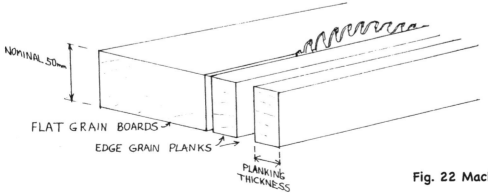

NOMINAL 50mm

FLAT GRAIN BOARDS

EDGE GRAIN PLANKS

PLANKING THICKNESS

Fig. 22 Machining Planking

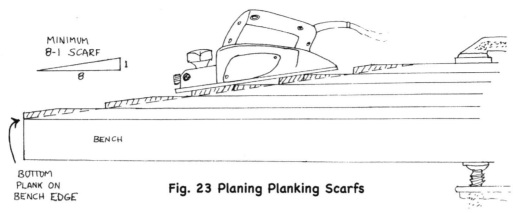

MINIMUM
8-1 SCARF

BENCH

BOTTOM
PLANK ON
BENCH EDGE

Fig. 23 Planing Planking Scarfs

with all scarfs facing up as in **Fig. 24**.

Brush or wipe unthickened epoxy onto all of the scarfs, and you will see it begin to soak in quickly. Top up any particular dry areas. Mix more resin, this time thicken it to a runny honey consistency with microfibres and apply this to all surfaces. Cut a long continuous strip of plastic a bit wider than the area covered by each scarf joint and place one end of it on the floor near the planks. Take one from the right-hand side, turn it over and press the scarfs together. Scrape away the glue as it squeezes out so you can ensure that the joint is tight.

Check that the planks both sides of the scarf joint are in a continuous line. Fire a staple or a small screw through the scarf joint to stop slippage, and make sure it does not protrude above the plank surface. Do the same with another pair of planks laying them on the plastic only 40 to 60mm from the first pair.

Drape the plastic across both scarf joints and place another pair of scarfed planks on top. Keep adding planks to the piles remembering to put the plastic in between layers and ensuring that the planks are in line either side of the scarf. Once all

Tongue-and-Groove Planking

There are companies that supply WR Cedar strip planking in several sizes with a loose tongue-and-groove machined into it. This works well on many hulls, the main advantage being that it makes sure the planking stays in line between moulds, and you do not need to scarf as long as you stagger the butt joins. The disadvantage is that it is more expensive and on some difficult hulls you will have to cut off the tongues in some areas. We used it on two Salvo class yachts without problems.

Estimating Quantities

The rule of thumb with quantities is to work out the maximum girth of the hull and divide it by the chosen plank width to get the number of planks. Multiply this by the overall boat length to get the number of lineal metres of planking to order. The total square meterage is greater than the actual hull area but includes an allowance for wastage and scarfing, and usually works out very close. If machining the planking yourself, work out how many planks you can get out of the chosen timber size.

Scarfing

Cedar is not usually available over six meters, so scarfing is necessary to get the length, and should be done before fitting to the hull.

The easiest method considering the number of scarfs is to use a power plane to cut the scarfs on six to eight planks at a time stacked on a bench as in **Fig. 23**. Plane the scarf on two groups of planks which when joined will make up the required length. Take the planed stacks to the floor and form two piles of one length

Fig. 24 Scarfing Planks

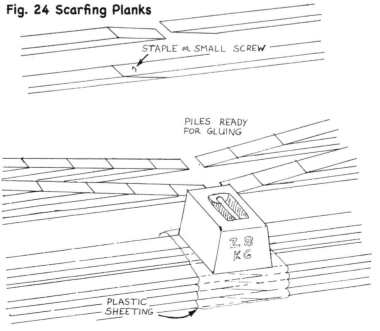

STAPLE or SMALL SCREW

PILES READY FOR GLUING

2.8 KG

PLASTIC SHEETING

are done, place a very heavy weight on plastic on top of both piles, exactly over the glued scarfs, and leave at least overnight. When you need to use the planks clean up the glue dags on the planks edges only with a block plane, and remove the staple or screw, and you're ready to plank.

If using Durakore you will find that the sheets come with scarfs already machined at each end, so all you need to do is select the width of the planking (45mm is a good size for a boat over 20 feet) and rip the sheets into strips and join them with epoxy on the floor as for the cedar strips.

Clamping planks on to work out the best position for master plank.

The First Plank

A great deal of care needs to go into the positioning of the first plank. Basically it needs to follow the turn of the bilge, but be allowed to lie naturally without either end being forced up or down. You will plank up from this plank, and then down. As the planks do not taper but are an even width, the lesser girth at both ends of the boat means that the planks will close up towards the hog and the sheer faster at the ends than in the middle, as in **Fig. 25**.

The position of your first plank must be such that the remainder of the planks will be able to take the increasing curve as they approach both the hog and the sheer.

Place your first plank approximately halfway up mould five, at about the turn of the bilge. Allow it to drape and lie where it wants to, with no edge set, but with each end roughly equal distances from the sheer. Tack it in place. Measure up about 600mm (about 13 or 14 planks' worth) on about every second or third mould and pencil a mark, then do the same down the same amount. Bend a

plank to these marks, and see how it lies. If the upper plank easily takes the bend and sits well but the lower plank cannot be bent to the marks, you need to move the first plank down a little and try again. The reverse applies if the upper plank will not sit.

If both sit well at this stage or after adjusting the first plank, measure a slightly greater distance both up and down the moulds such that you are plotting the position of a plank only four or five planks away from the hog and the sheer. If these sit well, everything is fine. If one of them doesn't, move the first plank slightly in the direction of the offending plank and try again. If neither plank will sit, you have a slight problem.

Most modern designs where the beam is carried well aft to a broad transom will not give any problems in the planking, but designs with lots of beam and narrow sterns could cause a problem. Most traditional hulls are okay, but double-enders usually present a problem.

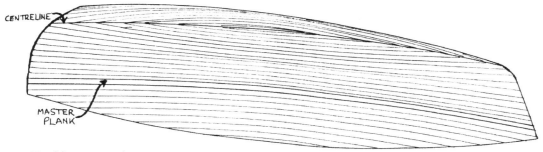

CENTRELINE

MASTER PLANK

Fig. 25 Planking Layout

Fig. 26 Beamy Hulls

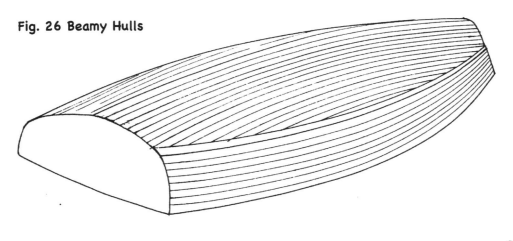

Beamy Hulls

You may have to plank the bottom as one unit, and the top-sides as another, with a joining line in between. First decide where the joining line will be. It is best to choose a line that will be parallel to the topside planks somewhere around the turn of the bilge. Plank the bottom first, roughly parallel with the keel, allowing the ends of each plank to curve down past the line. Trim to this line, then fit your first topside plank to it and plank down to the sheer (see **Fig.26**). Be careful to pull the joint into line or you will remove too much planking thickness once hull fairing begins.

Variations on this procedure can be followed for other difficult hull shapes. You may find it helpful to notch a temporary stringer into the moulds to support the plank ends at the join.

If you are part of the way through the planking when you realise there's a problem, you can fudge it by introducing a similar system. Sometimes it may be simpler to cut the remaining planks down the middle so that the narrower planks can take the bend, however this doubles the remaining plank work.

Double-Enders

Canoes and other long narrow boats usually have no problems, but full-bodied double-enders are difficult to plank (even in traditional planking methods) because the planks must twist from neat vertical at the stem, through near horizontal amidships on the bottom, to near vertical again at the stern while also taking a strong curve and they don't like it.

You could plank from two separate areas as for beamy boats, but it is generally simpler to taper the planks at the stern. If you taper them to half their previous width, they will close up at half the rate towards the hog and sheer, and the amount of curvature is greatly reduced and they become quite easy to fit.

Tapering can be done for any hull where the planks are closing up so fast near the stern that the curvature is becoming excessive and the plank edges want to lift.

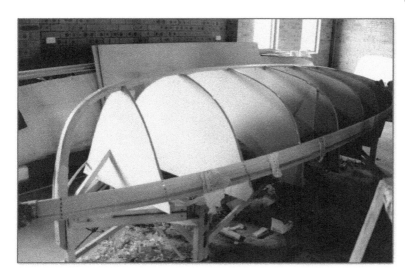

On some slim hulls you can start at the sheer and easily plank all the way to the keel using narrow strips.

Tapering Planks

The tapering process is quite quick and easy with a power plane. Simply clamp together just enough planks for the blade of your power plane to span, and taper away. Start with short strokes near the end and increase the length of the stroke with each stroke reaching the end of the planks until your last stroke is continuous along the entire tapered area, which should be from a little aft of centre, or from a little forward of wherever a problem has appeared.

It would be helpful to mark the taper on one or both sides of the group of planks with a batten. The ratio of the new width at the end to the width amidships should be similar to the ratio of the girth at the stern to that amidships.

When you start with a master plank at the turn of the bilge the planks will run out over the sheer.

The Planking Procedure

Now comes the part you've been waiting for. As each plank goes on, more of the boat's shape emerges. I always find it a fascinating part of boatbuilding - like reading a good book that you can't put down - you have to keep going to see how it turns out!

It is possible to plank alone, but it is easier with one or more helpers. With help, you should be able to fit five planks at a time, and it will be all over before you know it. Before you begin it is very important to cover the edges of all temporary moulds with plastic tape so the epoxy will not stick. Fasten your first plank in its chosen position with temporary screws (fast drive chipboard screws with an electric screwdriver are best) or double-headed formwork nails. You may use both of these without drilling but be prepared to split an occasional plank - generally it is better to drill first.

Clamp up five planks together side by side on trestles and apply epoxy thickened with microspheres to a peanut butter consistency (if it drips off the knife it's too thin) to the combined edges. Spread some also on the side of the stem and transom (if it is in the setup) far enough to cover the number of planks you are preparing.

We always use microspheres with resin for planking. While not as strong a glue as epoxy/microfibres, it is strong enough, as its strength is greater than the grain strength of the cedar. We always proved this to doubting students by test-breaking some of the offcuts from plank run-outs. The samples always break in the wood, not the glue line. The increased strength of microfibres is therefore not necessary, and in fact would cause problems in fairing because it is incredibly hard to plane and sand.

You should wear plastic gloves. But whether you do or not, it is better to work clean. There is a great temptation with gloves not to worry about getting resin on the skin. So instead it gets all over the gloves, the job, the clamps, the drill and anything else you touch. Keep rags handy and wipe

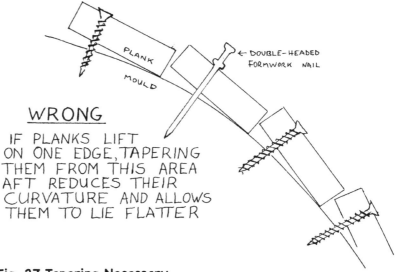

WRONG

IF PLANKS LIFT ON ONE EDGE, TAPERING THEM FROM THIS AREA AFT REDUCES THEIR CURVATURE AND ALLOWS THEM TO LIE FLATTER

Fig. 27 Tapering Necessary

89

any glue off your fingers as soon as possible whether you're wearing gloves or not.

Release the clamps and take a plank to the boat. Make sure it reaches both ends, and press it on top of the first plank, wriggle it just a little bit to evenly spread the glue and fasten it to the moulds with the same chipboard screws or formwork nails, starting somewhere in the middle and working towards each end in turn. With hand pressure, force the plank against the previous one as you drill and screw. Put the fastenings in slightly closer to any edge that is trying to lift. Glue and fasten to the stem as the first plank was. Use a quick action clamp as a lever to give any necessary twist to the planks as you fasten. Don't stop, you'll have to work fast to fit all five planks before the glue goes off. Stagger the scarfs by end-for-ending every second plank and by using any extra plank length so that the overhangs are at alternate ends.

You will find that the planks are not quite lining up between frames. Don't be tempted to edge nail or dowel, these all take too much time. Use shorter quick-drive screws through 3mm plywood strips (with plastic under) to bring the offending planks into line as in **Fig. 28**. The plywood helps to keep the planks to a fair line around the hull. You may have to fit these strips in more than half the bays between frames. **Fit these after every group of planks is fitted while the glue is still wet.**

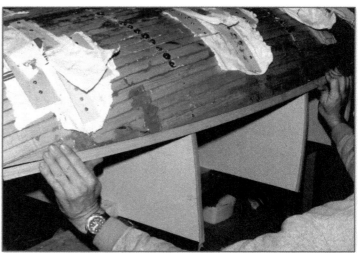

With beamy hulls you may need to stop when planks get too hard to fit towards the sheer, cut to a new line parallel to the sheer (see also next photo on following page).

Scrape out the excess resin that has squeezed out and force it into any seams that appear dry, both outside the hull and inside it, if you can easily reach. Once the inside becomes difficult to reach, ignore it, as you will be grinding a lot inside anyway later on.

Once you're happy with this group of planks (go ahead, stand back and admire it for a while), start on the next five. With one or more helpers you should be able to fit, adjust and clean-up five planks in around one hour.

It is standard procedure in boatbuilding not to plank too much of one side at a time, to even out any stresses on the setup. But because the planks at

Fig. 28 Bringing Planks into Line Between Frames

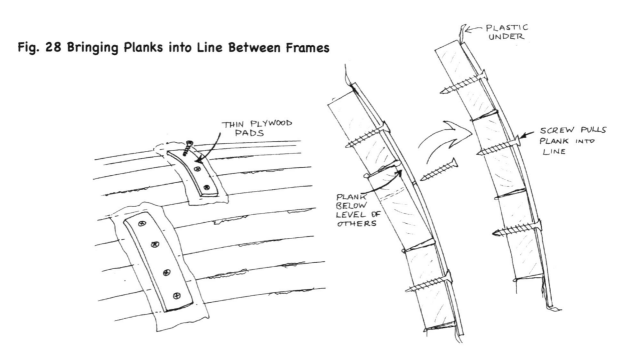

THIN PLYWOOD PADS

PLASTIC UNDER

SCREW PULLS PLANK INTO LINE

PLANK BELOW LEVEL OF OTHERS

the stem will probably protrude at the moment you may as well keep planking on one side per day. Plank the same area on the other side on the following day and so on.

The planks on the straight stem should be trimmed off parallel with the moulds and flush with the stem. If you were sensible you left a bit of wood on the stem around the hard knuckle just below the eventual waterline. This is the most difficult area of the boat to fair for the planking, so it is best to leave it until the planking is getting close

Last planks parallel to sheer. Note ply strips to bring planks into line between moulds. Pretty messy at this stage!

to it, then shape it to receive each individual plank with a chisel and rebate plane. Meticulously clean off any wet glue that got on before it sets. You should need to do this for three to five planks per side at the knuckle.

Plank up to the hog from the first plank on both sides, then down to the sheer. This enables you to use the sheer clamp as a platform to stand on to reach the inner planks. At the centreline on the hog, it is best to let the first planks there simply run out over the centreline and trim them back to the line when dry with a shallow-set circular saw, chisels and perhaps a rabbet plane. The planks on the

opposite side should be cut to fit here before gluing. A tight fit is not essential , but wood is cheaper than glue so a reasonable fit is preferable. The planks should be glued down to the hog as well as to each other. Some designers call for the use of stronger timber such as Mahogany or Oregon close to the keel because of the greater stresses here, especially in fin-keel boats.

At the sheer, allow the planks to run out over the sheer line. Make sure the planks you select to run out over the sheer are long enough to reach the next mould at both ends. Fixing them to the next mould ensures that they stay tight on the sheer clamp where they go past it.

Once dry, remove all remaining temporary fastenings and trim the sheer line but leave about 20 to 50mm over. Trim the planks running out over the transom or the transom mould.

Plane a flat on the planked hog to receive the fin-keel stub (you didn't leave any permanent fastenings here, did you?), locating it exactly (if you didn't mark it as you planked) by drilling up from a reference point inside the boat.

Plane a flat on the stem, and laminate several veneers of hardwood around the knuckle to

Planking nearly finished.

a thickness of 8-12mm, and one single thickness of hardwood to the straight part of the stem for ding protection in this vulnerable area. Hold them in place with lots of temporary screws with large washers under the heads. Remove the screws within 24 hours or they'll become part of the boat.

Fairing the Timber Hull

Seeing that you machined the planks a little oversize you have an allowance for fairing. With a No. 3 or No. 4 hand plane, plane diagonally in alternate directions, knocking off the high spots. Keep going until the surface is reasonably fair unless a plank in a particular area seems particularly low relative to its companions. If you planed right down to this one the planks around it might end up too thin. It is better in this case to fill the low parts with an epoxy/microsphere bog. Use a flexible batten over the hull held at different angles to identify the high spots to remove with the plane. Don't worry about hollows much at this stage unless they have stepped edges that glass cloth could not lie over without trapping an air bubble underneath.

Final fairing to establish a good-looking hull, especially on the topsides should wait until after glassing, but it is good to get it reasonably fair at this stage to save the time and expense of extensive bog fairing. But there is no escaping the fact that some bog fairing will be necessary, especially if you planked with Durakore.

Fairing the Durakore Hull

It is important not to remove much of the veneers on the outside of these balsa-cored strips, so fairing with a plane is not possible. The crux of the matter is to get the hull smooth enough so that glass cloth will lie without having small hollows and indentations that will trap air behind the cloth.

Go over the whole hull fairly lightly with a 175mm disc sander with a coarse grit, which will knock off any local sharp high spots and glue dags. Then go over the entire hull surface with a rubber squeegee and a not too thick epoxy/microsphere bog, which will fill all screw holes and local low spots. A day or two later, sand the whole hull with a foam pad disc sander or an orbital sander. Vacuum or blow off the dust, then check the hull to find any areas you missed which will need a spot fill.

A foam pad with 80 grit paper on a disc sander makes short work of glue dags.

PART 4 Sheathing

Preparing the Hull for Glassing

Even the cedar hull needs a wipe over with bog. It serves two purposes - it fills the screw holes and any small local hollows, and it allows the hull to soak up some resin. If it were not done, the cedar would absorb the resin from out of the glass cloth, possibly leaving it dangerously dry in patches. Sand the hull, dust off, and check for any spot filling necessary as for Durakore.

Sheathing the hull with fibreglass cloth is a big job but if well organised can be done in a day.

Choice of fibreglass cloth is important. The plans will usually contain the specifications, but if you are altering plans designed for a different method, please consult a designer, builder or resin manufacturer familiar with the method. Some designs call for unidirectional cloth, some for double-bias or even triaxial cloth, but some smaller designs simply rely on light woven cloth. **Do not use dynel or polypropylene cloths in this type of hull construction. The fibreglass cloth is an essential ingredient of the structure, and these other cloths do not have sufficient strength.**

Regardless of the weave of your cloth, it is always laid across the hull from gun'l to gun'l off the roll in order to maximise strength as in **Fig. 29** (with the exception of plain-weave cloth which may be laid lengthways or diagonally).

If a designer feels that unidirectional cloth is best, the panels can be butted up to each other. For any other cloth weave, overlaps of at least 75 to 100mm are essential for continuity of strength. Because of the curve of the hull surface, the panels will overlap considerably more towards the gun'l than they do at the centreline of the hull. The excess should be cut off to save resin and weight.

It is best to start at the stern and add panels forward. At the bow, it will not hurt to leave a double thickness wrapped around the stem. Cut and drape all cloths dry, after making sure the hull surface is clean by vacuuming and then wiping with a cloth. Measure the longest side of each panel from the keel to the sheer and multiply by two, so that each panel drapes all the way across. Leave a little extra for safety. Use a marker pen on the hull to mark the position to place each panel, and roll, do not fold them up and store them in order of demand.

Glassing

Round up at least two friends, promise you'll take them sailing, and tell them to bring clothes that they won't want to wear again. One or two more people would be even better. Make sure they all know what they are expected to do. There are several things to check before you start:

Make sure you have enough buckets, rags, squeegees, rollers etc to do the job, and enough plastic gloves to give everyone several changes. If you value the floor, place some plastic or thick cardboard directly under the gun'ls to catch the drips. If any time has elapsed since cutting the cloth, clean the hull again.

The Technique

Drape the first panel over the hull on its marks, making sure it reaches the sheer on both sides. The best procedure is simply to pour the resin on the cloth and allow it to wet through. Use a rubber squeegee to bulldoze the resin round, moving it from areas where it has already soaked in to drier areas, and using the squeegee to force any air in or beneath the cloth out through the weave. Use firm but not hard

Fig.29 Glassing the Hull

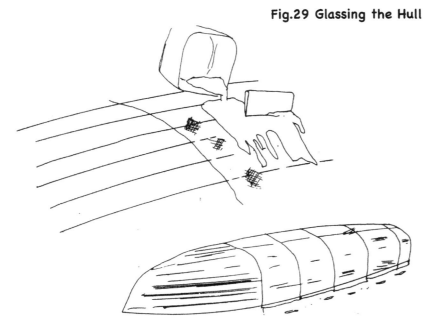

pressure - it is possible to force so much resin out of the cloth that the laminate is too dry.

Move the resin with slow, steady strokes. If you move it too fast you will aerate it (it will turn milky), and this will reduce its wetting-out power. On the flat areas of the bottom of the boat simply pour it out of the bucket and you will see it begin to wet out the cloth of its own accord. On the steeper topsides of the boat you will have to apply the resin with a roller and a tray.

You can speed up wetting-out here by lifting the near vertical hanging section of cloth and rolling thick coats of resin underneath (be careful in handling the cloth not to stretch it out of shape), and carefully putting the cloth down on the wet resin. You will probably have small problems in laying out the cloth evenly again in the wet resin, which is why we do not use this method for the whole panel.

Squeegee the surface to move excess resin from wet areas to dry areas and to work the air out, but don't force all the resin out of the cloth. Thicker cloths (over 400 gsm) can benefit by the use of a consolidator, a ribbed roller to remove air from the cloth.

Screw holes and low spots need careful filling.

The Crew

Put the lightest person, or possibly two, on top of the hull, wearing shoes that should be especially cleaned - these shoes should be left on the boat and another pair changed into when leaving the boat, and with instructions not to put all their weight on any flat areas of the planking not supported by the hog or moulds. This person is given the buckets by whoever is mixing the resin, and pours it out and generally concentrates on the sections which can't be reached from the ground. If there are only three of you, the other two each take a side and concentrate on the more vertical parts of the hull, both sides at a time.

Keep the wet area continuous - do not work on two separate areas because you may end up bunching the cloth up in between. If there are more than three of you, one person could be used almost exclusively to mix resin.

Considering the high demand, a small pump system may be too slow, and it is preferable to be able to mix about a litre at a time, using calibrated containers to ensure the right ratio of resin and hardener. Stir the resin well before handing it to the user.

Work Clean!

The secret of enjoying the process is to work clean. It is impossible not to spill resin, not to have drips on the floor, and not to get resin on your clothes or hands, but the greater the effort towards minimising the mess, the more pleasant the job will be. Change gloves and roller covers when the resin

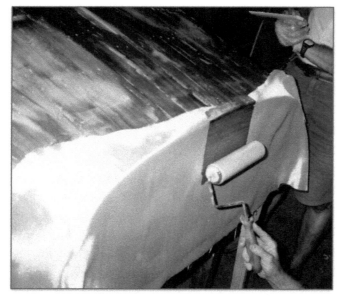

Foam rollers spread the epoxy resin on vertical surfaces.

on them starts to cure, and clean resin build-up from squeegees regularly with rags. Always pour from the same side of the bucket and attempt to keep one side dry for handling.

Time

Get the resin out of the bucket and onto the hull as soon as possible - it will go off much faster in the bucket than on the job. Work thoroughly but quickly, so that you are always adding each batch of resin to a wet edge of uncured resin from the last bucket. Work methodically to ensure this wet edge. It would be possible to do a hull like this alone in cool weather using the manufacturer's slowest, setting hardener, but three is the minimum crew to effectively do the hull in one go.

If for any reason you have to stop overnight or longer before completing all panels, the joining area with the new work will have to be ground and cleaned to ensure bonding between the areas.

Peel Ply

A nylon cloth called peel ply is laid over the wet-out glass (if 400 gsm or heavier) and squeegeed to minimise the resin in the laminate, flatten the weave to maximise its strength and to reduce grinding later. Immediately the width of a panel of peel ply has been wet, lay the peel ply over the hull and use the squeegee from the top out and down to wet out the peel ply and evenly spread the resin around. This resin will be forced to fill the weave of the cloth. Be particularly careful not to press too firmly; it is possible to remove too much resin from the cloth. If this happens, the surface will tend to look dry after the squeegee has passed over it. If you are trapping air under the peel ply, lift it up and add more resin. The peel ply will tear off after curing, whenever you are about to start the next stage, leaving a smooth and clean surface that will need only spot grinding (locate the spots such as where loops of glass threads are sticking up by feel and remove the peel ply locally only to grind, to minimise dust on the surface).

If Not Using Peel Ply

If you finish glassing one afternoon, and the night is expected to be cool and you can commence work again first thing in the morning, roll a coat of resin on the hull to help fill the weave of the cloth as soon as the surface is touch-dry; that is, if a finger leaves a print, but resin does not stick to the finger. This is the optimum time for recoating. Once the new layer is touch dry, or first thing next morning, commence the fairing process. If any of the stages are separated by more than 10 to 12 hours, less if it's hot, sanding will be necessary But what we must avoid is sanding through the glass fibres, which not only reduces the strength of the hull but is extremely unpleasant.

Fairing

Fairing means getting the surface free of bumps and hollows, so that a refection in gloss paint on the hull will show up distortion free. The only way to do it is by hard physical work, so it is tempting to skimp, but nothing looks worse that a hull that has not been faired well, and it will affect your pride as well as your resale value. The difference between a fair surface and an unfair one can often be measured in fractions of a millimetre. The greatest proportion of time needs to be spent on the topsides. Below the waterline it is less important.

The Bead Bog Method

You can simply smother your hull with bog and carve the boat back out of it, but it is less wasteful of time and materials if you use the bead-bog method. Your hull should be just tacked off from a weave-filling coat of resin, or have peel ply just removed, or have been lightly sanded and cleaned.

Mix resin and microspheres to a

Fig. 39 Bead Bogging

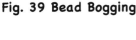
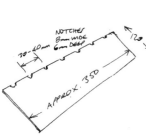
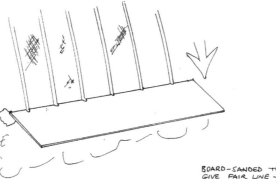

mayonnaise consistency. Cut triangular notches in a straight edge of a 350mm x 120mm x 3mm plywood board about 30mm to 40mm apart, 8mm to 10mm wide and 6mm to 8mm deep as in **Fig. 30**.

Spread the entire contents of one bucket on the hull relatively evenly with a squeegee or trowel, and bulldoze from the centreline of the hull down with this board, leaving a series of lines of bog in front of the board further along the hull. Use the build-up of bog in front of the board further along the hull. Cover the entire hull at one go to avoid sanding. A day or more later, commence sanding with an aptly named torture board, as in **Fig. 31**. With 40 grit paper, sand diagonally across the hull, and push the flexible board to the surface so that it conforms to the curve, or nearly so. You will probably need at least two different ones made of plywood of say, 4mm and 6mm thickness for different areas of the hull, the more flexible for the more curved areas. By doing this, the board reduces any high spots which do not conform to the shape of the hull.

Keep the board moving, don't stay too long in one spot and in one direction. Stop sanding in any particular area as soon as the board touches the glass surface anywhere. You will finish up with a hull where the sanded tops of the bead strips represent a fair surface.

After dusting, the next stage is to grout more bog into the valleys between the bead strips, with a lightly held squeegee or trowel. Using the same torture boards, fair this surface. A plane works well on any over-filled areas if kept sharp, and a fair proportion of the surface can be faired by plane but sanding with torture boards will have to commence at some stage, and is the only way to ensure a fair surface. Disc sanders will not do it, even those with random orbital action, and orbital sanders will definitely not do it.

Use small battens held at different positions on the surface to monitor your progress. If your hull has extensive very flat areas (as in some power boats), it might be necessary to make up a two-man board of around 1400mm to 1500mm, but on more

Fig. 31 Fairing the Bogged Surface

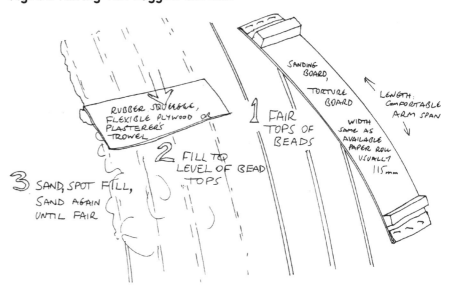

curved yacht hulls, a one-man board will be sufficient, because the fairness over large distances has been taken care of by fair moulds and the natural longitudinal fairing ability of the planks.

Even with the bead-bog method, you will go through several cycles of filling and fairing, hopefully on increasingly local areas. Don't worry too much about areas below the waterline, as long as they are reasonably smooth. Concentrate on the topsides until they are faultless.

Fairing a bead-bogged hull.

The bigger the hull, the bigger the fairing job.

Marking the Waterline

It is best to mark the waterline while the boat is still upside down and all the reference points on the temporary frames inside the boat are still intact. Use a clear plastic tube longer than the boat, filled with water (and no bubbles), one person with one end inside the boat and another with the other end and a pencil outside. Place the hose against a mould inside, and outside on the hull roughly where you expect the waterline to be. The person inside moves their end of the hose until the level of the water is right on the waterline marked on the mould, and because water finds its own level, marking the hull at the level of the water in the tube on the outside gives the correct height. Repeat the procedure, moving the outside end all around the boat making a series of marks which can be joined with a batten (see **Fig. 32**).

NOTE: This line represents the line at which the designer intends the boat to float when loaded. For anti-fouling purposes you may wish to mark the line 40mm to 70mm closer to the sheer.

Alternatives

You could use the water level to establish two straight edges on trestles at both ends of the boat level athwartship and with each other. A tight string line held between them will enable a third person to mark wherever the string touches the hull. By moving one in and one out, most of the hull can be reached and any parts that can't, can be marked by projecting the string line height in to the hull with a spirit level.

However these days laser levels are cheap and as long as you have one reference point you simply mark in the laser-generated line.

Permanent Marking

If you wish to permanently mark this line, you can either carefully scratch a line into the bog if deep enough, or glue on some fishing line - tape some

Fig. 32 Marking the Waterline

WATER FINDS ITS OWN LEVEL

WATERLINE AS ORIGINALLY MARKED ON MOULDS

OUTSIDE WORKER MOVES HOSE SLOWLY UNTIL INSIDE WATER LEVEL MEETS MARKED WATERLINE

nylon fishing line to the marks, and dab some resin between the bits of tape. When the resin goes off, remove the tape and coat the rest with resin. Even if the fishing line comes off later during sanding, a permanent ridge of resin will remain to mark the waterline.

Priming the Hull

The bog surface is slightly porous, so it is best to roll two coats of resin over the surface. I suggest that you add a little white pigment and graphite powder to the second coat, enough to colour it slightly grey. This serves two purposes: when sanding the hull at any later date, the grey colour is an indication that you don't want to go any further; and the graphite in the mixture makes it harder to sand if you do ignore it, thus protecting the glass surface beneath.

NOTE: Anytime a cured epoxy surface is to be prepared for any overcoating, whether of resin, hi-build primers or paints, the surface should be scoured with warm water and a kitchen scourer to remove the amine blush, a waxy bi-product of the epoxy while curing, otherwise it may interfere with bonding of the subsequent coats. The wet surface should be dried with cloths or paper towels. If the surface is more than 24 hours cured, a light sanding will also be necessary. To avoid scouring and sanding, it is best to apply succeeding coats of epoxy, or of high-build epoxy primer wet-on-tacky, which means the best time is when the resin is still soft enough to show a fingerprint, but not wet enough to stick to the finger. This usually occurs 3-5 hours after application, depending on temperature. Paint should not be applied directly to epoxy for at least

3 days, or the solvents may attack the fresh epoxy surface and retard drying of the paint.

You could sand this surface lightly and leave it until painting time; or apply a high-build easy-sanding epoxy primer either after lightly sanding the cured surface, or straight onto an almost cured surface. These high-build primers are a good, easy sanding base for later paint systems.

Painting

Don't do it at this stage for several reasons:
1. The hull will be marked many times and experience resin splashes etc between now and completion.
2. The fairness of the hull will change slightly over the building period because of minute movement in the wood, and final fairing of sandable undercoats before painting should be left as long as possible.

Turning the Hull Over

There are systems you could work out for building a rolling jig on the hull; or if your boat is small enough, a large group of people may be able to manhandle it over on mattresses or suchlike. But it would be easiest to find out from local boatbuilders which company they use - an experienced crane driver can roll a boat over very smartly and reasonably cheaply. Whatever means you choose it's a good excuse for a party. Leave the moulds in the boat to keep it stiff, simply disconnect the bolts holding the legs to the strongback (this is why we used bolts, right?).

You will of course need some sort of receiving jig. The best method is to build a cradle on the hull while it is still upside down, as in **Fig. 33**, and mark on the hull where it sits in the cradle. Lift the cradle off before rolling the boat over.

Use the marked waterline and/or the grid lines on the moulds to set the boat up dead level both ways, adjusting the cradle with wedges. This is very important when fitting bulkheads and furniture.

Fig. 33 The Cradle

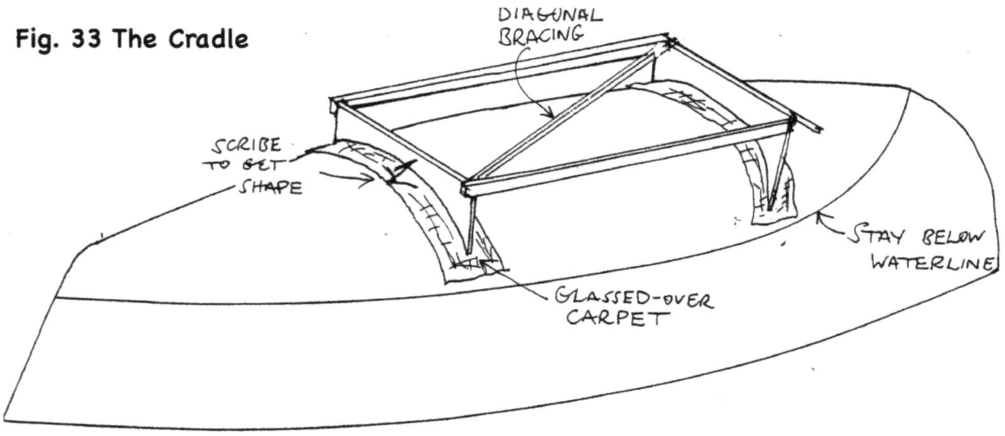

DIAGONAL BRACING

SCRIBE TO GET SHAPE

GLASSED-OVER CARPET

STAY BELOW WATERLINE

Preparing the Interior

Run a pencil line on the hull along the control edge of several moulds as reference points for locating the bulkheads. Remove all of the moulds, but place at least two braces across the boat before doing so. The hull is still floppy and it would otherwise be hard to re-establish the true deckline and beam.

Grind off all glue dags with a disc sander. The inside does not need to be faired like the outside, but it does need to be smooth enough for the inside laminate of glass to sit on. Do not delete the inside glassing - it is an essential part of the integrity of the hull in this building method.

If your inside laminate is of 330gsm plain weave cloth or less, you will still be able to clearly see the grain of the wood through the wet-out glass. Any thicker than this, and unfortunately you cannot. If you wish to have certain areas with visible woodgrain and your laminate is transparent, a fair amount of sanding is needed. Any paper rough enough to remove the glue dags will definitely scour the grain, and considerable sanding will be necessary to remove these marks. Fill all holes and seams before final sanding, and ensure that all traces of filler on the surface are removed.

For areas that will be painted, grind enough only to get a reasonable surface and then squeegee the entire area with resin/microspheres to fill screw holes, open seams and any indented planks, as for the outside of the hull. Sand, refill if necessary and sand again before glassing.

Filleting

Keeping in mind that the glass must not have any air trapped behind it, any sharp corners on the keelson, stem and sheer clamps should be removed, by rounding off any timber not done before, and by filleting any hollow corners, as in **Fig. 34**. A stiff resin/microsphere mix is knifed into the corner, and a stick

Grinder, spokeshave and round soled planes are used to clean up the inside.

with the end rounded to the required radius is used to spread it evenly, and then to wipe along the whole line in one long smooth stroke. This leaves an even, rounded fillet in the corner, and bulldozes the excess bog into two ridges on either side, which are then cleaned up with a metal putty knife.

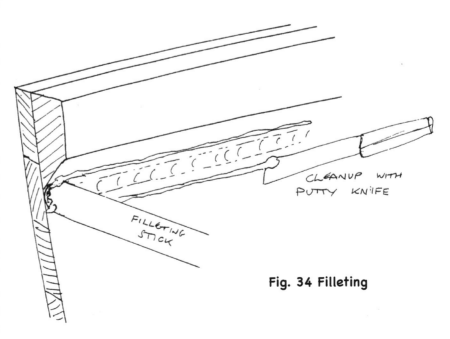

CLEANUP WITH PUTTY KNIFE

FILLETING STICK

Fig. 34 Filleting

It really pays to work neatly and to clean up well. If you leave bumps, holes and rough spots they will need considerable sanding before the glass cloth will safely lie over them. You will soon pick up the technique, which is just as well, because from now on in your boat's construction you will use it a lot, around bulkheads, interior furniture, cockpit and cabin structures.

Next day sand these fillets enough to ensure the cloth will conform to them (run your finger along them to test for smoothness), clean the hull, and you are ready to glass the inside.

Salvo 24 hull filled and sanded and ready for glassing.

Glassing the Inside

Exactly the same techniques and general comments for glassing the outside of the hull apply to the inside. Start from the bow so as not to glass yourself in, and work aft. The panels of glass are cut in two pieces which overlap on the hog, as it would be much too difficult to do it in one continuous panel. Tack the glass on top of the sheer clamp to hold it, roll it down to check its position, then carefully roll it back up.

You have to be actually standing on the hull where the glass will actually lie to reach the upper areas to wet them out. Roll a thick coat of resin on the topside area, and unroll the glass over this area and wet it through. Once the more horizontal bottom is reached, you may spread the glass dry and wet through it by pouring it on. One or two people could handle it if they worked on only one side of the hull at a time. Have a separate pair of shoes for inside the hull to cut down on the amount of dirt you walk into the hull.

It is very important to ensure that the glass lies into the filled corners under the sheer clamp and alongside the hog and stem. As you work the cloth elsewhere it will constantly pull away here, so keep going back and checking. Resin will try to pool in the channel either side of the hog, so try to keep moving it aft.

Peel Ply

If you wish to use peel ply do it only on the planking areas of the hull. Trying to get it to conform to the tight curves at clamp and hog will only lead to heartbreak. You will have to apply it immediately after wetting-out the cloth.

Filling the Weave

You need to roll more resin to fill the weave (if no peel ply is used), as on the outside of the hull, but it is harder to reach. Get a painter's screw-in extension and roll the resin from outside the hull, leaning over the gun'l. Remember it should be rolled on as soon as the original resin has tacked off. Two coats would be best. Don't wipe any bog into the inside, there is no bog fairing to be done.

Plain-weave glass cloth ready to wet out.

Fitting Bulkheads

Decide where the bulkheads are going by measuring from the original mould positions (if you forgot to mark these you can get it accurate to within a couple of millimetres by using the still-visible lines of filled screw holes through the planking).

Grind an area 200mm wide, 100mm either side of the bulkhead line everywhere it will touch the hull. This is an itchy job so it is well worth covering up with disposable suit, mask, goggles and gloves and doing all the grinding in one go (clean up well by vacuuming and wiping with a cloth).

If you lofted the bulkheads and cut them out earlier, now is the time to bring them for a trial fit. Expect that there will be slight discrepancies. Plane off any high spots. If the bulkhead touches the hull at several places and there are gaps of less that 6mm, all is okay. If the gaps are larger than that, you really should plane the high spots down further, but if this then makes the bulkhead too small you will have to do it again.

Bulkheads bonded in up to 18' Durakore-planked trailer-sailer.

Hold the bulkhead in its exact position, straight and plumb, between pairs of small nails tacked to the hull. Do not force the plywood into position or you may distort the hull.

Alternatives for Shaping Bulkheads

If you didn't loft the bulkheads, you have to start from scratch. There are several methods of doing this, all illustrated in **Fig. 35**.

1. Make a template - by stapling or screwing together small sticks ensuring they touch the hull on the line of the bulkhead. I find this way is best because you can shape the entire outline in one go and lay it straight onto your plywood.

2. The joggle stick method - draw the joggle stick outline on a piece of plywood held on the plane of the proposed bulkhead, then take this piece to your plywood stock; laying the stick in each position in turn and marking their points gives the hull outline.

3. Small part-bulkheads can be scribed by compass. It is important to hold the compass at a constant angle.

Bulkheads are glued to the hull. Pretty ugly at this stage, but keep

Fig. 35 Shaping Bulkheads

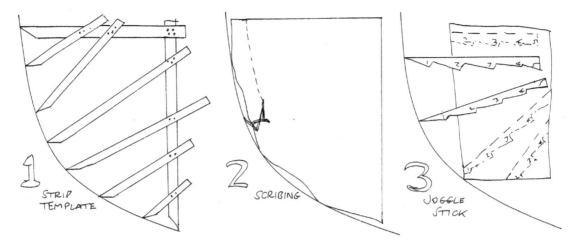

1 STRIP TEMPLATE

2 SCRIBING

3 JOGGLE STICK

Check that all doorways etc are plumb, and that under decks you have allowed enough plywood for the required deck camber.

Whatever method you choose, give it a trial fit, adjust if necessary, and apply a peanut-butter consistency of resin and micro-fibres to the joining edges, very thickly, and put it back in position between the nails.

With the excess that squeezes out, and with more resin microfibre mix, lay a neat fillet along both sides, as in **Fig. 36**. Avoid the nails, remove them once the resin has cured and fillet those areas.

Once dry, sand the fillet and apply glass strips 200mm wide, with 100mm landing on the bulkhead and the hull. Double bias cloth is best for this. Wet it out with a brush and consolidate with a metal consolidator roll.

Your hull is now ready to fit some deck framing.

Dinghy interiors are quite simple.

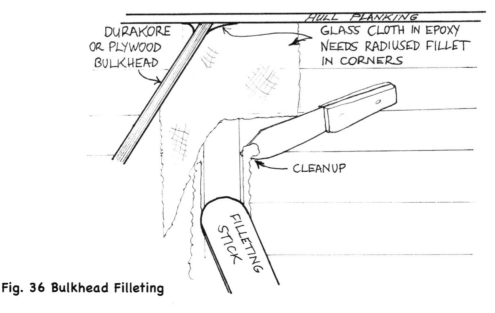

DURAKORE OR PLYWOOD BULKHEAD

HULL PLANKING

GLASS CLOTH IN EPOXY NEEDS RADIUSED FILLET IN CORNERS

CLEANUP

FILLETING STICK

Fig. 36 Bulkhead Filleting

PART 5
Decking and Fitting Out

You could proceed to fit out the interior right now, but your hull will be a lot stiffer if you first fit the deck beams, and probably the deck. But don't build the coachhouse yet. The work on the interior will benefit from having more light, more headroom, and more open space to move large sheets of plywood around. The actual plywood deck will not reduce this a great deal, but having it there gives a true indication of the final spatial relationships between the furniture and the deck overhead. If no deck at all is on, you may have some surprises when you do fit it.

Laminating Deck Beams

As mentioned in Part 2, your boat may have all of the deck beams set to one curve or camber, or each may be different. Use the method described there for drawing the curve(s) you need. This is illustrated in **Fig. 37**, along with alternate constructions for the jig you need to laminate the beams over.

Clear Oregon is so ideal for beams you can hardly go past it, but you could use Mahogany, Kauri, Alpine Ash, or for ultralight construction, Sitka Spruce. An ideal deck beam has 5 laminations. Any more means timber wastage. Any less and you may get excessive springback. If you cut the laminations on a good saw bench, the surface produced is ideal for epoxy gluing. If you have to plane them, rough up the mating surfaces with rough sandpaper before gluing. If two or more deck beams are made to the same curve, cut the timber more than twice the width and cut through the centre to produce two beams after the glue has cured. But no matter what width timber you use, leave at least 4-6mm on each side to make sure you will be able to clean the beam back to an all-wood surface.

Deck beams and bulkheads on Haven 12½.

Assemble everything you need, including clamps, gloves, friends, sticks or knives for mixing and spreading the epoxy, and plastic sheeting or tape to prevent the beam becoming part of the jig. Bend your laminations dry on the jig as a practice run. Mix the epoxy and microfibres to a mayonnaise consistency, and apply it to both mating surfaces. Assemble the stack, and take it to the jig. It would be best to wear plastic gloves, because you will inevitably get glue on your hands,

Fig. 37 Laminating Deck Beams

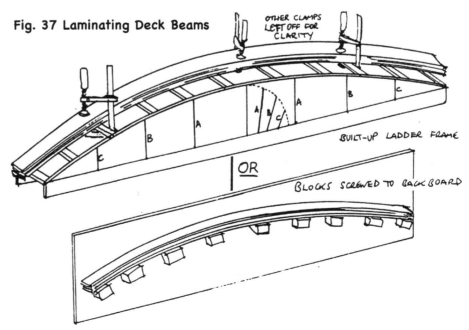

OTHER CLAMPS LEFT OFF FOR CLARITY

BUILT-UP LADDER FRAME

OR

BLOCKS SCREWED TO BACKBOARD

but make efforts to keep this glue off the clamps. A gloveless helper here would be invaluable. Don't let the fact that you're wearing gloves lead you to create a greater mess. Clamp the beam in place, but don't overtighten. Fit and tighten the clamps from one end, working progressively to the other. Scrape away as much squeezed-out glue as possible with a metal putty knife.

Release the clamps after 24 hours, and cleanup the beam with a power plane with tungsten-tipped blades, or possibly a belt sander to remove the glue dags. Final trimming should be done by hand plane. Thickness it evenly by machine or with hand tools. You may wish to round or mould the bottom edges, and possible even to apply two coats of unthickened epoxy resin before fitting.

Short side deck beams and possibly even some longer beams could be cut from straight stock on some boats saving a lot of work.

Fitting Deck Beams
The stages are illustrated in **Fig. 38**.

1. Mark the location of the deck beams on top of the beam shelf or sheer clamp, and lay the beam on these marks and extend them further onto the clamp. Square a line across, fore and aft, not further out than one third of the width of the clamp. With a combination square or other small spirit level, draw in two vertical lines the width of the deck beam on the inside of the sheer clamp. Measure down from the inner top edge of the sheer clamp the depth of the beam on the side nearest the closest end of the ship and square a line across. Use a non-prized chisel to cut away the glass within these lines, and with saw and chisels, remove the timber within the boundaries, making sure the back edge of the notch is straight and is slanted at least slightly outboard.

2. Place the deck beam in place, only upside down. Mark the beam exactly where it touches the back of the notch, on both ends of the beam, being careful not to move it during marking. Amidships, where the beams meet the clamp fairly square, the beam ends and notches can afford to be square.

3. Towards the ends of the ship, the beam ends should be parallel with the clamp, and the marks just made need to be made on both sides of each beam end, and then <u>squared across</u> before marking the angle to cut, simply because the beam was upside down.

4. Put the beam right side up resting half-over the notches, and place a sliding bevel with its body on top of the beam, and its blade arm resting on the back slope of the notch. Slide the beam in or out until the mark made in Section 2 is against the outer edge of the bevel blade, and mark that angle on the beam. Cutting the beam to both lines, this and the one on top whether squared across or angled, will match it to the back slope of the notches on both sides. If you did it perfectly, the beam will drop exactly into place. If you were cautious, you may have a little trimming to do. Do not hammer the beam in place, it will push out the sides of the boat - it must sit home gently. Apply thick epoxy to both ends and both notches, fit the beam, and cleanup the glue. You may wish to fit an angled screw to hold the beam in place, but it is not really necessary unless the beam is slipping. A loose wood fit can still be strong with the glue, but many of these joints are visible inside the boat and for that reason tight joints become more important. Do the longest beams first in case you inadvertently take too much off the beam end, so you can use it for the next longest beam, provided both beams are of the same camber.

Deck beams, carlins, bulkheads and centreboard case on David Payne's 17' Snapper Boat.

104

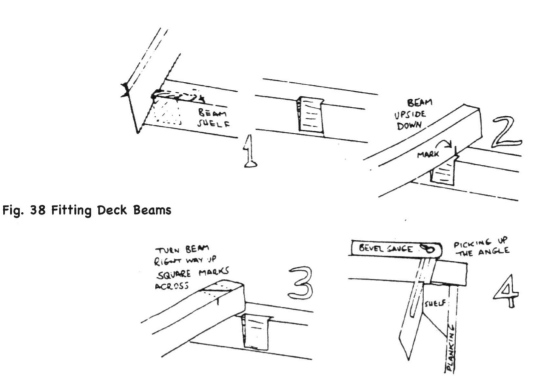

Fig. 38 Fitting Deck Beams

Carlins

Carlins are the fore and aft members that run either side of any opening in the deck, either the coachhouse, cockpit or hatches. They are let into the deck beams at both ends, so these beams, referred to as king beams, are usually slightly wider than the other deck beams to allow for this. The best way to join carlins to the deck beams in this form of construction is exactly the same as for fitting deck beams to the clamp (see **Fig. 38**). The longer carlins such as cockpit and cabin carlins will need to be cut or sprung to shape and held in their required position by some sort of temporary framing which can be as simple as notches in a temporary beam (see **Fig. 39**).

The carlins have to follow any curve to the cabin sides (usually near parallel to the gun'l) and also the sheer curve, and should agree with the designed deck camber. They should also visually fair in at both ends as if they continued for a few more beam spaces, otherwise the deck will have a sudden change of direction here. They may also be sloped inboard at the intended angle of the cabin sides, or be fitted oversize with an allowance for planing off at this angle. The short side deck beams are then fitted and glued. These should provide enough support to enable the temporary framing to be removed.

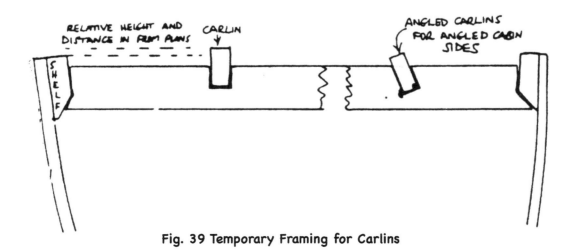

Fig. 39 Temporary Framing for Carlins

The King Plank

The foredeck needs some further support in the form of blocking between the foredeck beams to help take the thrust of the mast, to reinforce the foredeck cleat for mooring and anchoring and to act as a good joining area for the deck plywood (see **Fig. 40**). we refer to this as the king plank because it takes the same role as a thicker central deck plank in more traditional construction. It is notched slightly into the beams, but do not take out too much here or you may weaken the beams.

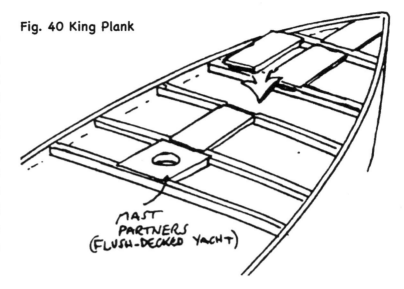

Fig. 40 King Plank

MAST PARTNERS (FLUSH-DECKED YACHT)

Fairing the Deck

All the deck framing must now be faired to receive the deck. Even if all the beams are at exactly the correct height, one edge will have to be planed off because of the slope of the deck in line with the sheer curve as in **Fig. 41**.

In addition to this, it is possible that small inaccuracies in height may have been incorporated, and battens and small sheets of plywood laid across the deck are necessary to ensure that they all end up at the correct height and bevel. Work methodically on the basis that you plane a little off each one and constantly check that you are on the right track, rather than attempt to complete one deck beam at a time. Along the gun'l, grind the hull glass completely away for 10-15mm down from the expected sheer line to keep it out of the road of plane blades when fairing the gun'l, and feather a further 25-30mm. The deck glass will overlap these areas.

Marking the Deck Plywood

Work out the layout of your deck plywood either at scale on the plans or with tape measure on the boat. The king plank is an ideal landing area for a join on the foredeck, presenting such a large gluing area. It is better not to join sections right at the corners of the cabins or hatches. Joining can be either with plywood butt blocks acting in a similar fashion to the join at the king plank, or preferably by scarfing. Lay the sheets on the deck and pencil underneath where they overlay the gun'l and the carlins and cut them roughly to shape. The area to be scarfed should be cut dead straight, and the bottom scarf edge should land on a beam. The plywood is scarfed at a ratio of 8 to 1, as in **Fig. 42**.

The scarfs should be planed dead straight (start with a power plane, finish with a hand plane), or slightly hollow to ensure the feather edge will sit down. Make sure the scarf on the first sheet to be fastened down faces up, and that on the sheet to join it faces down. Fit all sheets in place with temporary screws, and ensure the scarfs match. Mark the position of all beams, carlins etc, underneath with a pencil. Remove the sheets, and roll on two coats of unthickened epoxy to the underside. Sand between coats, as the first coat will raise the grain. Lay off the second coat with a brush or piece of foam roller in a cleft stick. Sand this with a 100 grit when dry, and apply one or two coats of a good sanding undercoat, either epoxy or oil based, but put plastic tape along the positions of all beams about 2mm inside each line. The idea is to completely paint the underside to avoid the necessity for overhead work and fine cutting in around the beams, unless you want the beams painted as well. The tape is there to keep paint off the areas to be glued. If the beams are to be epoxied and/or varnished, this can be done between coats on the deck ply. Finish with a gloss or semi-gloss white. I don't care what you say, white overheads (or at least light colours) brighten and

Fig. 41 Fairing Deck Beams

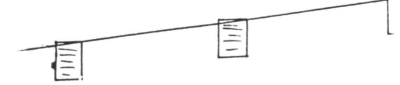

visually enlarge an interior. Remove the tape and ensure it leaves no residue. Drill 1.5mm holes along every area which will be glued at about 100-120mm spacing. Tape along the outside of each line, and possibly also the upper vertical sides of each beam to aid in glue removal. Apply epoxy and microfibres to the tops of all beams, carlins and sheer clamp for the first sheet and fit it in place with the same temporary screws. Drive silicon bronze boat nails into all the drilled holes (they do not need to be drilled into the beams). They can be of a relatively light gauge, as the glue is what really holds the deck on. Work methodically from one end of the sheet to the other, cleaning underneath meticulously before fitting the next sheet. Punch the nails below the surface, and overfill the holes with excess glue.

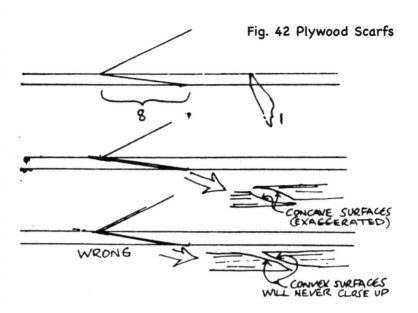

Fig. 42 Plywood Scarfs

CONCAVE SURFACES (EXAGGERATED)

WRONG

CONVEX SURFACES WILL NEVER CLOSE UP

Fitting out the Interior

This is a subject that has already filled whole books, so we will only touch on it here. There are several things to remember, some applying to this form of hull construction and some more general:

1. The hull will be stronger if large flattish unsupported areas of the hull have shelves, partitions etc filleted and glassed to the hull as bulkheads.

2. However the chainplates are attached to the hull, this area needs to be very strong and the loads tied into as many strong parts of the structure as possible.

3. Non-structural partitions can be simply filleted to the hull.

4. Electrics and plumbing: at least plan these early in the piece so as not to build in so much furniture that it is difficult to fit these systems. They should at least be in before decorative trim and paintwork are commenced.

5. Partitions not touching the hull can also be filleted together, or light offcuts of Cedar planking can be used for cleats (but not for unsupported beams), Oregon is best here.

6. Roll two coats of resin on all plywood, and especially any exposed end grain (which is better to avoid anyway). It is especially important to seal any hidden end grain. In areas out of the sun, no further finishing is necessary, but you can varnish or paint for decorative purposes.

7. Light colours brighten and enlarge an interior. Too much dark wood and varnish makes it look like the inside of a hollow log.

Cabin Structures

The cabin sides are usually of plywood, fastened and glued to the inside of the carlins which were installed or shaped to the required inboard shape. The joint where the cabin side meets the deck is filleted to a largish radius, and will be glassed over shortly. Do not cut windows until after the plywood is fitted and filleted, and preferably after glassing.

The cabin roof can be built in a similar fashion to the deck with beams and plywood, or it can be laminated from various combinations of plywood, Cedar strips or Durakore according to the designer, over temporary beams. Modern sloping and curve cabin fronts are also laminated over temporary beams.

Cockpit

Cockpit structures are basically boxy, and are built from plywood with fillets in corner joints or possible wood cleats on inside surfaces. Exposed edges are well rounded off.

Glassing the Deck and Cabin

Any overlapping edges should be planed off and well rounded, and the glue-filled nail heads should be ground or belt-sanded. The surface should receive a rolled coat of resin which is then sanded before glassing, and the whole area double-checked for holes. The glassing operation is the same as that for the hull, but a lot easier because of the near-horizontal surface and thinner cloth (no thicker than 330gsm). Simply pour the resin on, allow it to soak in, and bulldoze it around and work out air bubbles with a rubber squeegee. After tacking off, roll one or two coats more on to fill the weave. The glass should overlap the deck edge about 40mm onto the hull. Run plastic tape with at least 300mm wide plastic sheeting hanging to catch the drips, and cut the part-cured resin with a Stanley knife along the top line of the tape and pull it off. This line may be covered by a rub-rail, but if not, you will have to fair it in to the rest of the hull.

Laid Decks

You may wish to customise your deck with thin Teak strips set in epoxy coloured black with graphite powder, or with a flexible black polyurethane sealant such as Sikaflex. You will not need to glass these areas, but their perimeters such as the cabin-deck joint and hull-deck joint should be glassed with wide tape.

If you do not, a painted non-skid finish is best, especially if small areas can be masked to produce a pattern.

Deck Fittings

There is one vital thing to remember when installing deck fittings. More timber decks have deteriorated through fresh water getting in through leaking deck fittings than any other cause. Do not be lulled into a false sense of security because your deck is glassed and your plywood is epoxied underneath. Any exposed plywood in the hole is just waiting to suck up moisture, and you will soon have a rotten deck.

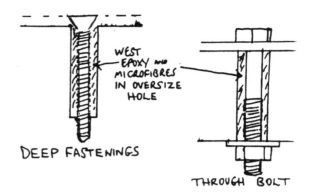

Fig. 43 Epoxied Fastenings

Any metal fastenings through the deck should be drilled for well oversize, and the hole filled with epoxy, whether through fastenings or not as in **Fig. 43**. The tenacity of a fastening buried in epoxy is immense, but any major items such as chainplates, rudder fittings etc should be bolted through oversized holes with epoxied threads. Careful work is necessary to ensure the effectiveness of this system.

The fastenings can be removed at a later date by applying heat with a soldering iron. They can be refitted once cool after being dipped in more epoxy.

Keels

Keel bolts too should be epoxied in through oversized holes. It is difficult to fit modern keels anyway if the holes are not oversize. If you follow keel fashions and wish to change it at a later date, a homemade hole saw from a piece of tube should be able to remove timber and glue from around the bolts, or apply mould release wax to the bolt threads when fitting.

Deadwood Underwater

You may have a long keel with plenty of deadwood, or you may have a wooden stub to which your ballast keel is fitted. The jury is still out on how best to construct these. Some boats have experienced problems, some have not. I favour deadwoods being glued up from any reasonably dense, good gluing timber such as Mahogany, Iroko, even Oregon, and tightly bolted as well as thoroughly and heavily glassed, preferably including the mating surface with the metal keel.

Expanding wood when wet has tremendous strength, enough to sheer light to moderate glass. On any boat kept on a mooring, water vapour penetrating the epoxy barrier will eventually raise the moisture level inside the wood, but thorough and thick glassing will minimise this and restrict expansion.

Since we fitted the deck, we have skimmed lightly over ground that will take you at least half the time you take to build your boat, but most of the material has been amply covered elsewhere. My purpose here, has been to get your hull and deck structure together, and to cover some new applications in interior construction and deck fittings which have been developed through years of building epoxy strip-planked boats, and I believe this method is the best available for anyone to build a one-off boat.

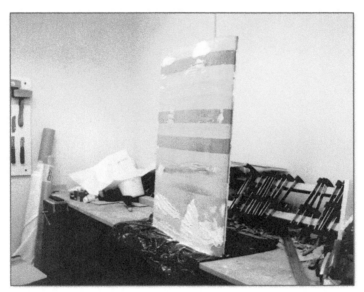

Keel stub of Salvo Class is built up from lifts of Western Red Cedar cut to foil pattern.

Plywood Clinker Construction

This manual was originally written for those who attended our classes in the 1990's, but an abbreviated version was published as a series of articles in Australian Amateur Boatbuilder magazine in 1995-96. I have always said that you have to get your hands dirty actually doing it before you can say you know how, and in the absence of classes you'll just have to go into your workspace after studying the manual and work it out in three dimensions.

Twenty-something years after it was written Ply Clinker Construction is still one of the most popular methods for home builders, but watch out, it's addictive!

I will mention one of my favourite bugbears here: many builders fall in love with wood like I did, but cannot bring themselves to paint over it. Ply Clinker Construction is a method that particularly benefits from some painted surfaces. I would strongly recommend that you consider picking out the solid

Another Iain Oughtred St Ayles Skiff joins the fleet, this one from Rathmines Men's Shed.

timber for clear finishing (thwarts, knees, rails) and painting most of the plywood except for highlighted areas such as the transom, the sheer strake and possibly the upper planks of the interior. This is particularly the case over exposed thick chunks of epoxy in joints. While you and I know that it is perfectly sound, if it is clear-finished your work is bound to gather some criticism, but if it is smoothed and painted it will look perfect.

Now get out there and build your boat!

David Payne's Clinker Ply 14' Rowing Skiff.

Plywood Clinker Construction

Plywood clinker construction is becoming one of the most popular methods for home builders to create an attractive and useful boat. You get the advantage of good looks and a traditional feel to the boat, while benefiting from the advantages of modern epoxy construction such as strength with lightness, ease of construction and elimination of leaks as a problem.

Briefly, plywood planks are cut to shape and epoxy glued to each other over temporary moulds, and glued to a permanent backbone of stem, hog and transom (see **Fig. 1**).

Each plank is shaped and bevelled so that each succeeding plank will fit, following exactly the same techniques as used in traditional clinker construction, except that instead of fastening the planks with copper nails, and roves, and fitting steam-bent ribs, the planks are glued together while being held with clamps or temporary fastenings, and no framing (or very little) is necessary. Compared with traditional construction where wood-to-wood contact and possibly a little old varnish or other bedding compound is all that keeps the water out, the epoxy glued plank can tolerate a less-than-perfect fit and still be structurally sound and permanently leakproof, making it ideal for first-timers. For most smaller boats, the addition of epoxy-glued seat supports and seats, gun'l rails and knees is all the internal bracing needed.

The other advantage of epoxy is that it simplifies several parts of the boat that are relatively difficult to do on traditional boats. The first plank, or garboard on a traditional hull must be fitted into a rabbet (rebate) along the keel and up the stem, which is a challenging woodwork project due to the constantly changing bevel. In ply clinker construction, this rabbet is unnecessary; you simply bevel the hog and stem at the correct angle to receive the plank, and run the plank out both over hog and stem. You later plane a flat landing for gluing on a separate outer keel and stem, with no compromise of structural integrity. Details of this process will be featured later, but for the moment it is enough to point out that ply clinker construction simplifies many aspects that were difficult and time-consuming in traditional clinker construction.

Designs

Many designs are already available for ply clinker construction. These include the excellent designs of Iain Oughtred, who was the first to design boats specifically for this method. David Payne, whose attractive boats were mostly originally designed for strip planking, but some of which we adapted for ply clinker construction; and Selway Fisher, whose wide variety of craft can provide a boat for almost everyone's taste. In fact, almost any small boat design with round-bilge lines can be built with this method. This manual will contain enough information for you to plank any small round-bilge hull.

The designs available range from canoes and dinghies, through open sailing boats, traditional trailer sailers and small yachts, and now Aussie-style clinker ski boats. The simplest designs call for 3-5 wide planks per side, and are either specifically designed for this method or can be adapted from designs for multi-chined stitch and tape boats. These include, Iain Oughtred's beach boat series of designs from 14-19 feet modelled on the Shetland Islands fishing boats, our own *Whiting Skiff* design which is an 11 foot rowing and sailing dinghy as featured in this volume and Selway Fisher designs for everything from canoes to traditional looking trailer sailers.

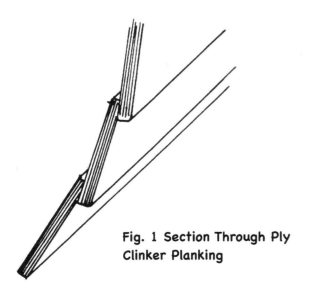

Fig. 1 Section Through Ply Clinker Planking

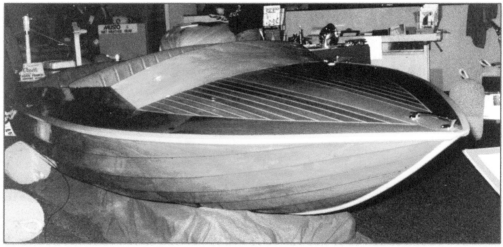

Plywood Clinker Construction has been used on these three boats of David Payne;
the 14' Putt-Putt (top); 16' Ski Boat (middle) and 14' Rowing Skiff (Bottom).

Lofting and Marking Out

Lofting is drawing out the plans full size so that you can mark out accurate temporary moulds over which to bend the planking, and mark accurate stem and transom shapes. Lofting is necessary only if the plans do not come with full-size patterns for mould shapes,stem etc. Most small boat designs, including all of the ones mentioned above, do come with such patterns. These patterns are tracings of someone's lofting, but because there are some designs that do not have full size patterns, we will cover the subject briefly here.

It is the **Lines Plan** of the boat that must be drawn out. This comprises three views as in **Fig. 2**, the **Profile** or side-on view of the boat, the **Half-Breadth Plan** of the boat viewed from above (or below), and the **Body Plan** or end-on view. The hull shape is drawn by plotting out a series of lines representing the intersection of several **plane or flat surfaces** with the curving hull surface. The easiest of these to grasp are the **Waterlines**, and the most obvious of these is the Designed Waterline (DWL) or Load Waterline (LWL), that line around the boat at which the designer expects the boat to float when carrying its normal load. The surface of the water is a plane or flat surface which intersects with the hull at the DWL. Every other waterline the designer calls for is another horizontal plane surface at given distances above and below the DWL. Just as the crocodile-eye view of the boat from side-on shows the DWL as a straight line, every other waterline is also a straight line in the profile view. From end-on, all waterlines in the body plan are also straight lines, but when viewed from below, the intersection of these horizontal

planes with the curving hull surface means that each waterline will be a curved line.

The **Sections** or **Stations** are vertical plane surfaces through the boat at right angles to the centreline. Once drawn these are directly useful because they are the shapes of the temporary moulds over which you will bend the planking. Sections are straight lines when viewed in Profile; they are straight lines also when viewed from above or below (in the half-breadth plan), but they are curved lines when viewed from end-on in the body plan.

The **Buttocks** are vertical plane surfaces parallel to the centreline of the boat. They are therefore straight lines in the half-breadth plan, and curved lines in the profile. Each of these lines then has a counterpart in each of the three views, and the essence of lofting is to ensure that the position of a line on the hull surface in one view agrees with its position on the hull surface in each of the other views, and how to do this will be described shortly.

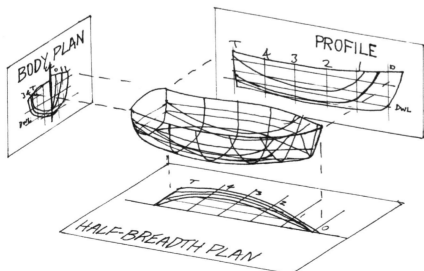

Fig. 2 Lines Plan

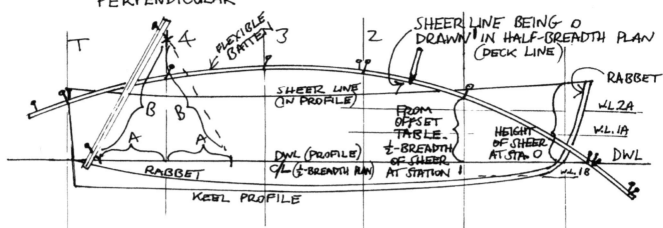

ESTABLISHING PERPENDICULAR

Fig. 3 The Grid and First Lines

Diagonals are a special case. They are plane surfaces starting on the vertical centreline of the hull at given angles between horizontal and vertical. They will therefore be straight lines in the body plan, but they are not actually drawn directly on the other two views. Rather they are plotted out on a drawing of their own, and how this happens is best described later. At the moment it is enough to consider that if the diagonals were drawn on the hull surface, they would generally be much closer to the trend of the plank laps than either the waterlines or the buttocks, and this fact makes them very important as we shall see shortly.

To save space it is normal to loft the three views of the boat superimposed on each other; this also means the basic grid need only be drawn once. You will need a space where you can lay down sheets of 12mm chipboard that will cover an area big enough to draw the three views superimposed. The chipboard is best painted white or light grey, and with any boat over 2.4 metres, more than one sheet will need to be used and they must be cleated together to prevent movement. The grid, comprising the straight lines of waterlines, sections and buttocks should now be drawn. Many designs use the DWL as a basic reference line, but others use a base line below the profile. Whichever line you choose should be drawn in, either with a straight edge if you have one longer than the boat, or by stretching a string line and marking a series of points beneath it which can be joined up by shorter straight edges. The straight-line stations common to the profile and half-breadth views are next. They are of course at right angles to the DWL

or base line, and one of these towards each end of the boat should be drawn using the school geometry method in **Fig. 3**. The highest waterline should be drawn in next, and the rectangle thus completed should be checked for squareness by measuring and comparing both diagonals. If these are different, something is wrong. An error of over 2mm could cause problems later. All other sections and waterlines can be measured and drawn in. Buttocks in the half-breadth plan will often have a common position with waterlines in the profile view, but not always.

Select a central station line to be the centreline for the body plan, and it is best if possible if the whole of the body plan can be drawn on one sheet of chipboard, and draw in the vertical buttock lines, and the diagonals as specified in the lines plan.

A Note about Colour-Coding

The grid should be inked rather than pencilled, and it is a definite help to colour-code the grid lines. I would normally draw Sections in black ink, waterlines in blue, buttocks in green, and save red for corrections and for the construction plan. Diagonals are usually black ink also. Label each line at intervals in large print for ease in locating positions later on. It helps if this labelling is colour-coded also.

Short-Cuts

Since the shapes of the sections are what we need to cut the moulds over which we bend the planks, you might assume that lofting all three views is unnecessary, and that only the sections need to be drawn, but this is not the case. At the scale at which the designer works, small errors in his or her measurements will be multiplied when drawn full-size, and if the sections only are drawn and contain errors, planks bent over moulds cut to these shapes may bend unfairly, that is, there may be bumps and hollows. We need to draw the longitudinal lines of the boat to prove that the relationship between each of the sections is correct; if a waterline is a smooth, fair curve, then the hull planking in that area of the boat will be a smooth curve also. There are no short-cuts.

Like this 14' Whilly Boat by Iain Oughtred, most small boat designers supply full-size patterns with the plans so no lofting is needed.

The Offset Table

Every position where one of the curved lines we are about to draw crosses the straight lines of the grid has a co-ordinate called an offset. Offsets for the curved waterlines are given as half-breadths on each station measured out from the centreline. Offsets for the Sheer, profile and the curved buttocks are given as heights relative to the DWL or Base Line, at each station. Diagonal offsets are distances along each diagonal from the centreline at each station. Newer designs will have these in millimetres, but many designs still available have Imperial measurements. Traditionally these are given in feet, inches and eighths of an inch. For example, an offset of 2-5-3 means two feet, five and three-eighths of an inch; 1-0-4 means one foot and a half inch.

The Sheer

The first curved line to be drawn is the Sheer line, the top of the highest plank in the profile view. It is one of the most noticeable lines in the finished boat, so it is worth taking some time to get right. Its position is given as heights above DWL or base at each station. Simply measure and mark each of these positions in pencil, tack a nail into each mark, and bend a flexible batten around the nails. The batten may not want to touch every nail without being forced, and when it does touch every nail, the batten may not be a fair line when viewed from each end, with your eye sighting along the batten. If there seems to be just one rogue nail allow the batten to take its own line between the two adjacent nails. If several nails cause the batten to wobble, pull some and try to get the batten to take a fair line in a position which will be the best average through the scatter of points, that is, some original points will be above the line, and some will be below it. It should not be too far from where the designer intended it, but it is vital that it is a smooth and fair line. When you are happy with it, ink it in as it will not change. Label it clearly at intervals.

You now draw in the same Sheer line, but in the half-breadth plan, that is looking down on the boat. You will have already selected the line which will become the centreline for the half-breadth plan view, and the offsets at each station should be laid off from this. Follow with nails and battens as before, ensuring that the line is fair. Ink this line in also, and label it. You now have two views of the same line, but in some plans the latter is referred to as the Deck Line to distinguish which view you are looking at.

Keel Profile and Rabbet Line

You next draw in the keel profile and rabbet line, first in the profile view. The keel profile is the bottom of the boat when viewed from the side; the rabbet line is the line at which the lowest plank meets the keel, and where the forward ends of the planks meet the stem. Even though there is no true rabbet on ply clinker hulls, it is a very important line because any parts of the boat outside this line are not built at this stage, but fitted later outside the planked hull. A single batten will not usually bend enough to draw both the stem and the bottom of the boat, so draw in each part separately. The same rules for fairness apply.

115

These same lines are now drawn in the half-breadth plan view. There usually are offsets given for the half-breadth of the outside keel and the rabbet line, if they vary in width along the boat, and these must be plotted and faired as for the earlier lines, but on many small boats the rabbet line especially will be of constant width from the stem to the transom.

With the lines you have drawn so far, you have an outline of the vessel from side on, and an outline of one half of the vessel from above. Now we have to turn to the Body Plan.

The Body Plan

The lines already drawn give us the true position of the top and the bottom of the planking at each section, and these must be transferred to the body plan. It is wrong to use the table of offsets to locate these positions on the body plane as you most likely have changed some of the offsets when fairing the lines. Your own drawn line is the true position of these lines and they are transferred to the body plan with the use of tick strips (see **Fig. 4**), which are thin straight strips of wood 2-3mm thick and 15-25mm wide. The height of the sheer at each station is lifted from the profile view, and the half-breadth at each station is lifted from the half-breadth view. The tricky bit is that in changing from the half-breadth view to the body plan, the tick strip must be rotated 90 degrees, which may seem hard to grasp at first until you learn to separate the three views in your mind: the half-breadth of the sheer at any station is measured out

from the centreline in both views, it is the centreline that has a different position on each view, left to right in half-breadth view, up and down in the body plan. The height of the keel and rabbet is taken from the profile view, and the half-breadth is taken from the half-breadth plan.

For the rest of the coordinates at each section, use the figures in the offset table. There will be a figure for every place where the curved hull section you are about to draw crosses each straight line on the grid. At each waterline there will be an offset given as a half-breadth from the centreline, at each buttock there will be an offset for a height relative to the DWL or base, and for each Diagonal there will be a distance out along that diagonal from the centre. You will end up with a series of points that you tack nails into and try to bend a batten around. It is extremely rare to find that the batten will lie fairly around all points. Again the principle is to take the best average line between the scatter of points, ensuring that the line is fair. Use pencil only to mark in the line as it is quite likely to change. Do the same for all stations including the transom. You now have the shapes of the temporary moulds, but we have not yet proven that the lines you have pencilled in are correct, and for that we need to draw out the diagonals, waterlines and buttocks diagonally. File the offset table way, you do not need it any more. All the measurements will now be transferred by tick strip.

Fig. 4 The Body Plan

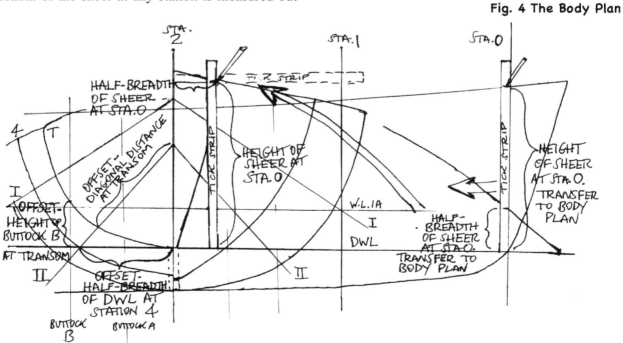

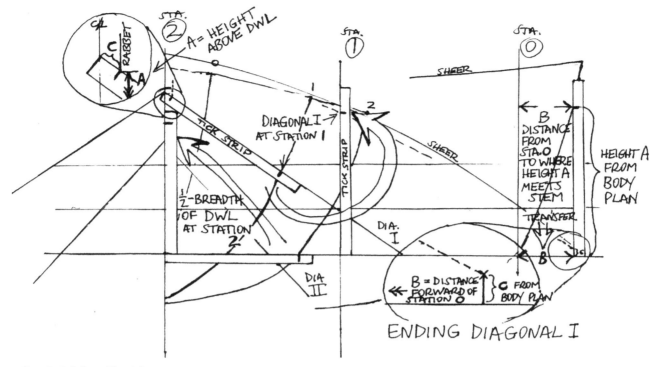

Fig. 5 Fairing the Lines

Fairing Diagonals

The diagonals are first because their intersection with the hull surface is generally close to the lines of the planking, and therefore they will show up any problems of planking fairness quite strongly. Conventionally on the Lines Plan the designer will plot out the diagonals on the opposite side of the centreline used by the half-breadth plan, and you can do the same full size if you have the room, but any line from left to right can act as the centrelines for the diagonals as long as there is room on the floor for the widest diagonal. Lift the distances at each station from the body plan and lay them out as in **Fig. 5**. The endings are the only tricky bit. Follow the diagrams in **Fig. 5**. Do the thing with the nails and batten, and see if the result is a fair curve; if not, pull a few nails and adjust positions until you get a fair line. Any nails moved mean that the new position of the batten at that point must be transferred back to the body plan as a correction. In effect, the batten has told you that the position you had pencilled in originally on the body plan is wrong. We usually mark the corrected position (transferred with the tick strip) with a short red mark to remind us that when we come back to redraw the sections in the body plan, the new line must go through this point. Repeat the process for all diagonals.

Traditional clinker designs are easily adapted to ply clinker construction like this 13'9" Fisher Waterman's rowing skiff.

Fairing the Waterlines and Buttocks

The waterlines are next, and are done in a similar fashion, except that the centreline used is the same one as the half-breadth plan view of the sheer or deck line. The half-breadths are lifted from each waterline in the body plan and laid out from the centrelines in the half-breadth plan. Locating the ends is again the only tricky bit. All corrections revealed when fairing the batten must be noted back on the body plan. Buttocks are laid out from heights at the relevant station in the profile view. The forward parts of the buttocks may need to be drawn with a more flexible batten. There are more points available for buttocks because of the point I made before about each line having to be in the same position on the hull surface in all three views. As illustrated in **Fig. 6,** the intersection of a buttock and a waterline in one view has to occur in the same position fore and aft as it does when they intersect in the other view. In order to have the buttocks fair, it is often necessary to redraw parts of the waterlines at this point, while not forgetting to stay on top of the corrections.

Back to the Body Plan

You now redraw the sections on the body plan, incorporating all of the corrections you marked in red. If you're lucky, this will work out, and lofting is almost finished. If you are unlucky, and you can't make all of the corrections fit, you have to go go through the process again, although it is rare for more than a few points to be out, and usually only on a minority of the sections. The answer is to pencil in a new fair line that is the best average of all the points you want it to go through, and draw out any diagonals, waterlines and buttocks that are affected by this change. It is rare that you will have to repeat this more than once.

A Note on Accuracy

While I must stress that you need to be as accurate as possible while marking out the grid and drawing the initial lines, by the time you are redrawing the body plan lines to incorporate the corrections, you can afford to be a little more liberal; for example, if a correction is just a pencil thickness away from a fair line you can consider that it fits.

Planking Thickness Deduction

Lines plans are mostly done to the outside of the planking, and to get the actual mould shapes over which to plank, you need to deduct the thickness of the planking. In most clinker boats this is as simple as drawing a line exactly the designed planking thickness inside the station lines. It is vital to keep the line exactly parallel; it is very easy to get a different shape when drawing this new line.

Fig. 6 Agreement of Waterlines and Buttocks

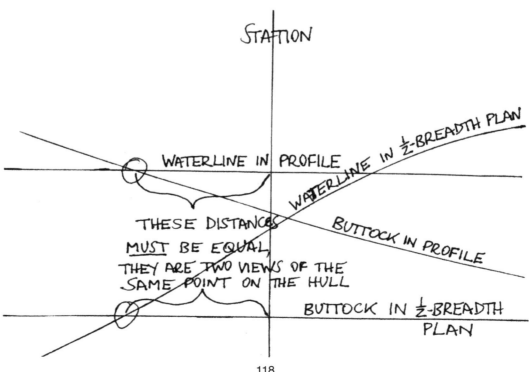

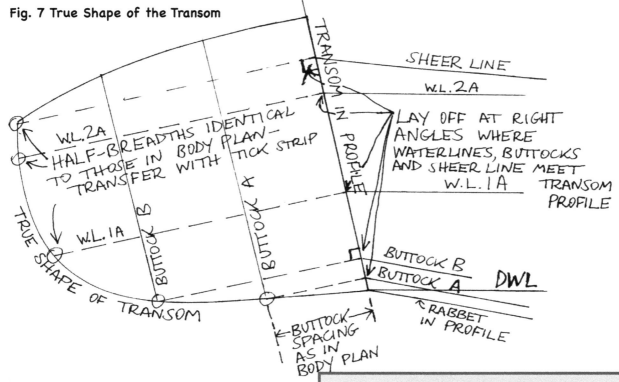

Fig. 7 True Shape of the Transom

Labels in figure:
SHEER LINE
W.L. 2A
TRANSOM IN PROFILE
LAY OFF AT RIGHT ANGLES WHERE WATERLINES, BUTTOCKS AND SHEER LINE MEET
W.L. 1A
TRANSOM PROFILE
HALF-BREADTHS IDENTICAL TO THOSE IN BODY PLAN — TRANSFER WITH TICK STRIP
W.L. 2A
BUTTOCK B
BUTTOCK A
W.L. 1A
TRUE SHAPE OF TRANSOM
BUTTOCK B
BUTTOCK A
DWL
BUTTOCK SPACING AS IN BODY PLAN
RABBET IN PROFILE

True Shape of the Transom

The transom lines drawn on the body plan will only be the true shape of the timber transom if the transom is dead vertical. Many boats however have a slope of some sort to the transom, and the lines on the body plan represent only the shape of that transom when viewed from directly behind. The true height of the transom will actually be greater and the shape on the body plan has to be expanded to allow for this. **Fig. 7** illustrates the method for doing this. Naturally you have to deduct the planking thickness also, but be careful when cutting out the timber, as the lofted shape is the outside of the transom, and the inside shape is actually bigger.

The Stem

The shape of the inner stem should also be drawn on the lofting. The face is normally on the rabbet line. The joint with the keel or hog should also be drawn in, and this is best done after first drawing in the keel at the forward-most station (after deducting planking thickness).

The sections should all be traced onto drawing office tracing paper for ease in transferring to the mould timber. The true transom shape and the stem shape should also be traced. Be sure to trace at least one or two of the waterlines also.

Lofting Chined Boats

Clinker boats with six or more planks aside are lofted as round-bilged hulls, and the planking doesn't come into it until the moulds are set up and you are ready to line out for planking. Boats with five planks or less per side are best lofted treating the hull sides as a series of flat panels in section, and waterlines, buttocks and diagonals are not used. Instead the lines of the plank joins, which are in effect chines, are lofted out longitudinally in both the profile and the half-breadth plan views. The sequence is: draw the sheer line in profile and in the half-breadth plan, draw the rabbet and keel in both views, laying the points from the offset table and correcting with a fair batten; ignore the body plan at this point. Lay out each of the chines or plank joins from the offsets in both views and ensure the batten that sweeps through them is fair. Use tick strips to locate these positions in the body plan, and join up each of the points on each station with a straight line. Deduct the plank thickness and you have your mould shapes.

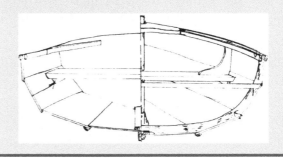

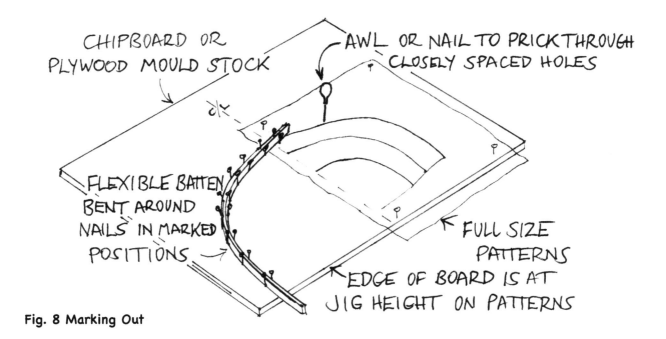

CHIPBOARD OR PLYWOOD MOULD STOCK

AWL OR NAIL TO PRICK THROUGH CLOSELY SPACED HOLES

FLEXIBLE BATTEN BENT AROUND NAILS IN MARKED POSITIONS →

FULL SIZE PATTERNS

EDGE OF BOARD IS AT JIG HEIGHT ON PATTERNS

Fig. 8 Marking Out

Marking the Moulds

The tracings of the lofting are the same as the full-size patterns supplied with many plans, so those who did not need to loft can start again from here. The full-size patterns consist of paper sheets with half of each mould shape drawn, and a centreline marked (see **Fig. 8**). Transfer these shapes by pinning the sheet to the mould stock (12mm chipboard or cheap plywood) and pricking through the lines with a nail or awl, being sure to mark the centreline and any waterlines marked, and the sheer mark or top of the gun'l. To mark the second side, simply turn the paper over, carefully locate the holes marked on the centreline and place the paper over these, and prick back through the same holes used on the other side. Most patterns will give you the line at which the mould will sit on the jig, but if not, you should draw one in at a constant height relative to the waterline of the boat. This line should be placed exactly on the edge of the chipboard sheet. Most designs will include a notch for locating the hog (the fore and aft inner keel) on the centreline, and sometimes notches for a sheer clamp or inwale at the sheer line. Somewhere between three and nine of these moulds will be necessary, depending on the design. Boats designed specifically for ply clinker construction will usually have

the suggested position of the plank laps marked around the perimeter of each mould and these should be transferred too. Later we will go into how you would decide on plank lap positions if these are not given. Join the dots made by the nail hole by tacking nails in and bending a flexible batten around, and pencilling in the line. Cut just outside this line with a jigsaw, but it is not necessary to cut too close or plane down to the line; simply just cut clear of the line so that the pencil line is always visible. Any planing of the moulds is only necessary just prior to fitting each plank. Cut any notches for longitudinal members exactly to the marked lines.

Chined boats like this Flattie are very easily lofted.

120

Laminating the Stem

The first part of the actual boat you will make is the stem. This can be laminated in several different ways as in **Fig. 9**. Clear Oregon, Kauri, or a light hardwood such as Silver Ash or Flooded Gum are best for the stem. The method pictured on the left side of the drawing can be used where there is not a great deal of curve in the stem, and is similar to the traditional method except it is epoxy glued rather than simply bolted together. The full-size patterns with the plans (or your lofting) will give you the shapes, and it is advisable to leave the sections oversize until after cutting and/or planing the scarf joints, then mark out the exact shape from the patterns with the same prick-nail-batten method as for the moulds, and cut and plane it to size.

The method in the middle is perhaps the simplest. Again leave the sections oversize until the epoxy has cured, then mark and cut the true shape. A bandsaw is handy for cutting out the shape in these two methods, but it can be done with a robust jigsaw or even handsaws and planed or spokeshaved accurately to the line.

The method on the right is marginally stronger, and requires more clamps, but you really need at least eight clamps for other parts of the boat later on, so this is a good place to start. Thin laminates are bent around a row of brackets or blocks fixed to a board, and clamped in position until the epoxy sets. The designer will usually suggest a thickness for the laminates, but it is wise to cut one to that size first and ensure that it will bend around the jig

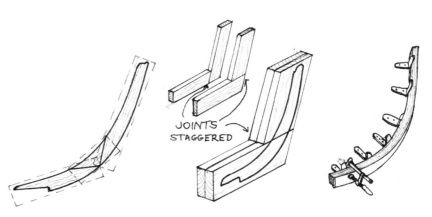

Fig 9 Alternative Stem Construction

before committing yourself to cutting the others. An individual laminate should bend around with relatively little pressure and no creaking sounds. The width of each laminate should be at least 6mm wider than the designer's suggested finished width to allow for cleaning up each side. Once all laminates are cut, <u>bend all around and clamp in a dry fit</u> to make sure it will work. Clamp at the end closest to the sharpest bend, and bend all around together, clamping on each packet in turn as the laminates bear on it. If it works, remove and mix the epoxy with microfibres to a just brushable consistency, and brush it onto both joining surfaces of each laminate. Protect the bench with plastic sheeting. Use gloves because of the mess, in fact using one glove is best to handle the wet laminates, and a clean unglued hand to handle the clamps. Put plastic sheeting also around the jig so the stem will not become part of it. Bend the laminates around the jig exactly as in the dry fit. Epoxy should squeeze out all joints. Cleaning up the squeeze-out is optional: sometimes the close clamp positions make it difficult at least to the point where you will inevitably get glue all over the clamps, and in fact the thick glue on top will help the rest cure a little faster. Leave the clamps on for at least 24 hours, or until the epoxy is hard enough not to dent with a fingernail.

When cured, cleanup the sides with a power plane, belt sander or grinder, and once the dags are off, true up the sides with a hand plane to the suggested thickness. Trim the end to be attached to the hog to the shape on the pattern, and use the pattern to mark in any waterline and station marks and the sheer height to assist in setting up, plus any suggested plank lap marks. Leave any extra length above the sheer line for fastening to the jig.

The inner stem can be laminated on the lofting or directly on the stem former.

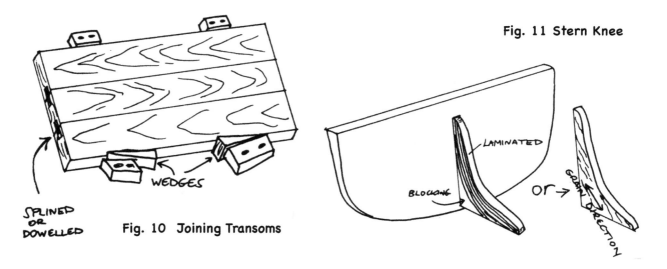

Fig. 11 Stern Knee

SPLINED OR DOWELLED

WEDGES

Fig. 10 Joining Transoms

LAMINATED

BLOCKING

or → GRAIN DIRECTION

The Transom

The transom can be cut from marine plywood marked from the full size patterns as with the moulds, but with a limited number of species of timber available in marine plywood, the transom is often made from solid timber to enable it to be a varnished feature of the boat. Kauri, Cedar, Mahogany and Queensland Maple have all been successfully used here. It will need to be built up from two or more boards, which should be planed to a light-tight fit against each other, then dowelled or splined and epoxy-glued as in **Fig. 10**. Large clamps are not necessary if you wedge the boards as shown. When cured, power sand any glue dags off and plane the boards flat. Mark out the transom shape as with the moulds, including the sheer and any suggested plank lap marks, but be careful to note which face of the transom the pattern represents: if it is the outside face, you will have to leave an allowance when cutting around the pattern because the forward or inside face of the transom is always larger, and the extra wood is necessary to allow for a bevelled landing for the planks. There is

no need to worry about bevelling this landing yet; leave extra wood, as the transom will be bevelled as you prepare to fit each plank. Leave the top straight with an excess of wood to assist in fastening the transom to the jig.

Stern Knee

Most designs will call for a stern knee between the transom and the hog. This can either be laminated as for the stem, with solid blocking to fill out the corner, or in boats under around 14 feet, cut from solid stock as long as the grain runs diagonally across the knee as in **Fig. 11**. It should be screwed and glued to the transom, central and dead square before setting up.

Setting Up

Most plans give details of the jig, but if not, a simple ladder frame is best, on four or six legs at a height which will bring the moulds to a comfortable working position, as in **Fig. 12**. Diagonal bracing of the ladder frame and the legs is necessary for rigidity. The jig should be fixed to the floor. It is not necessary to get the top of the ladder frame exactly level, it is easier to level up the moulds themselves.

It is necessary to understand how the moulds will sit on the jig before starting to build it. Each mould will sit on the line representing the given station spacing, but because the boat narrows towards each end, it is necessary to locate the forward moulds <u>aft</u> of each station line, and the aft moulds forward of the station line as in **Fig. 13**, so that the planking will actually rest on the drawn face of each mould.

A Kauri transom glued up.

Fig. 12 Mould Set Up

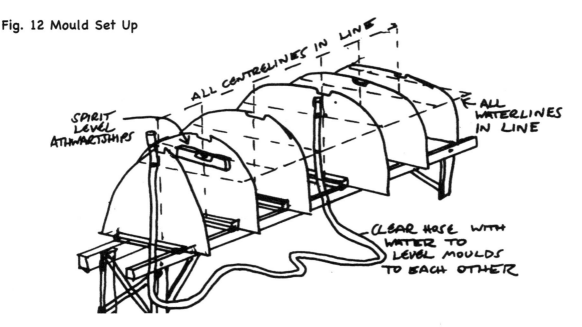

The station or mould spacing (given on the plans) should be marked on the top surfaces of the timber intended for the ladder frame before erecting it. Cross spalls should then be fitted at both ends on two of the station lines (forward of the line in the forward part of the boat, and aft of the line in the aft part) and the resulting frame checked for squareness by ensuring opposite diagonal measurements are equal. A diagonal cross brace should be fitted to hold this firm. Legs can now be fitted, also with diagonal bracing. All other cross spalls are now fitted, carefully ensuring they are on the correct side of the line, then a centreline is carefully drawn in with straight edge or string line.

The moulds are then erected, starting with the central mould, carefully levelling it using a marked waterline and checking that the vertical centreline is plumb and exactly in position over the jig centreline. Clamp it to the cross spall. Erect the most forward mould next, and level it similarly, but also check that it is level with the central mould using a water level, a clear hose with water in it. Do the same for the aftermost mould, and then erect all the intermediate moulds one by one. It is not necessary to use the water level on every one; the marked waterlines can be lined up by eye, that is all the waterlines should be visually on the one level. Screw the moulds to the cross spalls when you are happy with their position. Plumb the moulds fore and aft as well, and brace them diagonally to the jig.

Erecting the Stem

The stem can then be erected using the reference lines of station and waterline marked on it to locate its position relative to the forward mould. The most foolproof way is to cut a piece of chipboard to the shape of the space between the inside of the stem, the top of the jig, and the forward face of the forward mould, screw that to the centreline on the forward mould, and temporarily fasten the stem to that. It must be sufficiently well braced to take the pressure of planing it in position later.

Fig. 13 Positioning Moulds

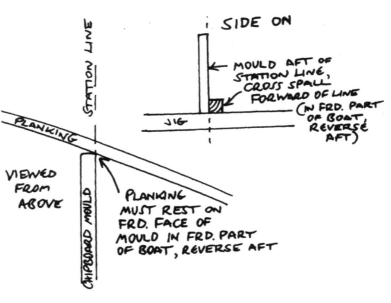

Erecting the Transom

If the transom is sloped the angle will be given on the plans. The height of the sheer on the transom relative to the jig is given or can be deduced, and the distance of this point horizontally to the aft face of the aft mould is given. These three coordinates enable the transom to be located accurately. The sequence is: first clamp timber braces to the jig at the angle of the transom, with their aft edge representing the inside face of the transom. Mark the height of the sheer relative to the jig on the aft edge of these braces, and move them forward or aft as necessary until this mark is at the correct distance from the aft mould. Screw them on position. Pencil in a straight line between the sheer marks on each side of the transom, across the inside face of the transom, and line this up with the marks on the angled braces. Line up the centreline with that on the jig and those on the moulds, and fasten it to the braces, screwing through the excess wood that will be cut off the top of the transom later.

A Note on Accuracy

With all the opportunities for errors to creep in through marking out, it is almost unheard of to find that all waterlines and aft centrelines line up perfectly over the whole boat. If a mark is obviously well out of kilter with all the others, suspect a major error and check back. If some lines disagree by less than two millimetres, it is best to average out the errors, that is if the waterlines line up but the centreline on one mould is out by up to two millimetres, move the offending mould to almost line up the centreline and disregard the fact that the waterlines may now be slightly out. If care has been taken in marking out, errors larger than this are unlikely.

Transom shape marked around batten held with nails to marks from pattern or tracing.

Fitting the Hog

The hog is glued and screwed to the stern knee, and either notched slightly into the transom or cut to butt against it. The forward end is fitted to the landing or scarf cut on the stem to receive it. Cleanup any glue squeeze out thoroughly.

The next step before planking is to shape the transom, hog and stem to receive the first plank, but we can't do this until we know how wide the plank is at each station. This is usually given on the plans, but if it is not, we have to go through the process of **lining-out** the planks.

Fig.14 Locating Sloping Transom

SHEER HEIGHT

TRANSOM BRACE

THIS DISTANCE FROM PLANS

AFT MOULD

LIFT THIS HEIGHT FROM PLANS OR PATTERNS

ANGLE FROM PLANS OR PATTERNS

JIG

OR DEDUCE
x = HEIGHT OF WATERLINE TO JIG MINUS VERTICAL HEIGHT OF WATERLINE TO SHEER AT TRANSOM

124

Fig. 15 Thickness of Plank Laps

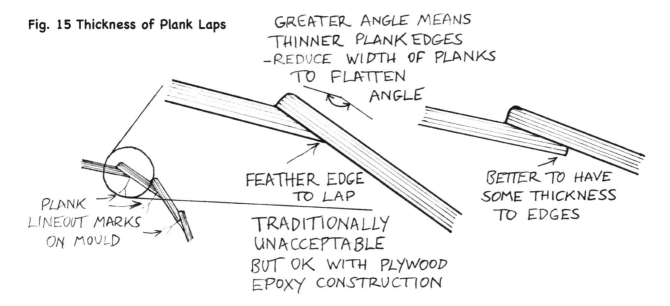

GREATER ANGLE MEANS
THINNER PLANK EDGES
-REDUCE WIDTH OF PLANKS
TO FLATTEN ANGLE

FEATHER EDGE TO LAP

BETTER TO HAVE SOME THICKNESS TO EDGES

PLANK LINEOUT MARKS ON MOULD

TRADITIONALLY UNACCEPTABLE BUT OK WITH PLYWOOD EPOXY CONSTRUCTION

Lining Out

The safest way to decide the number of planks and their widths is to refer to other boats of similar type, but you may have to change your original assumption in the light of what happens during lining-out. The simplest boats to line out are those with very semi-circular sections, as these can often be lined out simply by dividing the girth at each station, dividing each measurement by the number of planks, and this gives you the width of each plank at each station. Unfortunately, few boats are this simple. There are several factors that affect the line-out.

Keep the Garboard High

The bow end of the garboard or first plank should be kept fairly high on the stem. If this is not done, the plank end above it will generally tend to visually droop, and as the look of the run of clinker planking is very obvious, this can spoil the whole boat. It should not go too high, however. It could reach a point where the remaining space available for the rest of the planks means that each plank will be so narrow that there will not be room for the minimum two fastenings. It usually looks better if the planking is of even widths at each station, at least in the topsides. Remember that most boats have a rub-rail of some sort around the gun'l, and as the *exposed* width of each plank is what we are talking about, the sheer plank will be slightly wider. In areas other than the topsides, plank widths generally vary because of the following factors.

Narrower Planks at Hard Bilges

On boats that are fairly flat-bottomed or vee-bottomed and have a hard turn to the bilges, wide planks cannot be used at the turn of the bilge as illustrated in **Fig. 15**. To determine if your chosen plank width will fit at the turn of the bilge, draw the midship section full-size (use either the lofting or full-size patterns). The traditional rule was that no plank lap should be reduced to a feather edge. This is less important these days with epoxy-glued laps, in fact many designs with only a few planks each side are deliberately designed to have feather edges. The thinness of the edge is determined by a combination of the width of each plank and the angle at which the planks meet, and the planks can meet at such a large angle as to reduce the width of the lap. To thicken the plank edge, narrow down the width of the planks at the turn of the bilge; this reduces the angle at which they meet, and therefore thickens the plank edge. The width you deduct from these planks is usually best added to the bottom planks. The sections are usually flatter there, and wider planks here are acceptable, in fact they are traditionally referred to as the broad planks, first broad, second broad and so on.

The Shape of the Boat

The hardness of the bilges also affects the plank line-out because the planks in that region must follow the crest of the hill, as such: a plank cannot start on the flatter bottom of the boat, cross the hard turn of the bilge and end up on the flatter topsides. This applies equally to boats with a

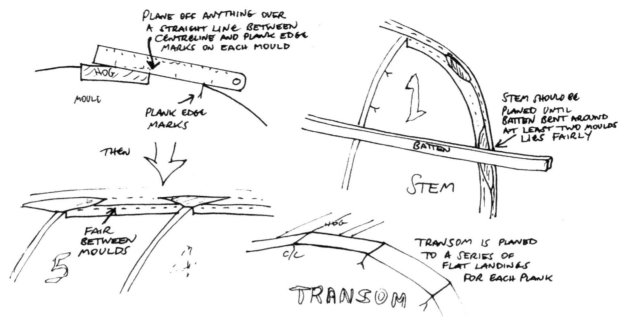

Fig. 16 Fairing the Backbone

reverse curve or hollow: a plank in this area must follow the bottom of the valley.

Shape also affects the way the planks run out at the stem. Boats with full flaring bows usually have the upper planks very thin high on the stem, and even in many cases one or two of the upper planks run out through the sheer line and do not even reach the stem, as on most clinker ski boats for example. This is because the full flaring shape means that in order to run out through the stem the planks would have to be very curved and would have to be cut from very wide boards. With plywood of course this is not a problem, but you may wish to follow the traditional look.

Line Out with Battens

Whatever widths you come up with, and even if these are given on the plans and patterns, it is essential to mark these on the moulds and tack battens around the hull (one side only) representing the plank laps, and stand back and view it from all angles. The visual effect of clinker planking is very important. It is almost certain you will want to adjust some of the battens to improve the look of the planking. Even if the marks were given by the designer, inevitable small errors in setting up will mean some of the marks will need to be adjusted slightly. When you are happy, mark clearly your revised positions. The important mark in each case is the outer plank lap mark, that is the one closer to the sheer, because this is the mark you take each plank to.

Bevel the Backbone

Using the line-out marks for the outer edge of the garboard or first plank, you now need to plane a bevelled landing for the plank along the hog, and at transom and stem. As each plank is a straight line across its width, at each mould the landing will be a straight line from the line-out mark to the centreline (or a line just off the centreline, depending on what the designer says), as in **Fig. 16**. So plane off anything above a straight line between these two points, whether it's timber hog or chipboard mould. Between the mould you have no exact guide for the angle, so fair in by eye. The secret of success is to remember what this is for: it is a landing for a plank, so the surface you end up with should be a smooth continuous curve fore and aft, and a straight line across the boat. To check, bend a section of plywood over the moulds and view it underneath to see if there are any gaps. At the stern, the transom should be planed for the garboard exactly as if it were another mould, except that is is important to have the fore and aft angle correct, and this must be checked regularly as you plane, using a batten bent over the next two moulds as in **Fig. 16**.

The batten is also used at the stem to determine the angle at which the plank approaches. With the garboard in particular it is important to use a section of plywood representing a plank, bent around the forward mould and stem in the forefoot area as a guide to how much timber to remove. It helps if this plywood is slightly more flexible than the planking material as the plank will probably needs some assistance from clamps to bend around here.

126

Spiling the Garboard

You will need a spiling batten, which is a strip of plywood of a thinner gauge than the planking, slightly narrower than the plank, and slightly longer. Get a sheet of cheap plywood and cut sections from it as you go. The plank shapes vary over the boat and no one spiling batten will do the lot. If the boat is longer than the plywood, screw two pieces together, and lay it with the screw heads down. Lay it on the boat so that it just lands on the hog all the way along. It is vital that the spiling batten lies naturally on the boat, that is without the ends being forced up or down, simply draped on the boat. Start by tacking to to the central mould, and work forward and aft tacking it to each mould in turn. If it begins to run out over the centreline or run off the edge of the hog, do not force it in the direction you want it to go. You must remove the nails holding it and realign it. Roughly trim the edge if it will not fit within the hog landing. At the bow it simply runs out over the stem.

With a set of compasses, mark a series of arcs all the way along the batten, with the point on the centreline or relevant planked mark, and the pencil describing an arc of about a quarter circle, about every 150-200mm , as in **Fig. 17**. If the marks for the outer edge of the plank are not covered by the batten, mark an arc from these as well. If they are covered ignore them. Mark the positions of each mould on the batten also. Take the batten to the plywood stock, and ensure that it won't move. With

Checking the transom for a good landing for the next plank.

the compass at the same radius as before, place the point on any two positions on each of the arcs, and mark two intersecting arcs which therefore represent the origin of the original arc. The line connecting all these points then represents the centreline of the boat in its correct relationship to your spiling batten. Cutting to this line will therefore give the plank a close fit to the centreline. Before removing the batten however, make sure you have transferred all of the mould marks (on both sides of the batten), and any of the arcs from the other side of the plank. Remove the batten, tack nails into the series of arcs and bend a flexible batten around the nails to pencil in the edge of the plank. Any missing marks from the other side of the plank can then be found by measuring the plank width on the relevant mould on the boat and transferring it to the relevant mould mark on the plank stock. Join these points with nails, batten and

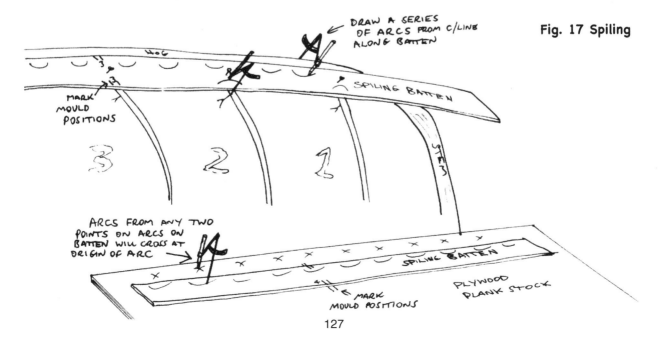

127

pencil and you have the shape of the plank. Jigsaw cut close to the inside line, and about 10mm clear of the outside line, and try for fit on the boat. It is not important to plane the edge on the centreline or even to worry about too close a fit, as in most designs this area will be covered later by the glued-on outer keel. At the bow the plank can simply run out out over the stem. It will be cut off later, and all planks will be planed flush with the stem before gluing on an outer stem cap. Temporarily screwing the plank to the moulds once you are happy with the inside line's fit is the best method to ensure that the plank does not change position while the rest of the work on the plank occurs, but if holes worry you, clamps can be used. The holes can be filled later with epoxy putty or wood plugs.

Scarfing Plywood

Any boat longer than about 2.2 metres will need the planks scarfed to get the length. In many ways it is simplest to scarf full width sheets together, but if you do not have enough space, it is possible with a great deal of care to scarf each plank individually, and in fact this is more economical with materials. You simply cut the plank in two sections, and scarf it together ensuring that the ends are in the correct relationship to each other. The best way to do this is to set up a section of chipboard longer than the longest plank (simply cleat it together) and about 300mm wide , on a bench or on the floor. As you spile the shape of each plank, spile it onto this chipboard first, then onto two separate pieces or plywood stock, and cut matching scarfs and glue it together on the board ensuring that it conforms to the spiled overall shape.

The scarf joints are cut by planing the end of the ply at an angle of 8 to 1, supporting the feather edge of the plywood right on the edge of the bench. If the plywood is 6mm, measure back 6mmx 8 = 48mm (or 50mm for ease of marking) and plane the slope from this line to the feather edge. The scarf should be flat and even, slightly hollow is better than rounded. The lines of the veneers in the plywood are a good guide here: a good scarf will generally have straight veneer lines revealed of even width. Bond the cut scarfs together with epoxy either by clamping them together, or by screwing right through from a scrap board on top into another (or the bench) underneath, remembering to put plastic down to prevent any glue squeeze-out bonding the ply to the backing boards. Give the cut scarfs a soak coat of mixed epoxy before adding microfibre powder to some more epoxy to thicken it to a mayonnaise consistency. A little vaseline or wax on the screw threads will make them easier to remove the next day. Heat from touching the screw head with a grinder will help any stubborn ones.

Fig. 18 Scarfing

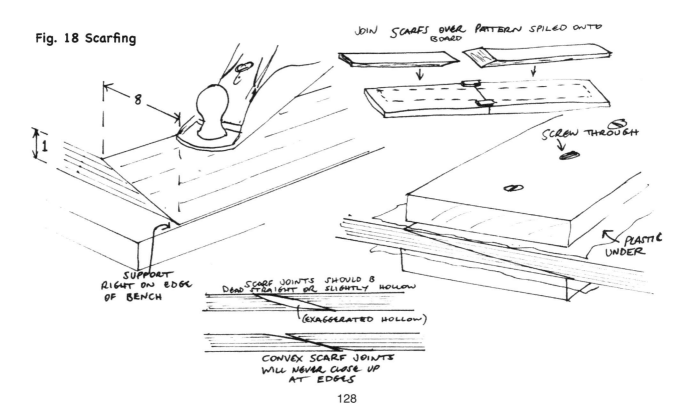

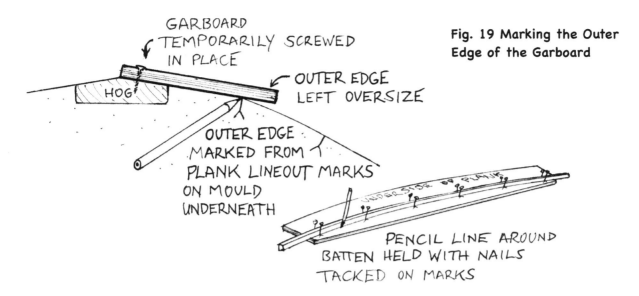

GARBOARD TEMPORARILY SCREWED IN PLACE

HOG

OUTER EDGE LEFT OVERSIZE

OUTER EDGE MARKED FROM PLANK LINEOUT MARKS ON MOULD UNDERNEATH

UNDERSIDE OF PLANK

PENCIL LINE AROUND BATTEN HELD WITH NAILS TACKED ON MARKS

Fig. 19 Marking the Outer Edge of the Garboard

Marking the Outside Edge of the Plank

The garboard plank, the first plank next to the keel, has been temporarily screwed or clamped to the stem, hog and transom with its inner edge just clear of the centreline. Remember that the centreline will have a flat landing for the outer keel planed on it, so perfect fitting of the plank edge to the centreline is simply not necessary, as it will be completely covered. The outer edge of the plank however is still oversize by at least 10mm. Transfer the lineout marks on the moulds, transom and stem to the underside of the plank as in **Fig. 19.** Remove the plank from the boat, tack a nail into each of these points, and join them with a pencilled line around a batten. If the batten is unfair, that is, if it has bumps or flat spots, try adjusting the nail positions slightly to improve it. Be conservative here however, because if you lined-out the planks fairly on the moulds any adjustments should be less than say 3mm. The resulting shape may well be

unusual, not at all what you expected. Some planks will be S-shaped.

You can cut and plane confidently to this line. Planing can be done either with the plank held vertically in two vices, or horizontally clamped to the bench with the plane held vertically (be careful to keep the edge square). Plane it fair, being careful not to plane too many strokes in in one spot or you will end up with a flat spot there. Keep the plane moving in overlapping strokes along the plank edge. Sight along the plank edge for bumps and hollows. The difference between a fair edge and an unfair one can be less than the pencil thickness, so it is better to sight along the side without the pencil markings.

Browing Off

"Browing off" is the term old Sydney boatbuilders use for the process of bevelling the plank lap as a landing for the next plank. The chosen lap width should be marked on the plank edge either with a marking gauge or by setting an adjustable combination square to the lap width and sliding it along the plank edge with a pencil held on the end. Screw the plank back on the boat, and plane the bevels at each mould as in **Fig. 20.** A small block plane is usually best for this. Bevel at stem and

Fig. 20 Browing Off

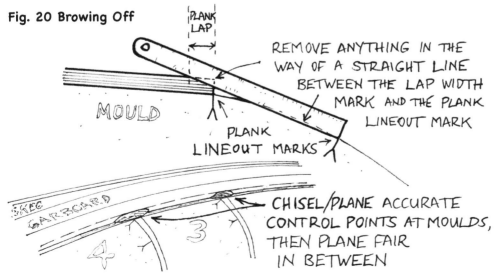

PLANK LAP

MOULD

REMOVE ANYTHING IN THE WAY OF A STRAIGHT LINE BETWEEN THE LAP WIDTH MARK AND THE PLANK LINEOUT MARK

PLANK LINEOUT MARKS

KEEL   GARBOARD

CHISEL/PLANE ACCURATE CONTROL POINTS AT MOULDS, THEN PLANE FAIR IN BETWEEN

stern as if they were just another mould, for reasons which will be explained shortly. With these bevelled areas as guides, fair in a continuous bevel. This can be done on the boat, but it is generally easier with small planks on the bench. You will notice that the angle changes from one part of the boat to another, and this change must be gradual, keeping in mind what this is for: it is a flat landing for the next plank. For the same reason, you should try to avoid wobbling the plane: the landing must be flat across the bevel. The veneers of the plywood are a good guide to the fairness of the bevel. If the veneers are wavy, it is a good indication that the bevel is uneven and unfair.

23' Lifeboat for the James Craig being planked with plywood. Note the staggered scarf joints.

Jerralds

Jerralds are rebates in both ends of the planks which let the planks into each other and allow them to sit flush on the stem and transom. Cutting them is a bit like riding a bicycle: difficult to explain, and your first attempt may be a bit wobbly, but once you've got the hang of it you'll wonder what all the fuss was about. If you follow the sequence outlined here you will have little trouble as long as you constantly check your progress. Traditionally, jerralds were usually cut before browing off, and this can certainly still be done once you have a feel for the correct angle, but for your first boat I strongly suggest you follow the sequence here. The

bevel has been continued right to the stem and transom. The jerrald starts between 150 and 250mm from each end of the boat, depending on the size of the boat, and is best cut with a rebate plane (either a No. 78 with an adjustable fence, or a smaller type running against a stick clamped to the lap width line). It can also be done with a sharp saw and chisel. The bevel is simply deepened into a rebate as in **Fig. 21**, at exactly the same angle as the bevel before starting. This ensures that the angle of the jerrald will be steep enough to accept the next plank. The angle of the jerrald must be at least equal to the angle at which the next plank meets this one, otherwise the matching jerrald underneath the new plank will be undercut. At the end of the boat, the jerrald should be just deeper than halfway through the plank. Depending on the angle, this may mean it will be close to a feather edge right at the end, but this is okay.

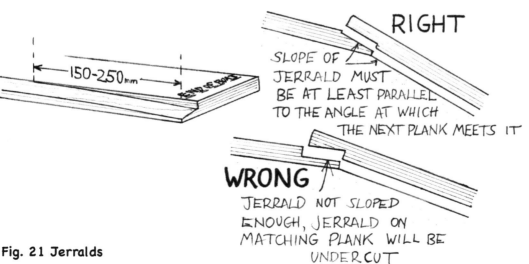

Fig. 21 Jerralds

130

Before Fitting the Plank

With jerralds at both ends, the plank is now ready to fit, but there are two things that must be done before fitting. One is to plane a landing for the following plank on the transom: at this stage a plane can get in there, but it is more difficult once the plank is glued in place. The other is to mark out a mirror image plank for the other side of the boat. Mark it well oversize, about 10mm all round. With these items done, the plank can be glued to the boat with epoxy thickened with microfibres. Clean up the glue with a metal putty knife meticulously, or you will regret it. Put plastic tape anywhere that glue is likely to squeeze through and stick the boat to the moulds. We generally run a line of low-tack tape along the inside of the plank just clear of the lap width to make cleanup easier.

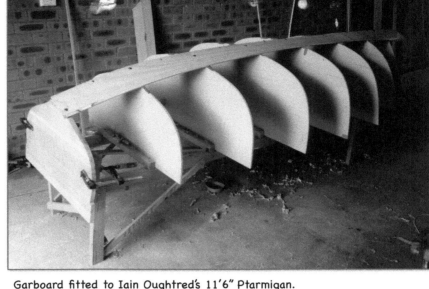

Garboard fitted to Iain Oughtred's 11'6" Ptarmigan.

Fitting the Other Garboard

The slightly oversize plank for the other side can be clamped in place, and any bumps along the centreline marked and then planed off so there is a reasonable fit to the original plank. Remember that the outer keel will cover this area, so a rough fit is perfectly acceptable, and a fine fit here would be a waste of time. Do not bend the plank to fit where you think it should go: it must drape naturally around the moulds and should be in contact with each mould. If an edge is lifting off a mould it is an indication that the plank is being forced. When you are happy with the way it lies, mark the underside with the plank lineout marks on the moulds, then remove the plank and join the dots with nails, batten and pencil, and cut and plane to this line as before.

Checking fit of second plank on 10' Robin.

The Second Plank

The next plank should now be spiled in exactly the same manner as for the garboard, laying the spiling batten around the moulds, preferably just landing on the edge of the garboard, but with the lap width line clearly visible, because that is the line from which the compass point starts the spiling process. Cut and plane accurately to the spiled inner line, but leave extra width on the plank. The other side is marked from the lineout marks on the moulds underneath only once the inner edge is fitted accurately to the boat.

131

Cutting the jerrald.

Plank held temporarily with nippers.

Bevel fairs into jerrald at stem.

What if the Spiled Edge Doesn't Seem to Fit?

With the first few planks on a stem dinghy there is a lot of twist, and it is quite likely that the spiling batten may not bend in exactly the same manner as the plank stock, and when you offer up your proudly planed plank edge it does not fit, particularly at the forward end. This is the one reason why you must leave plenty of excess plywood on the outside of the plank. With the garboard it is easy to trim back any bits that fit over the centreline. The fit of the second plank is more critical, but the solution is simple. Lay the plank in position over the moulds but with the inner edge only just landing on the garboard. If it is a different shape, it will be on the garboard more in some places than others. Simply draw a line along the underside of the plank where they overlap, and cut and plane to this line. Caution: before marking, check that the outer plank edge is beyond each plank lineout mark by at least the amount of your standard lap width; after cutting to your line marked from the previous plank edge, the plank will move inboard by this amount. If the plank doesn't cover these marks by more than the lap width this plank is a reject. It can be used however to mark an oversize replica which can be fitted in the same manner.

Matching Jerralds

After both sides of the new plank are planed accurately, jerralds must be cut to the underside at both ends to fit neatly into the jerralds on the previous plank. Hold the plank up in a position where it is parallel to where it will live, as in **Fig. 22**, and eyeball the angle at which the jerrald should be planed to match the other. Take to the bench and plane a few strokes at this angle, offer it up again, and check your angle and depth. Do a few more plane strokes, adjusting the angle if necessary. There is always less

Fig. 22 Matching Jerralds

HOLD NEW PLANK
PARALLEL TO LANDING
ON TRANSOM TO
EYEBALL ANGLE OF SLOPE
AND DEPTH OF JERRALD

to remove here than you first think, so I cannot stress too strongly that you should do only a few plane strokes each time and <u>check often</u>. If you go too far, epoxy will still fill it (unlike on a traditional boat), but it is far more satisfying to get a good fit. Remember that this jerrald starts flat and rolls to whatever angle is necessary at the end of the boat, so each plane stroke should roll as you go. The object is to get the inside of the plank to sit fair on its landing at the stem and transom. Where the planks fit fairly flat as on the upper stem and the bottom of the transom, this will also mean that the outside of the planks will end flush, but where the

planks meet at an angle as at the turn of the bilge, the outside overlap will still be proud, but this is okay a long as the inside of the plank is sitting down on the landing on the transom.

The plank is screwed in place on the moulds, and browed off, outer jerralds cut, and glued in place as before (after marking a sister and planing a landing on the transom for the following plank). The oversize sister is fitted to the previous plank on the other side as described above, marking from underneath from the edge of the previous plank, ensuring that it covers the outer plank lineout marks by at least the lap width.

David Payne's 16' Ski Boat.

Summary of Planking Sequence

Planking the rest follows in the same manner. The sequence is summarised thus:

1. Spile the plank. Cut and plane to the inner line, leave oversize on the outer side.

2. Fit to the boat. If it is a good fit, mark, cut and plane the outer side from the lineout marks on the moulds underneath. If it is a bad fit, mark as in Step 8 below.

3. Cut jerralds under the plank at both ends to allow the inside of the plank to sit flat on the stem and transom when in position. Temporarily fasten it off.

4. Brow off by bevelling accurately at moulds and fairing in between. Treat the stem and transom as if they were moulds.

5. Deepen the bevel into a jerrald (rebate) at each end, maintaining the same angle as the bevel.

6. Mark a mirror-image plank for the other side and cut it oversize. Plane a landing on the transom for the following plank.

7. Glue the plank on.

8. Mark the oversize sister by pencilling the edge of the previous plank from underneath, ensuring that the plank overlaps the plank lineout marks by at least the plank lap width, then follow the sequence as above.

The Outer Stem

The outer stem is usually fitted from thin laminates. Trim the plank ends and plane a flat landing on the stem. Dry fit all but one laminate by screwing them to the stem at 125-150 mm intervals. Remove and apply reasonably thin epoxy and microfibres to both surfaces of each laminate and permanently screw them in place. When dry, bevel to the required stem face thickness, adding the outer single laminate, glued on with temporary screws to hold it. Plug or epoxy-fill the holes.

Keel and Skeg

The skeg should be fitted by scribing its shape as in **Fig. 23**. The outer keel in the forward part of the boat should be scarfed into both the skeg and the outer stem.

Fitting Out

Don't be tempted to finish the outside of the hull completely at this stage, as there are a number of internal parts of the boat that will need fastening from outside the hull. If you are not going to dynel sheathe the hull you could fit the sacrificial rubbling strips to the keel and bilges at this point, but if you plan to sheathe then turn the boat right way up now. Boats under 14 feet are best freed from their moulds and lifted off as empty shells, but boats larger than this can get a bit heavy and are best lifted off by large, sober crews, or rolled over on tyres or mattresses with the moulds still inside.

Fig. 23 Scribing the Skeg

SKEG STOCK
PACKED UP LEVEL OR TO
DESIGNER'S SUGGESTED ANGLE
SET COMPASS TO
THIS DISTANCE

SKEG STOCK

SCRIBE SHAPE OF HULL
HOLDING THE PENCIL VERTICALLY
ABOVE THE POINT

There will inevitably be some glue dags to cleanup, though hopefully you will have cleaned up as thoroughly as possible after gluing each plank. Now is the easiest time to cleanup before there is any internal structure to get in the road. Sanding inside along the laps and even resin coating the interior is easier at this stage. Remember that if you want to finish the inside clear, i.e. varnished, then it is absolutely vital to remove all traces of glue, even to the extent of sanding out any stains from the glue so that they won't show through the clear coatings: you need clean, as-new wood to look good under a clear finish.

Ply clinker boats need little internal framing. Iain Oughtred's 10′ Robin sailing dinghy.

Seat Supports

The first parts to go into the boat should be the seat support system. This can either be individual cleats fitted to the hull for each seat, or a continuous riser on which all seats (or thwarts) sit. Seat cleats should be scribed to the shape of the hull and bevelled so that their upper surfaces are horizontal for the thwarts to sit flat, as in **Fig. 24**. They can either be simple blocks which do not protrude past the edges of the thwart, or protrude with some decorative shape cut into them. Fit a pair, one to each side of the boat by scribing and bevelling, and only cut any decorative shape into them after you're happy with the fit against the hull. They can be fastened with screws from outside the hull, and of course glued as well.

Risers are smaller in section but are fitted along the hull to support all thwarts, usually entirely within one plank, and generally stopping short of the ends of the boat. If they are on one plank only they can be glued and screwed from outside, directly to the plank. If they cross onto another plank, they will have to be mounted on regular spacer blocks. They are traditionally fitted with no bevelling to the hull....some designers may call for bevelling all the way along, but this is a masochistic practice with very little benefit and great room for errors to develop. The upper surface can be bevelled horizontally locally as a landing for each thwart, but even this is not necessary.

Thwarts

If substantial seat cleats have been fitted to the hull, the thwarts can be fitted without touching the hull sides, and this is certainly easier, but if they land on risers, they will need to be a dead fit against the hull sides. Follow this sequence: cut the thwart stock well oversize, locate one end on marks in its correct location, with the long end hanging over the side of the boat as near as possible to being directly vertically over where it is going to

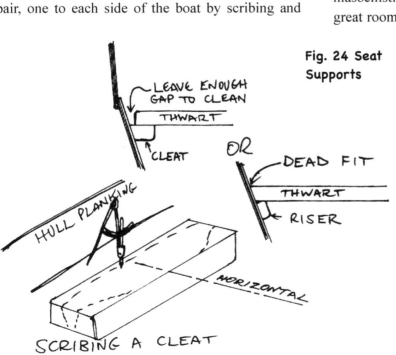

Fig. 24 Seat Supports

LEAVE ENOUGH GAP TO CLEAN

THWART

CLEAT

OR

DEAD FIT

THWART

RISER

HULL PLANKING

HORIZONTAL

SCRIBING A CLEAT

live, as in **Fig. 25**. Check that the boat is the desired beam at the relevant point, as sometimes the boat will narrow slightly when it comes off the mould. Prop it to the correct beam. Scribe the hull shape onto the boat end. Measure the maximum distance from one side to the other, (remembering that it will be greatest on the top surface of the thwart) either with a tape measure or by pushing two sticks out to the marks and clamping them together. The latter is the best system as it also enables you to measure the bevel angle of the end of the thwart against the hull. Set your jigsaw or bandsaw to this angle and cut to the first scribed line on the end of the board. Mark the overall width measurement onto the board. Put the board back in the boat, but this time with the uncut end down on its marks and the other end out over the side. Set a pair of compasses to a width that will pick up the distance from the hull side to the width mark, but allow an extra 10mm to the width of the thwart for safety on this first cut. Scribe the hull shape and cut to this line, with the same bevel setting on the saw as for the other side. The thwart should now almost fit into the hull ...... in fact it should be up to 10mm too big. Repeat the same steps, scribing again, but still leave a little extra on the width. There will usually not be enough meat left for saw cuts, so plane it down. A sharp low-angle block plane works best in planing the end grain. Plane towards the middle from each side to avoid splintering. When happy with the fit, screw and glue down.

A Note on Gluing

In almost every situation in ply clinker boatbuilding it is advisable to dry fit the parts before gluing. This way you know its going to work, and avoids any unpleasant surprises when the pieces are covered with messy and expensive glue. To ensure that the parts go back in the same place, use only a hand screw-driver and feel that the screws are going back into the same holes. A cordless screwdriver has no sensitivity and is just as likely to make a new hole and the parts will not fit correctly together. The best procedure is to leave enough time at the end of each session to glue up what has been made and dry fitted in that session. Leave plenty of time, it should not be rushed. Especially do not rush the cleanup job, or you will regret it. Cleanup squeezed-out epoxy with a clean metal putty knife. It is well worth the time spent in laying PVC tape along each side of a joint before taking the bits apart for gluing. Remove the tape immediately after cleaning up the excess with the putty knife. Areas to be varnished need total removal of even the wet stain of the epoxy; areas to be painted can have the stain, but any glue lumps or smears must be removed. Anything that you can feel (when dry) will show as a bump in a gloss paint coat.

Gunwales

Referred to by several names by different designers, gunwales, or outwales, or rub rails are fitted after the thwarts. They are quite simple to fit, the only actual fitting required being at the front where they fit against the sides of the outer stem.

Fig. 25 Thwarts

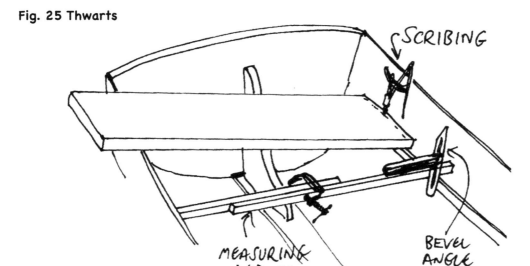

SCRIBING

MEASURING WIDTH

BEVEL ANGLE

Screw them into the stem, and bend them around the top of the sheer plank, clamping as you move aft. If the planking is of light gauge and the rail is quite stiff, it is best to bend both sides around together and tie the ends with a loop of rope to avoid localised stresses on the planks. Sight the rails from as many different angles and as far back as you can get from the boat to ensure that they lie in a sweet, fair curve. Nothing will spoil the look of a boat more than bumps in the gunwale. When happy with the position, fasten the rail on with screws through the plank from inside.

Knees

Knees are gussets that strengthen the boat. There are quarter knees on each side at the stern, a breasthook at the back of the stem joining the two sides of the boat together, and thwart knees bracing the hull sides over the thwarts. The secret to fitting knees is to fit one side at a time. Each knee (except for the breasthook) has one straight side and one side either curved or in two straight sections. With the quarter knees, the straight side is across the transom; with thwart knees, it is along the thwart. Fit the straight side first, and only start on the other side when you are completely happy with the fit of the first side.

For quarter knees take a sliding bevel gauge and measure the angle where the sheer strake reaches the transom. The plank side will invariably fit with its upper surface level with the top of the sheer strake; the transom side will normally slope a little up from horizontal towards its inboard end. If both quarter knees are horizontal and the transom has a curved top, visually the quarter knees will appear to droop. If the designer gives no specifications for the amount of rise, pencil a straight line from each corner to a common point on the centrelines just below the top of the transom. Position the bevel gauge at the correct attitude, then mark out a piece of timber with this angle. Knees can be cut from grown crooks with curved grain, or laminated from thin strips, or cut from straight-grained stock with the grain direction running across the knee as in **Fig. 26**. Cut the timber as a triangle; do not be tempted to cut the finer shape of the knee until you have dry-fitted a symmetrical pair. You then place the piece in position, and

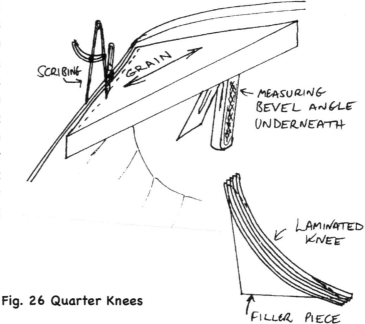

Fig. 26 Quarter Knees

ascertain the bevel angle of the side that is against the transom by pushing the bevel gauge up from underneath as in **Fig. 26**. If this is a slight angle, it can simply be planed in a vice; if it is a large angle it may be quick to set the jigsaw or bandsaw to the angle and cut it. Plane until the knee sits tight on the transom, with no rocking, and with its forward leg exactly parallel with the top of the sheer strake. Then use a compass to scribe the shape of the sheer strake onto the knee, measure or note any bevel, and plane until it fits tight. When you have a pair that fits, draw the required shape on one, cut it out and use it as a pattern for the other one. The extremities of a knee are always tapered. Thinner legs look best but are weaker, so you must find an eye-pleasing compromise. Fasten with one or two screws in each leg, either from inside or outside.

Thwart knees are fitted first to the thwart. Each thwart knee, if there is only one to each side per thwart, is fitted square to the thwart, so that the leg can be planed dead straight and square on the bench, and when it sits square and solid on the thwart, scribe the side against the hull. Thwart knees may fill the entire area or be hollow underneath, as in **Fig. 27**. On the mid thwart, a single knee is set in the middle of the thwart, parallel with the centreline, but on the forward and after thwarts, single knees are usually square with the side of the hull. That means that on the forward thwart the lower leg actually points a little aft, and the after thwart knee lower leg points a little forward. Thwart knees look best if the lower leg is

10-20% longer than the upper leg. To locate the forward and after knees in a visually balanced position see **Fig 27**.

The breast hook is the hardest to fit, so leave it to last so you've had some practice. It can be either one piece of timber with the grain going across the boat, or two pieces meeting on the centreline, each with the grain parallel with the sheer, or it can be laminated. If it is one piece, or laminated into one piece, cut the stock well oversize, because you are sure to reduce it considerably

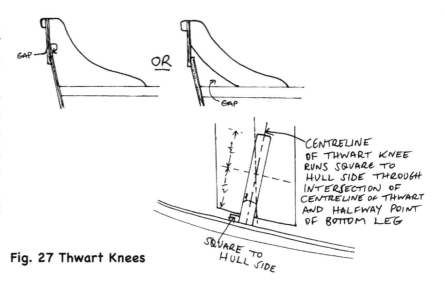

Fig. 27 Thwart Knees

CENTRELINE OF THWART KNEE RUNS SQUARE TO HULL SIDE THROUGH INTERSECTION OF CENTRELINE OF THWART AND HALFWAY POINT OF BOTTOM LEG

SQUARE TO HULL SIDE

while planing it to fit. Have it thicker that the other knees because when finished it should have some camber or curve across the boat. In some boats it is possible to fit one side first and then scribe and cut the other side but in most cases you will need to alternatively take some off each side. If you are making it from two pieces , ensure that your stock is large enough to still extend past the centreline when you have fitted it along the sheer. Each side should be raised a little towards the centre to allow for a little camber or curve on top. Fit both independently and mark the centreline on each in turn. Cut conservatively just clear of these lines, and plane some off each, literally a few plane shavings at a time until they fit snugly together all around.

A Note on the Sequence

The sequence of fitting the thwarts, then the gunwales, then the knees should not be changed. The thwarts are needed to hold the boat to the correct beam; fitting the gunwales first may distort the shape of the floppy hull. Likewise the gunwales should be on before the knees: if you carefully fitted the knees first, you may well find that they no longer fit, or cause a hard spot if glued in, because a stiff gunwale takes a slightly different shape to the flimsier plank. Floors, which we will deal with shortly, can be fitted any time after the thwarts go in.

Inwales

Inwales are companions of the gunwales or outwales, set on the inside of the planking, and are of similar or slightly smaller dimension than the outwales. They are not actually a necessary feature. Most traditional clinker dinghies around Sydney did not have them, and building is certainly simpler without them. If you do decide to leave them out, the size of your outwale should be slightly increased. Inwales can be fitted hard up against the planking, in which case they are fitted before the knees; or on spacer blocks to mimic the traditional look where the inwales were fitted against the top of the ribs. In this case the knees are fitted first, and notched to support the inwale at

Fig. 28 Inwales

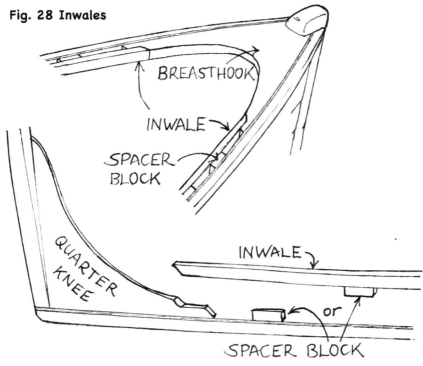

BREASTHOOK

INWALE

SPACER BLOCK

QUARTER KNEE

INWALE

or

SPACER BLOCK

the same distance from the planking as the spacer blocks. It is a fiddly job but one that is well worth the effort because it looks so good, and is very strong. The only drawback is that it is difficult to sand and varnish.

Fit the spacer blocks to the hull first (or fit them to the inwale) and notch the knees correctly. On the aft end of the breasthook and the forward end of the quarter knees, notch the landing at an angle as in **Fig. 28**. Start by fitting the end that is more difficult to hold the inwale to; sometimes it is the stern, more often the bow. Clamp it around in place as you go, ensuring that it is landing on each spacer block. This is vital: you are going to have to cut the other end to fit it in, and if the inwale is not forced out to the spacer blocks when you cut it, it will be pulled short when you do force it out when permanently fitting it. Cut the other end off in stages: always leave it a little longer than you think necessary, and worry it down. The best system is to use an offcut to make a template of the end, at least 300mm or so long, fit it into the notch and lay the real inwale on top of it as close as possible to where it is going to live, and pencil a witness mark across both pieces. Raise this setup onto the gunwale, put a protective piece of scrap ply underneath, and cut the end of the inwale to be an exact copy of the template, ensuring the witness marks line up. Add on a small margin for safety. When you are very close, it is sometimes easier to take a thin shaving out of the notch on the knee. It should be a firm fit.

Floors

Floors in dinghies are athwartship stiffeners to support the flat areas of the bottom, and support the floorboards or bottom boards. They are fitted by scribing off the hull as in **Fig. 29**. Just like the knees, they should be left well oversize until you are happy with the fit to the hull, then the required top shape can be cut. They are not set plumb or vertical, they should be set square to the planking,

because the floorboards which sit on top will be parallel to the planking. Where the hull shape changes towards the outer ends, especially forward, set them   square with the more inboard planking. They do not need to notch over the keelson or hog, as it is necessary to leave limber holes here so water can drain from one end to the other. In fact it is not necessary to notch them over every plank lap ….. they should definitely land on each plank lap because that is where the strength is in the double layer of planking, but there should be limber holes at the inboard edge of every plank. Screw down into the hog, and up from the outside through the plank laps as well as epoxy glue wherever they land. Before final fitting, remember to seal with epoxy all areas like the limber holes that will be difficult to reach once they are in place.

A Note on Fits

While setting up and planking it is quite acceptable to use less than perfect fits that rely on the epoxy for strength in the joint. While I am not encouraging sloppy work, epoxies form equally strong joints when they fill even quite large gaps. There are so many procedures in boatbuilding that take a lot of time, I can see no point in spending inordinate amounts of time getting perfect fits where it is neither visually or structurally necessary. However, most of the joints in the interior of the boat will be prominently visible, so even though there is no structural necessity, visually the joints should be as good as you can possibly make them. If painted, the glue lines are not visible, but the look of the boat will benefit from varnish in at least some areas.

Fig. 29 Scribing Floors

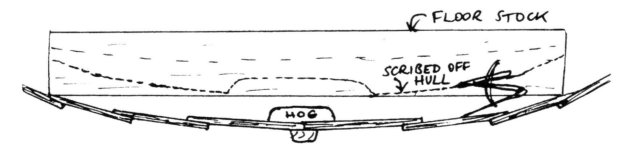

Floorboards

Floorboards can be straight, or curved on both sides just like the planking over which they lie. They can be directly screwed to the floors, or better still, fastened to cleats underneath so that the boards on each side of the boat can be lifted out together for ease of cleaning. They are held down by strategically located hardwood turnbuttons. If you've planked the boat you've already covered all the skills needed to shape and fit floorboards. They are usually not epoxy coated and varnished, but simply oiled because this is less slippery and easier to touch up.

We have now covered most of the procedure common to most plywood clinker boats. Different boats will have different items added, such as rowlock pads, centreboard cases in sailing boats, engine beds in launches, even decks on some large boats, but these are generally detailed in the plans.

Dynel Sheathing

Sheathing the hull is optional, but is highly recommended if the boat is expected to have a rough life, or if it will be moored. Fibreglass sheathing is not recommended as it is difficult to get fibreglass cloth to lay well over the plank laps on plywood clinker boats. Dynel, which is an acrylic fabric, is far easier to lay over the edges and hollows, but it is still necessary to round over the sharp edges of the planking, and work a small radius fillet of epoxy and microspheres into the corners, as in **Fig. 30**. The excess should be cleaned off thoroughly with a metal putty knife and used to fill any screw heads or dents on the outside of the hull. Any holes from temporary fastenings which go right through the planking should be filled with the same stuff but with a touch of cement colouring added if the inside of the hull is to be varnished, as some will inevitably squeeze through to the inside. After this cures, the hull should be sanded and cleaned off.

You cannot dynel sheathe any areas of the hull that you intend to varnish, as the pattern of the weave is opaque. It is quite common and very attractive to highlight the transom and the sheer strake in varnish. You may also choose to sheathe only those planks below the waterline. Lay the dynel cloth over the hull, and wet through with epoxy, applied with a brush on narrow-planked

hulls, or simply poured on and moved around with a rubber squeegee where it is possible. Pay careful attention to ensuring that the cloth lays into the hollows of the plank laps, and that it stays there when you move along further. Work methodically, keeping the wet edge as small as possible, that is, don't go too far along the hull before wetting-out right down to the sheer line (or wherever you are ending it). Keep moving excess resin to dry areas to avoid pooling in the grooves, and runs.

Dynel fluffs up a lot when wet-out with epoxy, and when dry the surface will be quite rough. Within 12-16 hours, go over the hull with a sharp scraper or spokeshave set for a fine cut, and remove a lot of the raised nap of the cloth while it is still reasonably soft. Trim edges and overlaps at this time also. Recoat with epoxy (rolled and/or brushed on). For the best result follow this coat with another in a few hours time while it is still tacky.

Rubbing Strips

The outer keel, and whichever planks amidships will take the ground when the boat lands or is dragged onto a wharf or pontoon should be protected with sacrificial hardwood rubbing strips. They are made sacrificial by gluing them on with only temporary fastenings, the holes of which are filled later, so that at a later stage if they become worn it is a simple matter to plane off the damaged surfaces and glue on new pieces in the same manner without having to worry about hitting fastenings with the plane. They still should be resin coated and incorporated into the paint scheme of the boat.

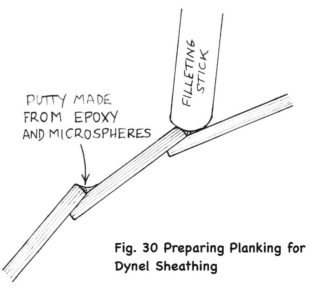

Fig. 30 Preparing Planking for Dynel Sheathing

Painting and Varnishing

Polyurethane paints or oil-based enamels can both be used over well-cured epoxies. Several coats of high-build undercoats should be applied and sanded back until you are happy with the surface finish: the top coats will merely repeat the surface of the sanded undercoat. Most paints and varnishes should not be applied until at least three or four days have past since applying the last coat of epoxy, as the solvents in the paint will attack the uncured epoxy and hinder the drying of the paint or varnish.

All bare timbers should receive at least two coats of epoxy. For the best finish, allow the first coat to dry, wash it down with a scourer pad and warm water to remove any waxy feel (amine blush) on the surface, and sand lightly to remove any raised grain or surface imperfections, and apply a second coat. Repeat the scouring with warm water and light sanding before any subsequent coats of paint or varnish.

Surfaces to be varnished should be well sanded to at least 150 grit, and preferably 180 or 220, and only exterior varnishes with U.V filters should be used. Do not leave any unprotected epoxy on the boat as it breaks down from U.V exposure.

A Note on Fastening

Plywood clinker boats are best fastened with stainless steel screws, but it is important not to leave any head exposed on the surface. Water will inevitably find its way beneath the heads of any exposed fastenings, and you will have defeated the whole purpose of sealing the entire boat with epoxy to exclude moisture. Fastenings in varnished areas should be covered with wood plugs, and with epoxy and microspheres in areas to be painted. Exposed copper nails and roves will also allow water penetration. If you like the look of steam-bent ribs and copper fastenings, build a traditional clinker boat. There is nothing wrong with the traditional method, and there is nothing wrong with the modern method, just don't try to mix the two together.

Good luck with your project.

Wetting-out dynel sheathing.

Building the Whiting Skiff

I drew up the plans for the 11' (3.3m) Whiting Skiff in 1993 to be a good introduction to a number of boatbuilding processes, particularly ply clinker construction, and to be able to be structurally completed in a class in two weekends. The bonus has been that it's a great little boat in the water, both for rowing and sailing and for motoring with a small outboard. It's big enough for two people but small enough to be cartopped. It has proved to be a great project for Men's Sheds. I still have and use one I built in the late 1990's.

The plans are available on the website **www.sydneywoodenboatschool.com.au**

Building the Whiting Skiff

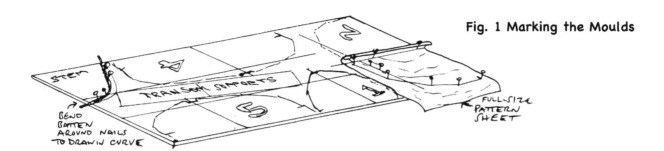

Fig. 1 Marking the Moulds

STEM

TRANSOM SUPPORTS

BEND BATTEN AROUND NAILS TO DRAW IN CURVE

FULL-SIZE PATTERN SHEET

1.   Mark out the Moulds from the Full-Size Patterns

On a sheet of 12mm chipboard or plywood 2400 x 1200mm, draw a line parallel with each long edge exactly 500mm from each edge, and position the full-size patterns so that this line becomes the DWL for each mould, as in **Fig. 1**. Prick the lines every 50mm or so with a nail or something similar. Flip the paper over, carefully line up the centreline, and mark the other side of the mould by pricking back through the same holes. Remove the patterns and draw the lines in with a ruler (each mould is a series of straight lines). All four moulds, plus the inside curve of the inner stem and two pieces to support the transom on the back of mould 5 should come out of the one piece of chipboard. Mark out the <u>inside</u> curve of laminated frame 3 either on another sheet of chipboard or somewhere on the original sheet (possibly on the other side) before you cut it out. The curved lines of the stem and frame will have to be drawn in by tacking a batten around nails tacked in the packed holes. Mark out the transom on 18mm marine plywood, and cut just clear of the line.

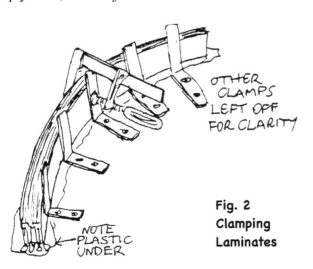

OTHER CLAMPS LEFT OFF FOR CLARITY

NOTE PLASTIC UNDER

Fig. 2 Clamping Laminates

2.   Laminate the Stem and Frame 3

Fasten metal angle brackets or blocks of wood every 150-200mm around the curve of the inner stem and the frame. Bend the 3mm laminates around the curve, dry clamping as you go in order to check everything before applying glue. When satisfied that all will work, remove the dry laminates and apply epoxy, mixing in enough microfibres to be just thin enough to brush, and brush onto both sides of each laminate. Bend around curve as before. Clamps need only be tight enough to bring the laminates together, they don't need to be tightened as hard as you can. Don't forget plastic under to stop the whole thing sticking to the board (**Fig. 2**). Leave at least 24 hours, preferably longer, and cleanup both sides with a belt sander or power plane and finish with a hand plane. Mark the perimeter of the frame and the stem onto each piece by pricking through the patterns and cut and plane to the line.

3.   The Setup

Cut and plane the chipboard moulds to the marked lines, and set up all moulds and stem, transom and frame 3 on a simple ladder-frame jig, with legs approximately 500-600mm to bring the moulds to a comfortable working height. You can either carefully level the top of the jig, or get the jig approximately level and level the moulds using DWL as reference. **Tip**: if you if you set up 1, 3 and 5 and check with spirit level and water level (clear hose with water inside), moulds 2 and 4 can be made correct by line-of-sight lining up of centreline and DWL. Brace the moulds plumb. Fix the stem curve pattern to the front of mould 1, and the transom supports to the back of mould 5.

Construction Plan
Whiting Skiff

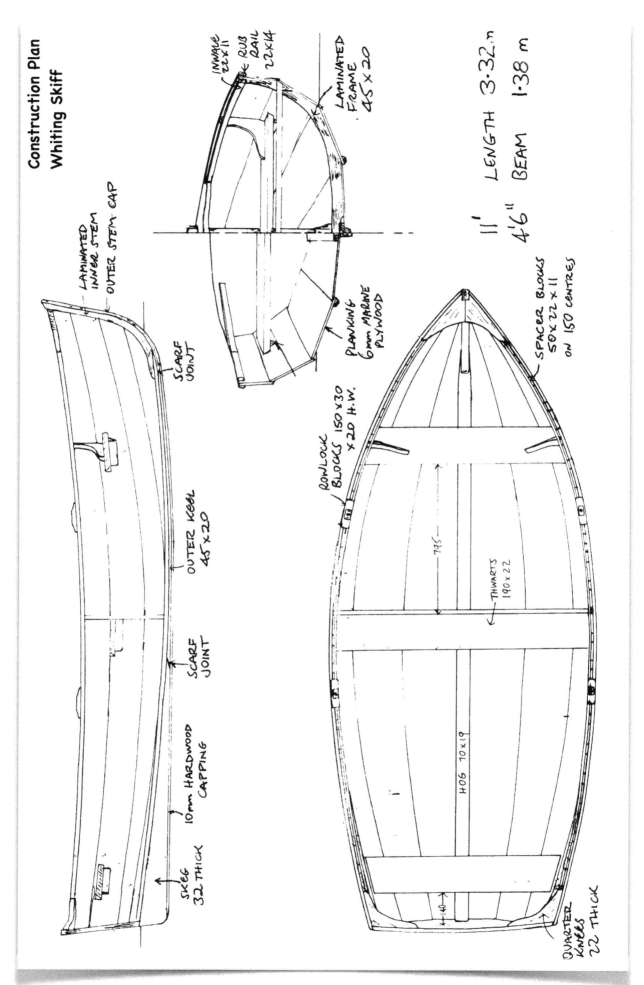

LENGTH 3.32 m

BEAM 1.38 m

11'

4'6"

INWALE 22×11

RUB RAIL 22×14

LAMINATED FRAME 45×20

LAMINATED INNER STEM

OUTER STEM CAP

SCARF JOINT

PLANKING 6mm MARINE PLYWOOD

OUTER KEEL 45×20

SCARF JOINT

10mm HARDWOOD CAPPING

SKEG 32 THICK

SPACER BLOCKS 50×22×11 ON 150 CENTRES

ROWLOCK BLOCKS 150×30 ×20 H.W.

THWARTS 190×22

795

HOG 70×19

140

QUARTER KNEES 22 THICK

144

Fig. 3 Bevelling the hog, stem and transom

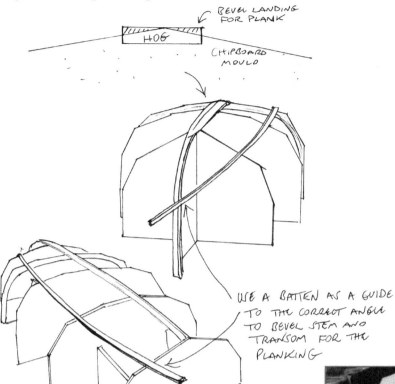

BEVEL LANDING FOR PLANK

HOG

CHIPBOARD MOULD

USE A BATTEN AS A GUIDE TO THE CORRECT ANGLE TO BEVEL STEM AND TRANSOM FOR THE PLANKING

4. Fit the Hog

The hog is then fitted across the top of all moulds in the notches cut for it, and screwed and glued to stem and transom. When the epoxy is cured, bevel the hog to make a landing for the plywood bottom panels. Shape the bevel at the moulds first, and fair in the areas in between by eye and with the aid of a batten following the line of the planking, leaving the front face of the stem 12mm wide, 6mm either side of a marked centreline. See **Fig. 3 and 4** and photos.

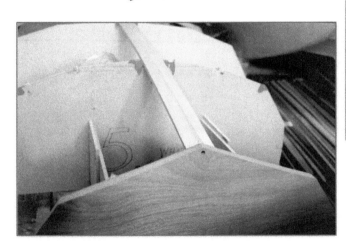

Two views of the hog, before and after bevelling.

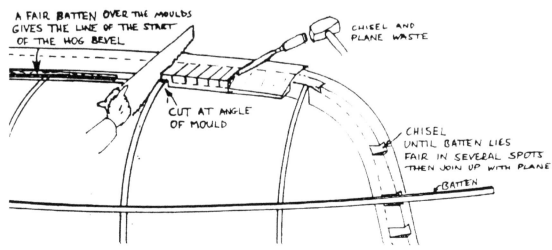

A FAIR BATTEN OVER THE MOULDS GIVES THE LINE OF THE START OF THE HOG BEVEL

CHISEL AND PLANE WASTE

CUT AT ANGLE OF MOULD

CHISEL UNTIL BATTEN LIES FAIR IN SEVERAL SPOTS THEN JOIN UP WITH PLANE

BATTEN

Fig. 4

5.   Scarf the Plywood Planking

Cut one of three sheets of 6mm plywood in half, and scarf the halves onto the other two sheets to make two new sheets approximately 3600 x 1200mm. The slope of the scarf joint is approximately 8 to 1, make it 50mm wide on the 6mm plywood, and plane the scarfs as in **Fig. 5**.

Join the sheets with epoxy and microfibres, fastening temporary screws through battens either side of the plywood in line with the scarf joint. When cured, remove the screws and battens and mark out the plank shapes as on the drawing, and cut just outside these lines.

6.   Fitting the Garboard Planks

The first plank, known as the garboard, is hung over the moulds and clamped and/or temporarily screwed in place so that it more than covers the area that it has to; that is, it should be just over the centreline along the hog, and be outside the plank edge positions on the moulds. Mark these positions underneath as in **Fig. 6**, remove the plank, turn it over and tack nails at these marks and mark a line around a batten bent fairly around these nails. Cut and plane to this line. Temporarily fasten the plank back in position on the boat, mark a line 15mm in from the outer edge, and bevel this area as a landing for the next plank. As with the hog, bevel at the moulds first, and fair in between by eye. At

Fig. 5 Scarfing the Plywood Planking

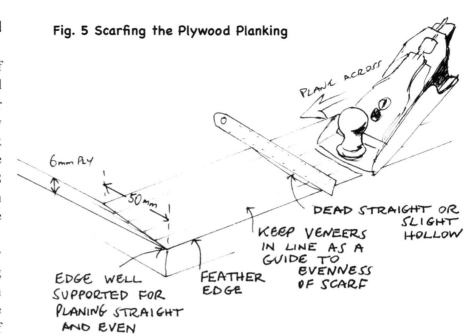

Fig. 6 Fitting the Garboard Planks

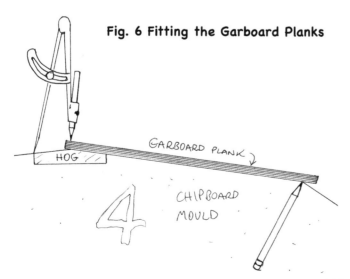

each end of the boat, treat the stem and transom as if they were just another mould. Remove the plank again, take it to the bench, and as in **Fig. 7**, make a jerrald by deepening the bevel over the last 200mm from each end into a rebate, finishing slightly deeper than halfway through the plank thickness. It is very important to maintain the angle of the bevel at each end as it is deepened into a rebate.

Mix epoxy and microfibres to a consistency approaching that of peanut butter, and apply to the transom, hog, frame and stem where the garboard will lie, and fit the plank permanently. Put plastic tape on the chipboard moulds where the plank joins will occur so no excess glue will bond the planking to the moulds. Cleanup all squeezed-out glue with a metal putty knife.

Fit the other garboard plank before proceeding to the second plank.

7.   Fitting the Other Planks

Lay the second plank over the moulds so that it only just laps onto the garboard. On the outer edge, it should protrude at least 15mm past the plank join marks on the moulds. Run a pencil along the outside of the garboard plank underneath, remove the plank and cut and plane to this line. The plank should now fit over the 15mm bevelled lap area. (see **Fig. 8**).

You now need to make a matching jerrald underneath this plank to fit the jerralds already done on the garboard plank. View the joint from end on, estimate the amount and angle of the

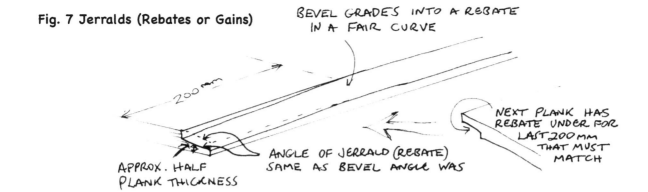

Fig. 7 Jerralds (Rebates or Gains)

BEVEL GRADES INTO A REBATE IN A FAIR CURVE

200 mm

NEXT PLANK HAS REBATE UNDER FOR LAST 200 mm THAT MUST MATCH

APPROX. HALF PLANK THICKNESS

ANGLE OF JERRALD (REBATE) SAME AS BEVEL ANGLE WAS

rebate, and plane less than you expect. Remove a little at a time, constantly bringing it back to the boat for a trial fit to monitor your own progress. If you go a little too far, don't panic, as the gap-filling properties of epoxy will make the joint structurally sound and waterproof, but if you want to get the best fit you can do I can't stress too strongly the need to remove only a little at a time and constantly monitor your progress.

Temporarily fasten the plank in position, and mark the outer edge from the mould marks underneath as for the garboard, remove the plank and draw a line with nails and batten, cut and plane to the line, re-fit the plank and shape bevelled lap for the next plank. The bevel on the later planks will be narrower than 15mm towards the stern of the

boat, in fact the angle is so great that no jerrald is necessary at the transom for these planks.

Fitting the third and fourth planks follows exactly the same procedure.

The garboard is fitted and the lap bevelled for the next plank.

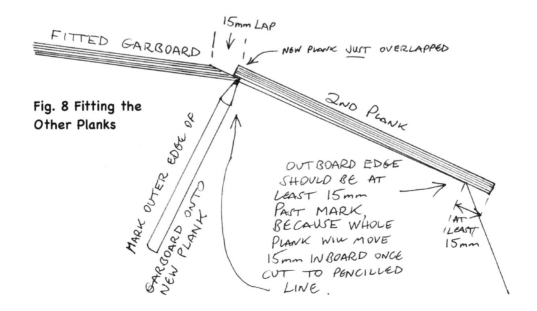

FITTED GARBOARD

15mm LAP

NEW PLANK JUST OVERLAPPED

2ND PLANK

Fig. 8 Fitting the Other Planks

MARK OUTER EDGE OF GARBOARD ONTO NEW PLANK

OUTBOARD EDGE SHOULD BE AT LEAST 15mm PAST MARK, BECAUSE WHOLE PLANK WILL MOVE 15mm INBOARD ONCE CUT TO PENCILLED LINE.

AT LEAST 15mm

8.   Fitting the Outer Stem, Skeg and Keel

You need to plane a flat landing for the skeg, keel and outer stem all the way from the transom to the top of the stem at a width to suit each part; the skeg is 32mm wide, therefore, the aft section of the boat needs a landing 32mm wide, the central section of the keel needs a landing 45mm wide, and the outer stem is 32mm wide. Cut off the protruding planks on the stem as close as you dare before planing them flush with the inner stem. If the resultant landing is slightly more than 32mm, don't worry, it is not important.

The laminates for the outer stem are laminated directly onto the boat. As usual, do a dry fit first. All but the last laminate are fitted first, fastened with stainless steel permanent screws every 150mm on the centreline, starting at the keel end and drilling and screwing each one in turn as it bears on the inner stem as you gradually bend the stack of laminates around. It helps to have three hands for this job. When you are happy with the dry fit, remove the screws in reverse order, and prepare for gluing. Mix epoxy and microfibres to a just brushable consistency and brush onto both surfaces of each pair of laminates to be joined as well as the landing on the boat itself. Fit to the boat exactly as you did in the dry fit. When the epoxy has cured, fit the outer laminate using short temporary screws with washers, and fill the holes with epoxy after removing the screws if painting here, or drill and plug with 3/8" plugs if varnishing.

To fit the skeg, hold the skeg stock on the boat exactly where it is going to live, with its upper surface (that is the surface closest to the roof of your workshop) horizontal and scribe the shape of the hull onto it as in **Fig. 9**, cut it to shape, and trim to fit with a spokeshave. Be careful to ensure that it stands vertically when fitted. Drill and screw from inside the boat to hold it in place while the glue goes off.

The keel is fitted between the skeg and outer stem, scarfed to fit at each end. The fit is not critical.

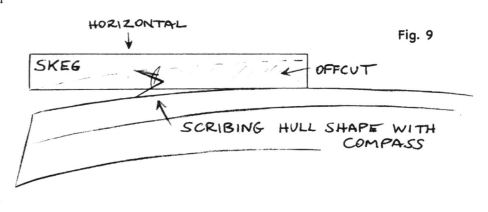

Fig. 9

A weekend class in 1993 gets stuck into planking.

148

9. Shaping the Outer Stem, Keel and Skeg

The stemhead is trimmed square-sided, reducing at the level of the bottom of the sheer plank to be shaped so that it is in line with the run of the planking, leaving the stem face around 12-14mm wide. Just past the turn of the knuckle of the bow, this face widens over about 200-250mm to be the full width of the keel about 100mm behind the scarf joint. The sides of the keel and the skeg should have a slight taper in from vertical, so that the underside of the skeg finishes at 22-25mm.

We are just about ready to turn the boat over. If you intend to dynel sheathe the bottom two planks for extra abrasion resistance, you could do it now, or at any stage after this that you are able to turn the boat over again. Dynel sheathing is described below.

A 10mm thick hardwood capping can be fitted over the keel and skeg, ending at the forward end in a notch into the outer stem. Hardwood rubbing strips are also fitted to the inner edge of the second plank. All these pieces are glued in place, held with temporary screws (which are removed and filled later). With no permanent metal fastenings, when these strips eventually become worn, it is quite an easy matter to plane the scuffed area flat, and glue on a new strip. If dynel sheathing, the hardwood strips should be fitted after sheathing.

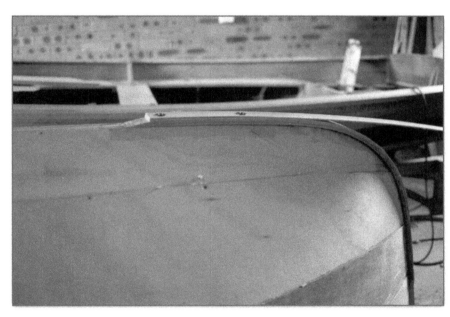

Outer stem cap laminates glued on.

Cutting in line with the planking is the first step in fairing off the outer stem laminates.

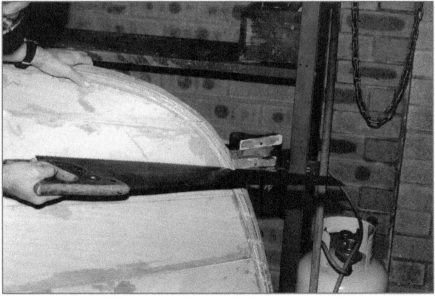

Dynel Sheathing the Hull

You may wish to dynel sheathe the bottom of the hull if you expect to give it rough treatment, especially pulling over rocks or gravelly beaches etc. An ideal perimeter line is the lower lap of the third plank, that is, you will be sheathing the bottom two planks

Turn the boat upside down, and round over any sharp edges on the planks and keel. Apply a radiused fillet of epoxy and microspheres to the plank lap at the top of the garboard and to the hull/keel joint. Use plastic masking tape to define the perimeter of the area you want sheathed. Lay the dynel cloth over the hull dry, cut darts where necessary, cut off any large overhangs but leave a good margin overlapping the perimeter tape. Mix epoxy and hardener, and wet out the cloth by pouring the resin on and moving it around with a squeegee on the flatter bottom areas, and with a brush in the corners and on the more vertical areas. The resin starts to soak into the cloth almost as soon as it hits the surface, but you will need to use the brush and/or squeegee to remove all of the air bubbles that form in and under the cloth. Be liberal with the resin, give it plenty of time to soak in before moving the excess to dry areas, because it also needs time to soak into the dry wood underneath. If you do not use plenty of resin you risk the wood soaking away resin from out of the cloth. When you are certain it is quite wet-out, move the excess resin to dry areas, otherwise it will continue to flow downhill and form heavy runs. Wet the cloth right to, and just onto the plastic masking tape.

When just cured, use a sharp utility knife to cut the cloth right along the line of the masking tape, and peel it off. This gives a clean edge. A couple of coats of resin rolled on or thickened with microspheres and screeded on will fill the weave of the cloth and sanding the cured surface (after scouring with a pad and warm water for the amine wax) should give a surface ready for undercoating, with perhaps a little spot filling necessary. You will need a little extra sanding (perhaps even light grinding) on cloth overlaps and the odd wrinkle.

Dynel sheathing the bottom two planks. Plastic tape makes edge trimming easy.

10. Turnover

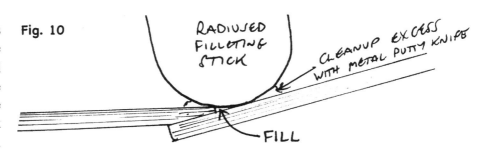

Remove any screws holding the boat to the moulds, and lift it off. Stand back and admire it for a little while, then remove the moulds from the strong back and put the boat onto it. Shore it up to be steady enough to work on. Two pairs of 200 x 25mm boards or something similar clamped or screwed to the cross-beams of the jig should be sufficient. Now is the best time to clean off all glue dags, and fill all holes with epoxy and microspheres, and fill the join between planks 1 and 2 with a radiused fillet of microspheres (see **Fig. 10**).

11. Seat SupportBlocks

These can be made from the offcut piece of the skeg, and are fitted to the hull in the positions you can scale off from the plan, bevelled to fit against the hull so that the top of each pair will provide a horizontal landing for the seat or thwart. You can check for this using two straight sticks clamped together, the same device you will use for measuring the width of the thwarts shortly (see **Fig. 11**). Screw from outside the hull and glue in place. Countersink the heads of these permanent fastenings slightly and fill over the heads with epoxy filler (microspheres).

The first job after turning the hull over is to fill the lower laps.

12. Thwarts

Start with the main thwart, laying the stock on the seat support on one side, and because it is still longer than it will eventually be, lay the other side exactly vertically above where it will live. Using a compass, scribe the hull shape onto the side lying on the seat support. Measure the maximum width

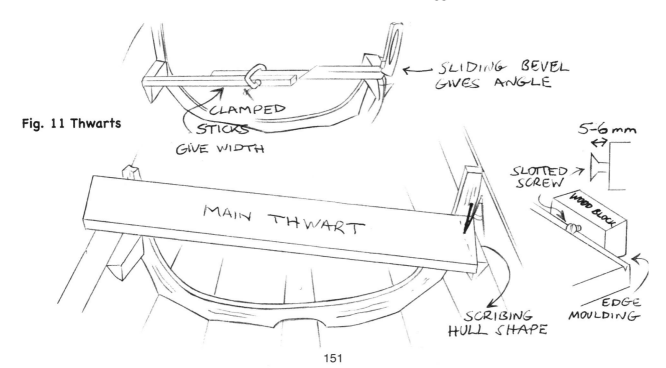

of the thwart with two sticks clamped together after being pushed out to touch each side 22mm above the seat support i.e. at the upper surface of the thwart. Lay this distance out on the thwart stock from the line you have already scribed. Lay the stock back in the boat, this time with the other side on its seat support, open the compass to the distance from the hull side to the width distance marked from the sticks, and scribe as before. Cut clear of these lines leaving about 10mm excess for safety. The thwart should sit lower in the boat now, enabling you to scribe again, probably a bit more accurately. Pick up the bevel angle as in **Fig. 11**, and cut/or plane to the line and angle. Check the fit regularly as you plane away. If you are painting all of the boat, a light-tight fit is not important, as the epoxy has great gap-filling properties with no loss of strength in such situations. If you are varnishing, these joints are all on show and you should take every care to achieve thin glue lines. Screw and glue in place. As in all cases from now on where the fastenings are permanent, countersink the heads

and fill with epoxy if painting, or drill for 3/8" plugs if varnishing .

The forward and aft thwarts are done in a similar manner, but allow a little more excess when cutting as a safety margin because these thwarts are more difficult to scribe accurately the first time. Round over or ease the edges of each thwart or cut a traditional edge moulding with the simple tool in **Fig. 11**, and sand thoroughly before fitting permanently.

TIP: If you will be painting the boat, cleanup all glue very thoroughly as you go - it is far easier to cleanup wet than after it is cured, and any bumps you can feel will show through paint. If varnishing you need to be even more thorough, as even the stain from the glue will show through varnished surface - in this case, fit plastic masking tape along both sides of any glue joint while the parts are dry-fitted, then cleanup thoroughly after gluing and peel the tape away before the glue cures.

Fig. 12 Knees

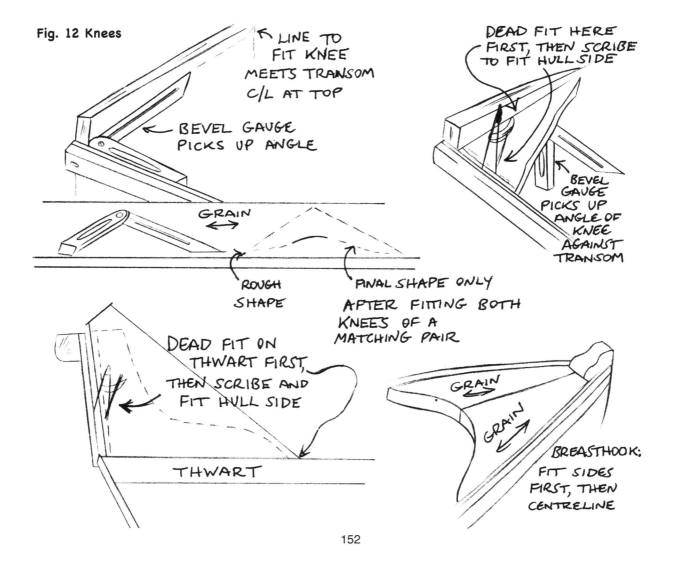

13. Gunwale or Rub Rail

The rails are simply screwed (from inside) and glued to the sheer strake, but great care should be taken to ensure that they curve in a sweet and fair line, because this is one of the most important visual lines on the boat. Clamp them in place and view from all angles and adjust if necessary before drilling for screws. A larger screw from outside into the transom and stem holds the ends in.

14. Quarter Knees, Breasthook, and Thwart Knees

These are fitted to brace the boat in the corners. The angles are picked up with a bevel gauge, and the angle laid on the stock so the grain of the timber is at right angles to a line bisecting the knee (see **Fig. 12**). The secret of fitting knees is to get the straight side absolutely correct first, and only then worry about the other side. In the case of quarter knees, get the side that fits against the transom dead right first, that is, a tight fit on the transom at the correct angle to allow the other leg to be parallel with the sheer line, not angled up or drooping down, and not rocking in any direction. Then scribe the hull side onto the knee and plane to fit.

The breasthook is made in two parts, and each is shaped individually to fit against the plank before striking a centreline and fitting them together.

The thwart knees are fitted by planing the thwart side dead flat and square first, then scribing the hull side and planing to fit. One screw through each leg is usually sufficient to hold them while the glue cures.

15. The Inwales

Cut notches on the breasthook and quarter knees and the central laminated frame to fit the inwales. Screw or nail and glue the spacer blocks to one side of each inwale, or alternatively fit them to the hull first. If you wish to cut the edge moulding as in **Fig. 8** and the photograph, now is the time to do it. Fit the inwale into the notches cut for it, being very careful when cutting to exact length. It is better to cut oversize and remove small bits at a time until it fits.

Spacer blocks fitted to inwale. Note the notches in the knee and breasthook to receive the inwale.

Inwales glued and clamped on, fastened with counterbored and plugged screws from inside through spacer blocks.

Hi-tech tool cuts moulding on inwales.

We fitted benches to "Black Dog", one of the boats we built. They work well if you plan to sail a lot.

It's a personal choice but I like to pick out all solid wood in varnish and paint all plywood (other than varnishing the transom and sometimes the sheer stake). Non-skid paint is best on the inside bottom planks.

16. Rowlock Pads

These are simply hardwood blocks screwed and glued to the top of the gunwales about 225mm aft of the aft edge of the two forward thwarts. Fit a filler piece under each pad to fill the gap between the inwale and the hull where the hole for the rowlock will be drilled, which will be as close to the hull as possible.

This completes the structural work for the rowing version of the Whiting Skiff. All that remains is a lot of sanding and painting or varnishing.

Whether you are painting or varnishing, every wood surface on the boat inside and out must have two thorough coats of unthickened epoxy and hardener rolled and /or brushed on, being particularly careful to ensure that all end grain plywood gets a thorough soaking. Between the coats, rub down with a scourer pad and warm water to remove the waxy residue from curing, allow to dry, and sand lightly with 120 grit before applying the second coat. Do the same before applying paint or varnish, this time with 150 grit, and if varnishing, finish with 180 grit. Do not paint or varnish over the resin until it has cured for at least three days.

17. Painting

You can brush or spray with either two-pack polyurethanes or regular hardware-store oil-based enamels. I find a brushed enamel finish is easier to apply and maintain. Whatever system you choose, use the relevant undercoat, but you don't need any wood primer (the epoxy does that) and remember that the quality of your final finish can only be as good as the surface you end up with after sanding your undercoats.

18. Varnishing

Epoxy is a sound base for varnish, but it does need to be protected from ultra-violet light, so use a good marine varnish contain UV filters, and apply at least 5 or 6 coats. Traditional varnishes are ok, but one-pack polyurethanes are better over epoxy, and you could use two-pack polyurethanes if you wish for the toughest surface.

It's now ready for use!

Rigging the Whiting Skiff for Sailing

The Whiting Skiff can be built purely as a rowing and outboard motor boat, but can also be rigged for sailing with a simple standing lug rig. The only parts of the boat itself that need to be added are the centreboard case and the mast step block and the mast hole in the forward thwart, plus rudder gudgeons on the transom. These can all actually be fitted at any time in the boat's life after launching if you're in a hurry to go rowing, but it is easier to fit the centreboard case before painting, and before dynel sheathing the bottom.

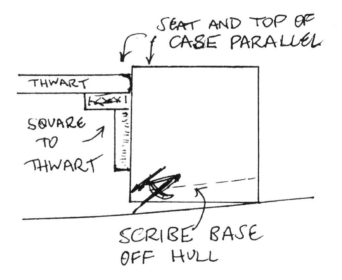

Fig. 13 Centreboard Case

19.   Centreboard Case

Mark the shape of the case sides as in the plans on 6mm plywood, cutting slightly outside the pencil lines. The exact shape of the bottom where it fits the hull must be scribed as in **Fig. 13**. Cut to this line and plane until you have a light-tight fit on both case sides. Glue and screw the case logs on the outside of the case bottom, leaving enough wood to plane back to the plywood edge you have just planed, after the glue cures. Fit the internal uprights of the case to one side only, screwing from outside for permanent screws and using plenty of epoxy

thickened with microfibres to ensure there will be no leaks. To resist abrasion from the centreboard inside the case it is best to sheathe it with dynel cloth, or fibreglass cloth. Sheathe the side with the uprights fitted so that the cloth turns up and covers the edges of the timber that will be inside the case, trimming excess cloth with a utility knife or sharp chisel after curing, and sheathe the other side flat across. When cured, the surface should be scoured with warm water, sanded and given another coat of epoxy, then glued together. When dry, plane the bottom logs back to the plywood and check its fit in the boat.

If you have a penciled centreline on the inside of the bottom, you can mark the fore and aft limits of the slot through the bottom, and mark the slot for width. It is safest to drill the hull right on the centreline somewhere in the proposed slot, then check underneath the boat that this hole comes through exactly in the centre of the outer keel. If not, adjust your slot accordingly. It is more important that the slot be in the middle of the outer keel. If you do not have a centreline marked inside, you must start from the outside anyway but always drill a pilot hole on the centreline first and use it to establish the fore and aft position of the slot which can only be determined from inside the boat. Drill a hole big enough for a jigsaw blade at each end and cut out the slot with a jigsaw. Cut clear of your line by at least 3-4mm as jigsaw blades are notorious for not cutting square, and chisel the slot to the line as straight and square as you can.

Assemble the whole case with its upper side supports going under the thwart, and drill and screw it in place without glue at this stage. Make sure the case is exactly over the slot by putting two temporary blocks that are the exact width of the slot into the slot as locators, and fit the case over these and drill and screw the logs to the hog, and screw into the upper side supports through the thwart,

Centreboard case parts.

ensuring that the case is at right angles to the thwart. Fit the case cap on top of the side supports (it needs a slot cut in it first), and trim it all round. When you are certain that everything is in its correct place, take it apart and put it all back together with ample epoxy thickened with microfibres.

20.   The Centreboard

The centreboard itself is cut from 12mm plywood to the dimensions in the plan, or made by laminating two 6mm pieces together, and shaped to resemble a foil, that is the leading edge is rounded and the trailing edge is tapered to about 3mm thickness. The veneer lines that appear as you plane the plywood are a good guide to keeping these surfaces even and fair.

21.   The Rudder

Twelve millimetre plywood is also used to make up the rudder blade to the pattern in the plans, with cheeks of 6mm, and the tiller fastened to the rudder head with extra plywood cheeks. you can either have the tiller fixed, or pivoting on a bolt through the rudder head. If you choose the latter, you will need to cut a notch and shoulder in the front of the rudder head at the position at which you want the tiller to rest.

Shaping the rudder blade.

156

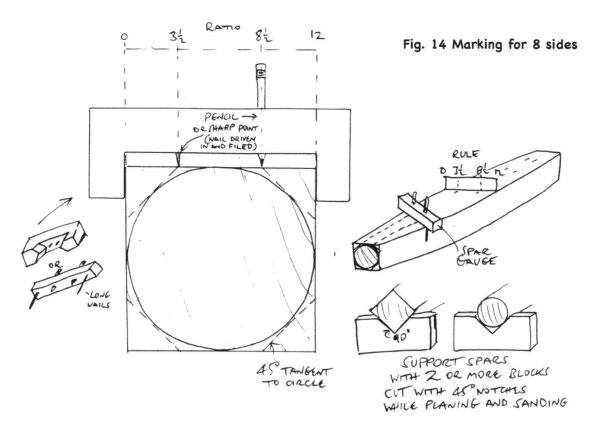

Fig. 14 Marking for 8 sides

45° TANGENT TO CIRCLE

SUPPORT SPARS WITH 2 OR MORE BLOCKS CUT WITH 45° NOTCHES WHILE PLANING AND SANDING

22. The Mast and Spars

The mast and both spars are shaped round from square stock selected from the best Oregon Pine (Douglas Fir) available, clear grade with no knots or sloping grain. Each of the three is tapered according to the dimensions on the plans. Looking at them from front on, they are all tapered evenly on both sides, but from side on, each is straight on the side that the sail is against, that is, the top of the boom, the underside of the yard, and the aft side of the mast, and all of the taper is taken off the other side. A power plane is the quickest tool for removing timber, but be conservative and leave plenty to finish off with a hand plane, preferably a No. 5 or No. 6.

The square spars are then made eight-sided by knocking off the corners down to lines marked by a spar gauge as illustrated in **Fig. 14**. Chocks as illustrated support the spars at the angle necessary.

The corners of the eight sides are then knocked off to make it 16-sided. Each of the sixteen sides should be exactly even with all the others at any point on the spar. The best way to gauge this is to colour in bands of pencil around the spar every 300-400mm. As you remove the corners and make new flats, the new flats (without pencil) should be exactly as wide as the old flats (still with pencil) at any point along the length.

You may be able to set a plane blade very finely and knock off the corners of the sixteen sides, or you may get straight into sanding. Sanding should be with the grain (along the spar) or slightly diagonally across the surface with 40 grit paper under a shaped foam block as in **Fig. 15**. Once the plane blade flats have disappeared, sand down through the grades, say 80 grit then 120 grit, finishing with 180grit.

Complete the spars with details of holes, mast heel tenon, and rounded ends, and apply the manufacturer's recommended number of coats of varnish.

Fig. 15

Pencil Shadow for Planing

HOLLOW TO SUIT MAXIMUM SPAR DIAMETER

APPROX 200-300 mm (THE BIGGER THE SPAR THE LONGER THE BLOCK)

Guide and Foam Block for Sanding

23. Mast Supports

The mast has no stays, but is free standing through the centre of the forward thwart, with a morticed block of hardwood glued to the hog beneath the thwart as in the plans. The thwart hole should be big enough to get a leather collar either around the mast or lining the hole itself. See **Fig 16**.

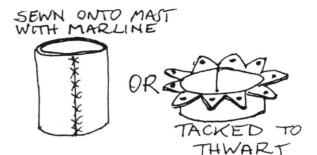

Fig. 16 Mast Collar Leather

24. Rigging

The sail should be lashed to the holes at both ends of the yard and boom by tying just over a metre of venetian blind cord to the cringle (hole) in the corner of the sail with a bowline, and taking three or four turns through both the hole in the spar and the cringle and then taking tight turns around the lashing until most of the excess is used up, then tying off by simply poking the end around a stand of the original turns, then around another strand as in **Fig. 17**. The yard can then be lashed with a simple spiral through the small cringes in the sail. The sail is essentially controlled by only two lines,

the mainsheet tied to the boom, and the halyard to haul it up. The end of the halyard on the yard is left long to take a loop around the mast to keep the yard close to the mast when sailing. A similar line should be used to keep the boom close to the mast. Getting ready for sailing is simply leading the halyard through the sheave hole in the top of the mast, standing the mast upright through the thwart, and hauling the yard up. The mainsheet should be led through the block aft. Launch the boat and fit the rudder when there is sufficient depth, and take off, dropping in the centreboard as soon as the depth allows.

Fig. 17 Lashing Sail

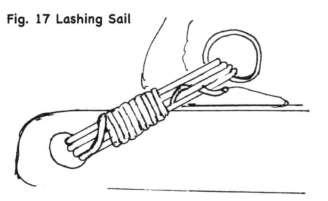

Enjoy your sailing!

Sailing on the Parramatta River.

Carvel Planking

Introduction

I could hardly put out a book titled *Wooden Boatbuilding* without including a section on carvel planking. There was never a Sydney Wooden Boat School Manual on the subject as we only ran a class on carvel planking once late in the active life of the School. So the following section is pretty much what a manual would have been.

This has to be a relatively brief description of carvel planking, but is I think a reasonable introduction to the subject. If you plan on building a carvel-planked boat I suggest you get the books in the Recommended Books list.

Carvel Planking has been around since at least the Bronze Age in Europe. There are all sorts of variations in how it is done, but the essential feature is that each plank in the hull is fastened to a structure of vertical frames and butted up against the one above and the one below it so that the planks are flush on the outside and the inside. It appears to have evolved in the Mediterranean region and Arabia and only spread into Northern Europe in the late Middle Ages. The ships that spread European influence out to the rest of the world were carvel-planked.

Historical and regional variations include fastening to frames with metal fastenings or wooden pegs, doweling or lashing the planks together and variations in the sequence of whether the framing or the planking is set up first. Boats down to around 12 feet (3.6metre) or so up to ocean-going ships of hundreds of tons were built this way.

The method that will be described here is basically framing first, then the planking is fastened to the framing with metal fastenings, which tends to be the way the method has evolved in the Western world, and the way in which most work and pleasure boats over twenty feet (6.5 metres) or so were built from the 18th century until the advent of glass-reinforced plastics in the mid-20th century.

Carvel Planking in Huon Pine.

Lofting

Guess what, every carvel-planked project will start with some sort of lofting. I have already covered lofting in three of the original manuals so I will not repeat myself here. The same details that apply to strip-planked and clinker-planked boats also apply to those carvel-planked. Boatbuilders in the past varied in the amount of lofting they did. I repeat my view that any time spent lofting will be more than saved later in the building programme.

But I do need to draw your attention to a few specifics that apply to lofting carvel-planked boats:

Designers generally draw their lines to the outside of the hull. Carvel Planking is generally thicker than what might be used on a clinker or modern design for strip-planking, and sometimes you will also have to allow for the thickness of the ribbands and ribs if the ribs are to be bent on the outside of the ribbands, so the notes on planking thickness deduction towards the end of the Lofting section of the Strip-Planking Manual are important when drawing the construction plan from which you will fashion your moulds. Drawing the true shape of a flat, sloping transom has been covered in the Building a Traditional Clinker Dinghy Manual, but some yachts will have been designed with a transom that is sloped but is also curved. I cannot improve on the description of lofting a curved and sloped transom found in Robert M. Steward's book in the appended List of Recommended Books.

Stems, keels and sternposts on carvel-planked boats generally have a continuous planking rabbet (rebate) on both sides. This should be drawn on the lofting as in **Fig. 1** so patterns can be made for cutting the rabbet. Draw in fairly closely spaced

Fig. 1 Lofting the Stem Rabbet

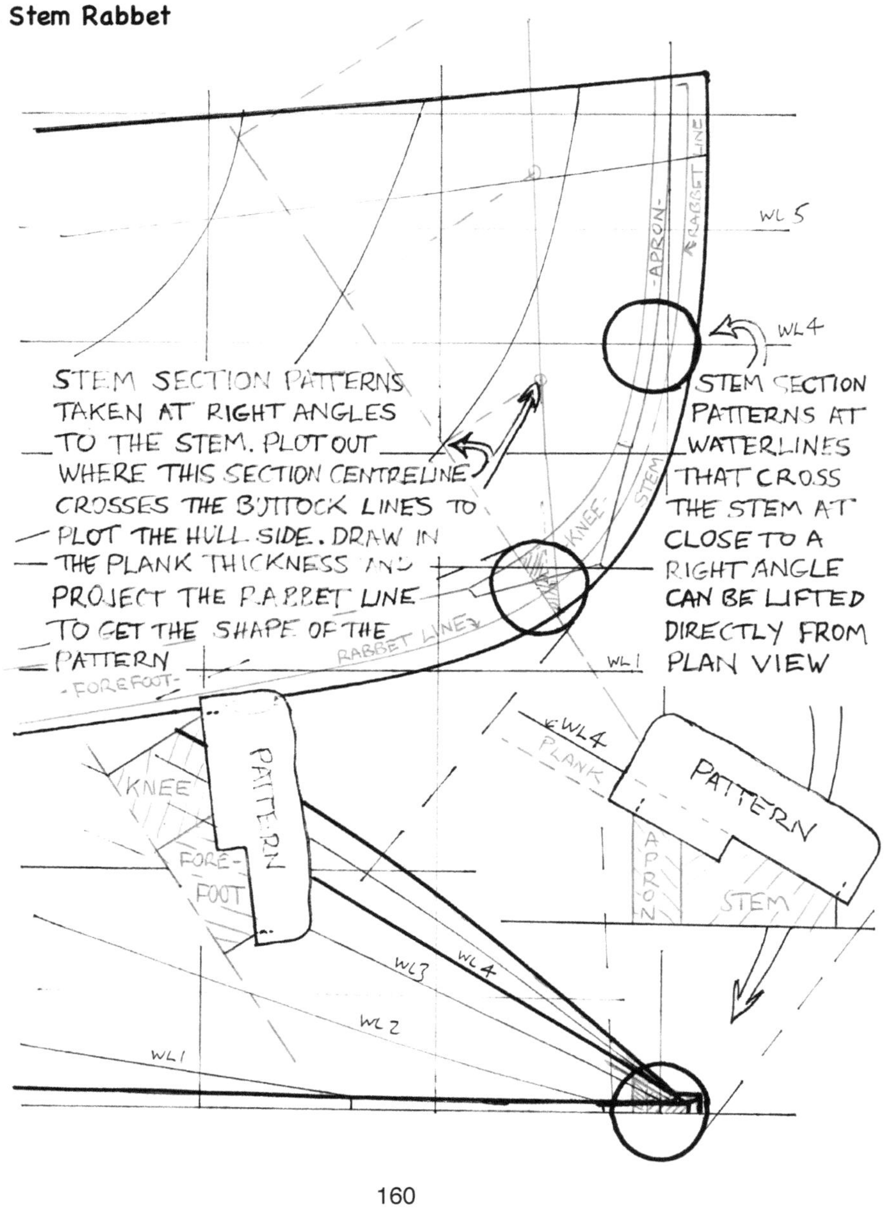

STEM SECTION PATTERNS TAKEN AT RIGHT ANGLES TO THE STEM. PLOT OUT WHERE THIS SECTION CENTRELINE CROSSES THE BUTTOCK LINES TO PLOT THE HULL SIDE. DRAW IN THE PLANK THICKNESS AND PROJECT THE RABBET LINE TO GET THE SHAPE OF THE PATTERN

FOREFOOT

STEM SECTION PATTERNS AT WATERLINES THAT CROSS THE STEM AT CLOSE TO A RIGHT ANGLE CAN BE LIFTED DIRECTLY FROM PLAN VIEW sections and you will be able to mark enough points to draw in both the back rabbet line and the bearding line. The latter is the most important because this indicates where the plank first touches the stem timbers so you can shape the landing for the planking in the rabbet. By all means make and use templates as illustrated, but be conservative in cutting the full depth until the moulds are set up and ribbands and battens can prove the angle at which the planking will land.

Marking out the Moulds

This has also been covered in the other Manuals. Because carvel designs are generally larger you will need to build up your moulds from smaller pieces so it is probably easiest to use the method where you put flat-headed nails in the lofting and press your mould stock down onto them to transfer the shapes of the curves and importantly the grid lines, but tracing film works as well.

The moulds are marked out and assembled directly on the lofted body plan.

Setting Up:
Upside Down or Right Way Up?

There tends to be regional variations in setting up a carvel-planked boat as well as practical considerations.

Pros for Upside Down

✓It is easier to work downhand when planking, framing, caulking and fairing, sanding and painting, but it is harder to lift heavier backbone timbers, so upside down tends to be used for smaller boats.

✓You can incorporate permanent bulkheads into the setup.

✓If producing more than one boat off the moulds there are savings to be made if the design and setup allows for lifting the boat off the moulds without having to dismantle them. Production firms such as Herreshoff in the USA and Halvorsens in Australia set their production boats upside down.

Pros for Right Way Up

✓You don't need to turn the boat over.

✓The heavy backbone timbers don't have to be lifted very high.

✓It is easier to rove over the nails on the inside. This is one of the reasons that many production boats built upside-down used screws in the planking.

Production boats at Halvorsens were built upside down.
PHOTO COURTESY RANDI SVENSEN, FROM WOODEN SHIPS AND IRON MEN
(See Recommended Books).

Fig. 2 Upside Down or Right Way Up

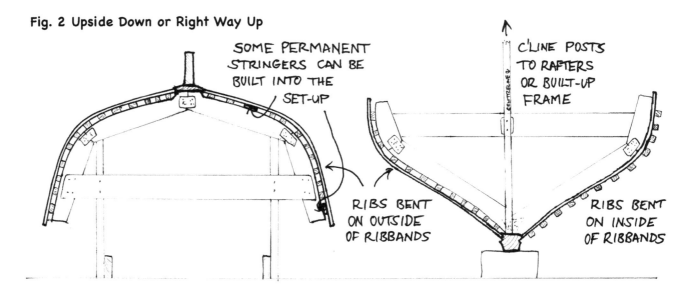

SOME PERMANENT STRINGERS CAN BE BUILT INTO THE SET-UP

C'LINE POSTS TO RAFTERS OR BUILT-UP FRAME

RIBS BENT ON OUTSIDE OF RIBBANDS

RIBS BENT ON INSIDE OF RIBBANDS

Fig. 2 shows some of the variations.

I have only ever built carvel-planked boats the right way up, so my descriptions will assume this. If you are building upside down you will have to do your own translation. If there are any big differences in applying my methods I will mention them.

There are variations, largely regional, in the number of moulds used. Many designers have conformed to a standard of ten station moulds equally spaced. Most production boats had even more closely spaced moulds. Most Australian boats and particularly fishing trawlers and other large work boats of the early to mid-20th century generally had fewer moulds, partly because they built multiple permanent stringers of hardwood into the setup and these tended to fair out just fine around widely spaced moulds, saving a bit of time on mould construction. I used seven moulds on the Ranger with the ones at each end more closely spaced than the ones in the middle.

Keels and Backbone Timbers

Keels are generally of one piece on all but the biggest boats such as large trading ketches where the keels would have to be scarfed together. On larger craft and many smaller boats the keel would be straight, but on most smaller boats and some larger craft they would be curved, or sprung so there is rocker in the keel. If a boat is built with a rockered keel the right way up, such as the Victorian Couta boats the curve must be forced into it by holding it down in the middle and bending the ends up. Boats built outdoors would be built over a buried log with chains or long bolts through the pre-cut keel slot to hold the keel down while the

end or ends were jacked up. On my Ranger class yacht which features in a lot of the photos I held the centre and aft parts of the keel down with threaded rod through holes where keel bolts would eventually go, epoxied into the concrete floor and used two ordinary car jacks to force the front end up. Nuts at pre-determined heights on the threaded rod ensured the keel bent exactly to the designed curve.

The designer will generally have drawn the keel and backbone arrangement in detail. **Fig 3** shows some of the variations. Stems can be cut

Taper being cut in a Spotted Gum keel timber.

Fig. 3 Some Different Backbone Arrangements

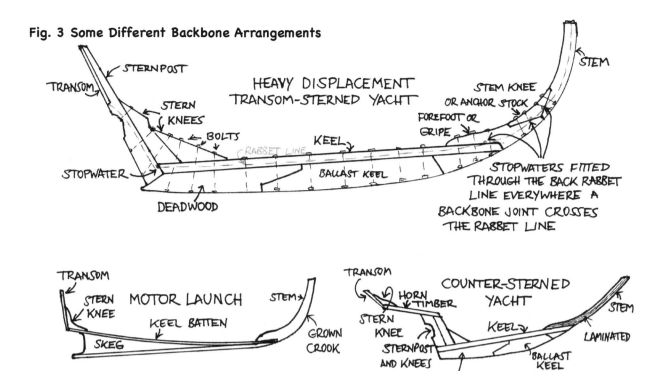

HEAVY DISPLACEMENT TRANSOM-STERNED YACHT

TRANSOM
STERNPOST
STERN KNEES
BOLTS
RABBET LINE
KEEL
STOPWATER
DEADWOOD
BALLAST KEEL
STEM
STEM KNEE OR ANCHOR STOCK
FOREFOOT OR GRIPE
STOPWATERS FITTED THROUGH THE BACK RABBET LINE EVERYWHERE A BACKBONE JOINT CROSSES THE RABBET LINE

TRANSOM
STERN KNEE
MOTOR LAUNCH
KEEL BATTEN
SKEG
STEM
GROWN CROOK

TRANSOM
HORN TIMBER
COUNTER-STERNED YACHT
STERN KNEE
STERNPOST AND KNEES
DEADWOOD
KEEL
STEM
LAMINATED
BALLAST KEEL

from curved stock, or laminated, or built up from smaller pieces bolted together.

The keel will almost definitely be tapered fore and aft. The widths are lifted from the lofting and marked on the Station lines on the keel, and these points joined with a pencil line around a batten held to those points. Cut just clear of these lines with whatever tools can handle it. Generally a hand-held circular saw is best. If the depth of the blade is not enough to cut through the whole depth of the keel in one go, get a long series drill bit of the width of the saw cut (generally about 1/8" or 3mm) and drill vertically in the slot through the rest of the keel. Turn the keel over, join these points with a pencilled line around a batten and cut close to this line. If you lofted the width of the bottom of the keel as well as the top, you can mark this on the underside and cut and/or plane this angle. A circular saw cutting at an angle is quickest with the keel upside down, but be aware that the bevel angle changes constantly and you should do the saw cut with the most conservative angle, then plane down to the lines (rabbet line and bottom of keel line).

Backbone timbers can be worked on with both traditional and modern tools. Adzes and axes are great tools for removing waste timber, but so is a power plane. You can easily ruin some expensive timber trying to learn to use an axe or adze properly. Final preparation is almost always down to hand tools. Large timbers with big surface areas to be joined must be planed straight and true.

The separate pieces of the backbone are bolted together. The designer will normally have noted the diameters and positions of all bolts. Copper and

Shaping the sternpost with an adze.

163

bronze rod is still available and both are easy enough to cut threads on. Any hole for a bolt longer a than about a foot (300mm) should be drilled 1/64" bigger. If you cannot tap the bolt in with light blows from a heavy hammer, stop and withdraw it (which may be difficult) and ream out the hole. If you persist in hitting it harder and harder it will jam up and you will never get it in or out. A little Lanolin grease will ease its progress.

Mating surfaces like on this stem knee must be planed straight and true.

On the use of glue in traditional construction…….

Smithy's Rule: It is okay to use glue (epoxy, resorcinol) to build up from smaller pieces an item that would have been available as a single piece of timber once upon a time, for example scarfing to get longer lengths, or laminating thin pieces to get a curve such as stems, knees etc. It is not okay to glue together different parts of a boat such as planks to frames, or planks to keels, or even planks to each other. Some builders in some parts of the world have gotten away with it, but in my experience the odds are that you will regret it, I have quite a collection of sad stories. It comes down to the philosophy of modern versus traditional construction: a modern laminated boat is a monocoque construction of wood glued together where water is totally excluded- a traditional boat is a collection of different pieces of wood held together by metal fastenings and you must expect water, or at least moisture to enter some parts of the system. If you pierce a laminated boat with metal fastenings that allow water in, or if you glue parts of a traditional boat together it will end badly more often than not.

Bedding Compounds

Every part of the backbone that joins against another piece must have a bedding compound on the joining surfaces. In Australia this was typically blackjack (pitch) or a lead-based compound. The best combination was to paint the joining surfaces with red lead paint (lead oxide) and then apply white lead putty (lead carbonate in oil) before bolting the parts together. I have pulled apart wooden members of a boat over a century old that had been prepared this way and the wood was perfect underneath. This is because the main effect of the lead was to kill all life (such as rot spores) that might try to live in there. But we found out quite a few decades ago that humans are one of the life forms lead tries to kill! So it is unavailable commercially and may even be illegal to sell in some jurisdictions. These days I use blackjack between the heavy timbers of the backbone after priming both surfaces with grey primer. All other wood-to-wood contact areas receive 2-3 coats of primer before assembly. In areas particularly prone to rot I have occasionally used Copper Naphthenate (the green stuff) but that is also so poisonous it is likely to be banned soon.

Polyurethane sealants have come to dominate the construction industry in recent decades and I reluctantly admit we will probably be using them in traditional wooden construction soon, in fact I have used them in a number of cases, particularly in traditional clinker construction and batten-seam

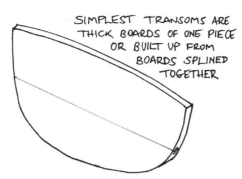
SIMPLEST TRANSOMS ARE
THICK BOARDS OF ONE PIECE
OR BUILT UP FROM
BOARDS SPLINED
TOGETHER

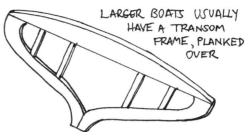
LARGER BOATS USUALLY
HAVE A TRANSOM
FRAME, PLANKED
OVER

Fig. 4 Varieties of Transoms

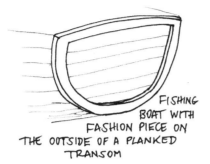
FISHING
BOAT WITH
FASHION PIECE ON
THE OUTSIDE OF A PLANKED
TRANSOM

FINE COUNTER-STERNED
YACHTS SOMETIMES HAVE
A STERN SHAPED FROM A SOLID
BLOCK NOTCHED OVER THE HORN TIMBER
AND RABBETED FOR THE DECK AND PLANKING

HORN TIMBER

carvel boats. My reservations are due to the fact that they have no fungicidal qualities, but their very *stickiness* and flexibility gives me hope that they will never give up in a joint where there is very little movement and they will keep moisture out. Use the low-modulus (flexible) ones and always prime the timber before bedding down. The polyurethanes are expensive but work out cheaper in the sausage packs rather than the tubes. Do not be tempted to use glue between large timber pieces (see box on gluing).

Don't Forget the Stopwaters!

Wherever a joint between two members of the backbone crosses the rabbet line there is a path for water to get into the boat. You must drill holes for softwood dowels right through the joint starting and finishing on the inner rabbet line on each side. The planking will therefore cover the ends of the dowel. See **Fig 3**. Any water seeping along the joint will swell the dowel which then blocks off the joint. The hole should be drilled 1/64" undersize. Do not use standard store bought dowels, you need to make your own. Whittle an oversized piece of softwood down to just larger than the diameter you want, then hammer it through a hole in a piece of thick steel, or a plumber's flaring tool. This compresses the timber so it has more chance to swell when wet. It should be a driving fit into the undersized hole in the joint. There's a natural control on having it too tight because if that's the case it will split or crush as you try to hit it in.

The Transom

Unless your boat is a double-ender you will need a transom (or *tuck* in Australia). On smaller boats this will often be one wide board or a number of boards jointed together, well thicker than the hull planking, in fact thick enough to form a landing for the plank ends and their fastenings. On yachts there will more often be a frame around the perimeter of the transom to make a bigger landing for the plank ends, and the transom boards may be no thicker than the hull planking. **Fig. 4** shows some of the variations. On most Australian boats the planking extends past the tuck for a distance about equivalent to the plank thickness, so when planking you simply run the planking past the tuck and trim it off later. Workboats and fishing boats generally had a fashion piece on the outside to help reinforce the tuck edges against knocks. Fine yachts in USA and Europe occasionally had the planking mitred to the transom planking. I have never done it (except on a repair job once) and don't intend to, but if you want to investigate it see Larry Pardey's and Bud McIntosh's books in the *Recommended Books* appendix.

The Planking Rabbet

The rabbet or rebate lets the planking into the stem, keel and sternpost so it ends up flush on the outside. On smaller boats this is easiest to cut on the bench, but once the timbers are large and heavy it is necessary to shape this in situ. Up to a certain size if you have the right equipment and plenty of room you can bolt the backbone pieces together, and lay it alternately on each side to cut the rabbet so you are always working downhand. Couta boats were generally done this way. The position, depth and angle are all lifted from the construction plan on the lofting. Patterns can be made from thin plywood or even cardboard at each Station and a notch chiselled out on the keel to fit the pattern as in **Fig. 5.** If you haven't already made the patterns and cut the notches on the stem do so now. The area in between your notches is then removed keeping it as fair as possible realising that the bevel angle is probably changing constantly. I have always found that it is safest to cut the rabbet about 12-15% less deep than the nominated planking thickness at this stage (say 1/8" less in 7/8" planking). The final cutting to depth should happen only when the moulds are on. The patterns should be shaped accordingly. The rabbet line should be planed fair and sighted up to check this for ease in fitting the garboard, a bumpy rabbet is a bugger to fit a plank to!

Fine-tuning the rabbet after the moulds are erected. A big slick is ideal for this.

Ballast Keel

If your boat is a keelboat, at some stage you will need to fit a ballast keel, usually of lead these days. It is not impossible to pour your own, but it is dangerous. Feel free to look up details elsewhere but I would advise against it. Sometimes keel bolts are cast into the lead, but I would also advise against that unless it is a tall fin keel, and not many carvel-planked yachts have those. Lead is quite easy to drill with regular twist drills. You should get the lead in place under the keel and drill down through the timber, at least as far into the lead as it takes to hold the drill bit in the right line once you separate the timber and lead to make it easier to drill the lead. This is because you will need to keep adding a little kerosene as a lubricant and it can get very messy with kerosene and lead swarf everywhere. But it is not impossible to do both the timber and lead in one go. There should be plenty of bedding compound between the timber and lead. And did I mention that the top of the lead should be dead flat?

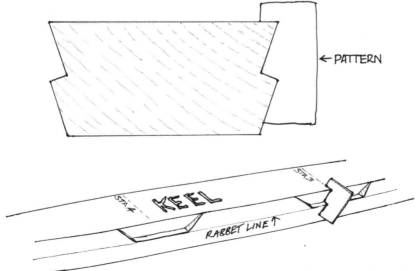

Fig. 5 Cutting the Planking Rabbet on the Keel

Deadwood

The area aft of the keel and usually a small bit in front of it is comprised of large lumps of timber called deadwood. The designer will usually have drawn these up and marked out bolt positions.

On some designs the sternpost is tenoned into the top of the keel and if this is the case you have the alternative of building the boat on its keel and adding the ballast keel and deadwood last thing. This is useful if you have limited height in your workshop as I have, and it means you have a shorter climb into the boat. If the designer has the sternpost tenoned into the lowest deadwood, you will have to fit at least these deadwood pieces first, and you might as well fit the ballast keel at the same time.

Erecting the Moulds

This has been covered as it applies to smaller boats and those built upside down earlier in this volume, and the same rules apply such as ensuring they are both level and plumb with all of the grid lines (centrelines, waterlines and buttocks) exactly lining up, and the forward moulds set <u>aft</u> of the Station lines and the aft moulds set <u>forward</u> of the Station lines. The more rigid the structure is the better. If possible attach each mould to a vertical

post attached to the rafters of the building you are in, and put props out to the walls if they are close enough. They should be rigidly fixed together longitudinally and diagonally. This is easy if you made the top edge of the cross spalls all on one waterline. Fore and aft and diagonal horizontal pieces can be simply screwed to the top of the cross spalls. Fitting the uppermost ribband around the sheer strake also helps lock everything in place with careful measurement.

Lining-out for the Planking

Once the moulds are erected the next job is to work out, at least roughly, where the planking will go. Fashion a batten just narrower than your expected narrower planks, thin enough to take the bend and twist around the hull with light pressure, and at least almost as long as the boat. On most hulls there is a clearly observable "ridge line" at the turn of the bilge, more pronounced the further aft you go (see **Fig.6**). It would be difficult to lay a plank that crossed this ridge, that is to start on the flat of the topsides, cross the ridge and lay on the flat of the bottom. Clamp or tack your lineout batten around the moulds on the peak of this ridge line. Try the batten first with no edge set (sideways bend). Clamp it first in the middle and simply

Fig. 6 Lining-Out for Planking

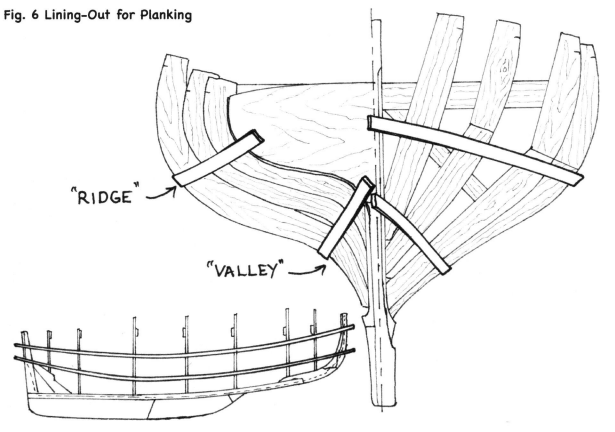

"RIDGE"

"VALLEY"

167

"wrap" it around the moulds. Clamp aft first because the ridge is more prominent there. Where it lands up forward is less important, but you need to consider that the distance from the batten to the sheer should be roughly equal at the stem and at the transom as the same number of planks will need to land in both places. If you get it right first go you will be lucky. On most hulls you will need to edge-set the batten **down** to keep it on the crest of the ridge on the aft sections.

Once you're happy that the batten is laying where you want it, mark its position on the moulds. Above here the plank lineout is easy, you simply measure the distance to be covered between the batten and the sheer at the stem, stern and amidships and divide these distances by the number of planks you expect to use. Adjust the dividing number to get a suitable plank width for the stock that you have. You can use a diminish board as pictured in Figure 12 in the Building a Traditional Clinker Dinghy Manual but it is easy these days to use a calculator.

Below the batten might be a different story. If the hull has much reverse curve in section aft you will need to run the lineout batten up the bottom of this "valley" for the same reason you had to run it along the ridge, that is because a plank cannot be expected to cross over this valley. If you have any slack in the decision of where the batten can lay, it is best to lay it so that when viewed from beam-on the bow and stern ends should be roughly the same distance from the floor, or a little greater at the bow. It should also be roughly the same distance at the bow and stern to the ridge batten line. When you are happy, mark its position on each mould. Below these marks, measure from the marks down to the keel rabbet at the forwardmost mould, the amidships mould and the aft one just in front of the sternpost. Depending on the shape of the boat it is likely that there will be far more territory to cover down aft than there is up forward. It might be worth doing the same exercise of dividing the distances forward, amidships and aft- if your plank stock is wide enough to cover the territory aft and the planks will be wide enough up forward to comfortably fit two fastenings (eg. on 7/8" planking they need to be at least 2" wide and preferably wider where they land on the stem or forefoot) that's probably all you have to do- except it would be wise to lay the lineout batten where the middle plank of this group lays and check that it

Lining out the planking.

will lay comfortably. If the forward territory divided by the number of planks comes up with a figure less than say 2", you will need one or more stealer planks(see **Fig. 7**). These are planks that are let in to a longer host plank and tapered to cover more territory where necessary. Naturally all of this lineout only needs to happen on one side of the boat.

If the forefoot or lower area of the stem is sloped enough to mean the planks would end in a feather edge or really small angle, you will need to nib them into the plank above as in **Fig. 8**. The width of the nib ends need to be 1 1/2 to 2 times the thickness of the planking and they should land on the back rabbet. You need to allow for the extra width of the housing for the nibs when calculating your plank stock.

Now it's time to fine tune the back rabbet on the sternpost, keel and stem so the planking will sit snugly, and to fair the transom edges to be a fair landing for the planking. A batten is used as a guide on the transom and the stem back rabbet, and an off cut of the planking stock will assist along the keel back rabbet as shown in **Fig. 9.** Keep the angle of the rabbet square or slightly greater than a right angle. You can check this with your plank offcut which should be exactly 90 degrees on its edge. The angle of the rabbet should be just enough so that the square-edged plank offcut is sitting tight on the inner rabbet line and a tiny gap is visible on the outside.

Fig. 7 Stealer Planks

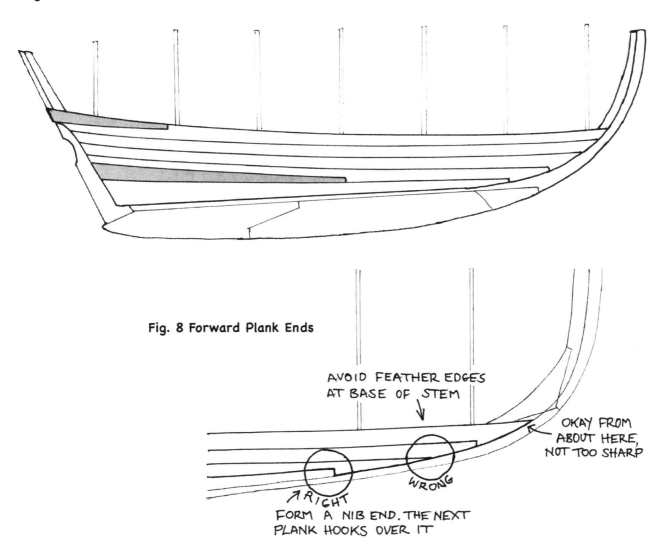

Fig. 8 Forward Plank Ends

AVOID FEATHER EDGES
AT BASE OF STEM

OKAY FROM
ABOUT HERE,
NOT TOO SHARP

WRONG

RIGHT

FORM A NIB END. THE NEXT
PLANK HOOKS OVER IT

**Fig. 9 Fairing the Transom Edge and Finishing
the Planking Rabbet on the Keel**

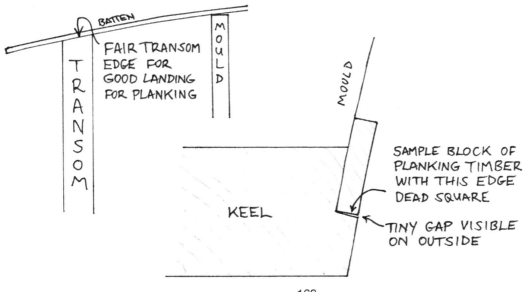

BATTEN

MOULD

FAIR TRANSOM
EDGE FOR
GOOD LANDING
FOR PLANKING

TRANSOM

MOULD

SAMPLE BLOCK OF
PLANKING TIMBER
WITH THIS EDGE
DEAD SQUARE

TINY GAP VISIBLE
ON OUTSIDE

KEEL

169

Ribbands

If building with grown or sawn frames you are ready to plank once the frames are all in place. If you are using steam-bent ribs you will need to fit ribbands around the moulds. Unfortunately the designer will not often specify the dimensions and spacing of the ribbands. They are made from cheap pine (around Sydney we use plantation Radiata Pine), squarish in section of a thickness at least as great as the larger dimension of the ribs. Scarf them together (see p.86) to get the length so they run from stem to stern. They should run roughly as you expect the planking to run. A good rule for spacing is to space them about every one and a half plank widths. The critical factor is that you don't want them to distort when the considerable pressure of bent ribs comes on. You may require extra shoring in tough areas. Locate the first ones where your ridge and valley marks are, then space the others out. They need to be closer together in areas where you expect load to come on when bending in the ribs, in other words clustered a bit on the ridge and the valley. If you are planning to bend the ribs outside the ribbands they must be set so their outer surface represents the inner surface of the ribs, so you will either have allowed for this when marking out and cutting your moulds, or you must let the ribbands in to the moulds. If you are bending the ribs inside the ribbands their inner surface represents the outer surface of the ribs, i.e the same as the inner surface of the planking.

Framing

For most of the history of carvel-planked boats frames were built up from solid pieces of timber cut from crooks of timber where the grain follows the curve known as **grown frames**. Heavier boats such as the British Pilot Cutters and many of the French heritage boats such as the Bisquines are still being built this way. As naturally curved timber began to get harder to get some frames were constructed from shorter futtocks of straight-grained timber fastened together known as **sawn frames** (see **Fig. 10).** If your design calls for this, you do not need to make up temporary moulds. During the latter half

Ribbands more or less follow the planking lineout. The ribs will be bent on the inside of the ribbands on this boat. Note the rib heel sockets in the keel.

of the nineteenth century steam-bent frames began to be used and came to dominate the construction of lighter boats including most yachts from then on. The combination of water and heat to bend timber had been known for at least centuries, by many different cultures around the world. Some cultures such as the Chinese and the Dutch thoroughly soaked their timbers and then applied heat either by holding the timber over a fire or by holding a fire up to the timber. Other cultures or regional areas boil the timber if a large enough container can be found, or pour boiling water over the timber often with the use of some thick cloth to hold the hot water on the surface.

Steaming the timber produces the most heat, and that is what we will describe here but first we have to prepare the boat to receive the frames, which I will refer to as **ribs** from now on. The designer will normally have indicated the rib spacing he wants. This spacing is marked along the keel. The starting point is important. Things to consider are the placing of floors, bulkheads etc. While sawn or grown frames were generally set up plumb, steam-bent ribs are difficult to set up plumb. The amidships ribs where the planking is roughly parallel to the centreline can be almost plumb, but depending on the shape of the boat the sheer or gunwale ends of the forward ribs tend to slope aft and the aft ribs tend to slope forward. You need to determine this before you start bending in

Fig. 10 Grown and Sawn Frames

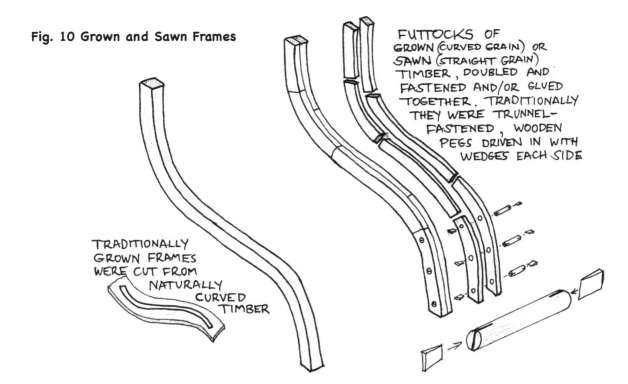

FUTTOCKS OF GROWN (CURVED GRAIN) OR SAWN (STRAIGHT GRAIN) TIMBER, DOUBLED AND FASTENED AND/OR GLUED TOGETHER. TRADITIONALLY THEY WERE TRUNNEL-FASTENED, WOODEN PEGS DRIVEN IN WITH WEDGES EACH SIDE

TRADITIONALLY GROWN FRAMES WERE CUT FROM NATURALLY CURVED TIMBER

the ribs. Fashion a piece of timber as long as the longest rib, the same width as the ribs but thin and flexible enough to bend in cold. Use this as a template to mark the position on the ribbands, ensuring that your template piece can lie flat on the ribbands at all points. Expect to modify the positions a little to ensure even spacing.

There are regional variations on whether to notch (socket) both sawn frames and steam-bent ribs into the keel or not. The argument for not doing it is that it may become a rot trap. However this is more of a problem in areas where the boats are stored out of the water in the Winter with the danger of fresh water from condensation gathering there. In a well-maintained vessel I believe the advantages of notching outweigh the disadvantages. One of the main advantages is quick location of the heel of the hot frame as you are about to bend it. Cut a sample piece of your rib stock to use as a template to chisel out the notches. A slide-in fit is what you want. A hammer-in fit at this stage will make fitting the hot wet ribs into the socket difficult as the wood will have slightly swelled up. Pay attention to the fore and aft angle that each rib will approach the keel. The sockets are cut in the back rabbet so their outer edge is flush with the back rabbet, so the back rabbet needs to be cut to the full depth of the planking by this stage.

Timber selection for steam-bent ribs is covered in the Building a Traditional Clinker Dinghy Manual. All four corners of each rib should be arrised (eased) with a block plane. The Australian tradition is to have flat ribs with the fore and aft dimension approximately twice that of the thickness. In engineering terms a square section frame of the

Many Australian Boats were built with the ribs bent around the outside of the ribbands. This is a Jack Pompei boat. Pompei boats have a great reputation for being sturdy vessels. PHOTO BOB CARTER, CLUB MARINE MAGAZINE.

same cross-sectional area would be stronger, in fact the rectangular rib would be even stronger if placed on edge, but there would be little to fasten the planks to and they would be practically impossible to bend. The European and American tradition is to have the ribs in square section. Australian ribs are generally a little closer together.

Water is heated in a boiler and piped into a box big enough to contain the timbers being used. The old rule of thumb was to leave them in the box for an hour per inch of thickness. With Spotted Gum and other Aussie hardwoods this is a bare minimum. The timber needs to be very hot. If you can handle it without gloves it is not hot enough.

Bending the ribs is a job for at least two people (though one person can manage it if bending the ribs around the outside of the ribbands and there is no reverse curve). One person pulls the rib out of the box and passes it to the other person standing by where the rib will go. The heel of the rib is jammed into the heel socket in the keel (this may require a tunk with a mallet on the other end of the rib) and leaned on to force it around the ribbands or out to them. If bending inside the ribbands the technique is to force it out to the ribbands with your foot or (padded) knee while bending the top back towards you. Work your foot or knee higher and higher on the rib, each time bending the top back, over bending it slightly each time, and sort of roll it up the hull. The photo sequence (page 173) shows this. The bending should all happen within about 30 seconds of coming out of the steam box or the rib may cool off too much. You have to work quickly but not jerkily...the rib is likely to snap if you try to bend it too suddenly or around a hard point.

The second person will fit clamps on the rib at any ribband it is not already laying snugly on. In reverse curve areas this will probably mean a clamp on every ribband. Make sure the rib is laying very close to its position marks. If it is just slightly off this is not a problem as long as you adjust before screwing it in place. A good tunk on top of the rib with a mallet will help it to lie firmly on the ribbands in the upper curve, but make sure you kneel on the rib lower down when doing it or it could be forced away from the ribbands in the lower reverse curve.

Start in the middle of the boat where the ribs are longest (if you break them there may be enough to use it in another part of the boat) and the bends are not extreme. Keep working aft and generally the curves will be getting tighter. When you run out of clamps you will need to start screwing the ribs to the ribbands. Every second ribband is enough as long as the rib is snug on the unfastened positions. In fact if the rib is already cool it may stay in place with just a screw or two at the turn of the bilge.

It is best to start with the moulds still in the boat but remove any additional longitudinal bracing you may have put in. Fit a few ribs in each bay and fasten them off to the ribbands before removing the moulds when they are in the way of a rib. Occasionally in the middle of the boat there will be moulds that do not interfere with a rib placement, and these can stay in at this point. You may feel that some parts of the boat need some more athwartships bracing temporarily fixed to ribs that are fastened to the ribbands before removing adjacent moulds.

If you are bending the ribs on the outside of the ribbands whether right way up or upside down you will not need to remove the moulds unless they hinder clamping of the ribs.

There may be a point at which you start breaking ribs as they bend. From this point on it is better to make up the ribs in two or more laminations. Traditionally difficult ribs were either split with a bandsaw cut down the middle or simply done in two layers. Steam-bent wood is under terrific stress. Even if the wood takes the bend without breaking, repairing boats over the last few decades has shown me that highly stressed ribs will give up eventually, from just a short time after bending to years later.

Over many years I have worked out where I expect the ribs to get difficult, and prepared the rib stock with two laminations in slightly difficult areas, and three laminations in extreme areas. They are cut slightly overwidth, with only the heel ends reduced to the correct size to fit into the heel sockets. They are then steamed and bent in (being thinner they need less time in the box) and allowed to cool. The laminations are then taken out of the boat, allowed to dry over a couple of days, then epoxy glued together back in the boat, held in place with temporary screws through some ribbands and clamps on every other ribband, with plastic sheeting underneath and in the heel socket to prevent the rib sticking to the keel and ribbands. After the epoxy cures they are then removed from the boat, the edges removed to take them back to the size of the original ribs, and fitted back into the

Step 1: The outside person passes the hot rib from the steam box into the boat.

Step 2: The rib is jammed into the heel socket.

Step 3: The rib is "walked" up the hull.

Step 4: The technique is to pull the top of the rib inboard bending it over your foot. Keep moving the foot higher up the rib and bend back again. You can see the outside person starting to attach clamps down low.

Step 5: Clamp in place once you're sure it is landing flat on every ribband.

This sequence is from my video Carvel Planking Episode 1: Steaming the Ribs on YouTube

boat. This takes considerably more time than just bending them in, but they will be stronger and last a hell of a lot longer than highly-stressed one-piece ribs.

It is best to remove all ribs one at a time and prime coat the heels before fitting them back into the heel sockets with a bedding compound and a nail or screw to hold them. Any ribs which will be varnished (in my boats usually only in visible areas) will benefit from being sanded clean before final fitting.

Planking

You already should have a pretty good idea where the planks will run as your ribbands should more or less show this. Now where to start? In commercial boatyards planking would generally commence at the sheer and continue down, at the same time as another team would start from the garboards and work up. A shutter plank at the turn of the bilge is then fitted to close up the hull. This system is great for commercial work as up to four teams can be planking at the same time. If you are working alone however it is unnecessary. It is easiest to start at the garboards and work continuously so the sheer plank is the last plank and no shutters are necessary.

The Garboard

The garboard is the first plank against the keel. On most traditional hulls where the keel is raked the garboard needs to be as wide as your widest available plank aft, and will generally taper forward, especially if there is a lot of curve to the lower stem. **Fig. 11** shows a selection of different types of hull with the garboards highlighted. You will also see on the different types of hull that the planking can be quite wide on the flatter areas of the hull, but needs to be narrower on the more

Fig. 11 Variations in Garboards

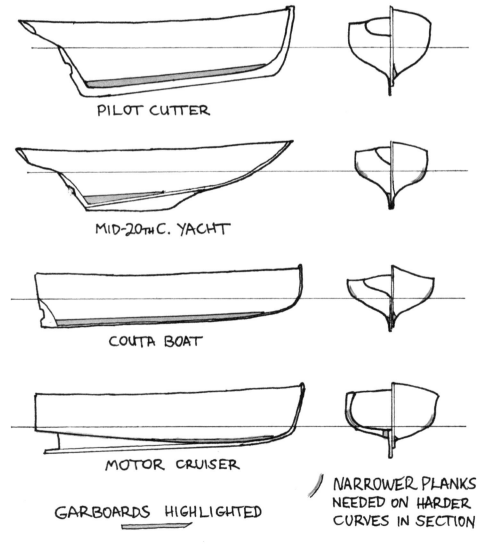

PILOT CUTTER

MID-20TH C. YACHT

COUTA BOAT

MOTOR CRUISER

GARBOARDS HIGHLIGHTED

NARROWER PLANKS NEEDED ON HARDER CURVES IN SECTION

Fig. 12 Allowing for Rounding and Hollowing of Planks

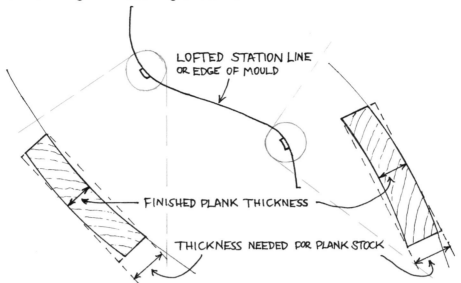

LOFTED STATION LINE
OR EDGE OF MOULD

FINISHED PLANK THICKNESS

THICKNESS NEEDED FOR PLANK STOCK

curved areas such as the turn of the bilge and any reverse curve lower down. You need to allow for rounding and hollowing of planks when selecting your plank stock. Hardly any of your planks should be machined to the exact finished dimension. **Fig. 12** shows a diagrammatic way of working out how thick a plank needs to be from your lofting, or you can work it out directly off the moulds. Most of the wider planks on flatter areas will still need an allowance for some rounding and hollowing.

Spiling

The shape of the edge of the plank that fits against the keel is found by spiling. A spiling batten is a piece of timber narrower than the planking and thin enough to be easily twisted to lie flat on all ribs. It should be simply tacked or clamped in place with no edge set just clear of the inner rabbet line. It needs to be as long as the plank being planned, but it can be made up of shorter sections overlapped and screwed together. Drive the screws from the back so that the batten can lie on the back rabbet and the plank stock.

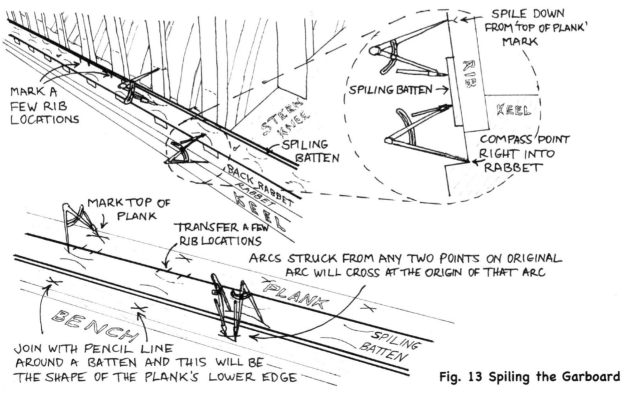

MARK A FEW RIB LOCATIONS

STERN KNEE

SPILING BATTEN

BACK RABBET

KEEL

SPILE DOWN FROM 'TOP OF PLANK' MARK

SPILING BATTEN →

RIB

KEEL

COMPASS POINT RIGHT INTO RABBET

MARK TOP OF PLANK

TRANSFER A FEW RIB LOCATIONS

ARCS STRUCK FROM ANY TWO POINTS ON ORIGINAL ARC WILL CROSS AT THE ORIGIN OF THAT ARC

PLANK

BENCH

SPILING BATTEN

JOIN WITH PENCIL LINE AROUND A BATTEN AND THIS WILL BE THE SHAPE OF THE PLANK'S LOWER EDGE

Fig. 13 Spiling the Garboard

A set of compasses or dividers is used, opened to a radius that will allow arcs to be drawn on the batten starting at the inner rabbet line as illustrated in **Fig. 13.** Space them about a hand-span apart. Pencil the positions where the batten crosses several selected marked ribs before removing the batten to the bench and placing it on your selected plank stock.

Selecting the Garboards from your Plank Stock

Your garboard planks are generally quite wide and it is best if they are one length of timber. But you can build them up from two pieces scarfed together, either because you simply don't have long enough timber or because with a difficult fit at each end you have decided to do it in two pieces because you can fit each end independently and then scarf them together in the middle. Do not be tempted to butt them together, some of each plank will butt on the back rabbet but a half-butt block would be problematic to seal. Traditionally, boatbuilders would try to book match the planks on each side of the boat, that is have them both ripped out of a thicker board, especially on smaller boats. Such timber is getting more difficult to find and it is really not necessary. What does help though, and this applies to all planking, is to check the growth rings on the plank ends, and if the rings show the plank is anything other than perfectly edge-grained (quarter sawn), orient the plank so that on convex sections such as the topsides the inside of the tree should be to the outside of the boat, and on concave sections, the inside of the tree should be to the inside of the boat, illustrated in **Fig. 14.** This uses the natural tendency of wood to warp away from the centre of the tree as it seasons.

Marking the Plank from the Spiling Batten

While locating the spiling batten ensure the line you are about to mark will be close enough to the the edge to allow for your planned width of the plank. If the plank is going to be considerably tapered, plan the spiled line to run close to the edge so that you are saving as much timber as possible, you may be able to use the offcut elsewhere. The only exception to this is if the grain of the board runs at a bit of an angle so you could angle the spiling batten to suit as it is always best for the grain to be relatively straight along a plank.

The forward end of the garboard can be quite wide in hull shapes like the Pilot Cutter or the Motor Cruiser in Fig.11, and if this is the case it will be best to make a thin template of this area, and another at the sternpost, and screw these to the spiling batten as in **Fig. 15.**

Make sure the batten cannot move on the stock and is laying comfortably with no edge set. Use the compasses or dividers set to the same radius to draw crossed arcs on the plank stock from 2 positions on the arcs on the batten, which finds the origin of those arcs and establishes exactly where the inner rabbet line was relative to the batten. Refer back to **Fig. 13.**

Transfer a few rib positions also to the plank stock. Tack nails into the crossed arcs, lay a flexible batten around the nails and clamp or tack it in place. Pencil around the batten. do the same for the top edge of the plank if you spiled that side. Cut just outside this line preferably with a circular saw set to cut just deeper than the thickness of the plank and supported on small offcuts on the bench. For safety clamp the plank to the bench, moving the clamps when they are in the way of your cut. Plane

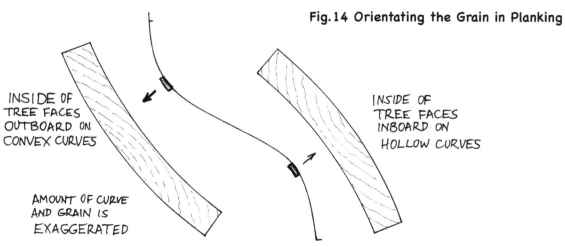

Fig.14 Orientating the Grain in Planking

INSIDE OF TREE FACES OUTBOARD ON CONVEX CURVES

AMOUNT OF CURVE AND GRAIN IS EXAGGERATED

INSIDE OF TREE FACES INBOARD ON HOLLOW CURVES

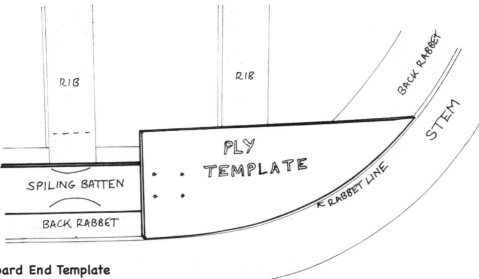

Fig. 15 Garboard End Template

the plank edge to the line, sighting along the edge to check that it is fair. Keep the edge square. If you didn't spile the top edge, work out the planned width of the plank every few ribs or so, mark it and join up the dots with tacked nails, batten and pencil. Cut about 10mmm (3/8") outside this line. Select the sister plank for the other side and mark it out by simply tracing around the first plank, naturally making it the reverse of the first one, that is lay inside to inside when marking. Cut a little bit outside these lines. Don't plane to the lines on the sister plank at this point.

Steaming the Plank

Offer the plank up to the boat. If it will take the bend and twist with light clamping pressure you can skip the next part and go straight into fine tuning the fit. If not, and this is usually the case, you will need to steam the plank to get it to bend and twist. If you have a steam box long enough and some helpers to assist in fitting the hot plank, that's the way to go, so put both planks in the box. If you don't, a technique only developed in recent decades is the go- put the plank in a heavy-duty plastic sleeve, clamp it lightly in the middle onto the boat, tie off one end of the sleeve and attach the hose from the steam generator to the other end. Fire up the steam generator and after about half an hour, start to force the plank into the bend and twist. Take it easy, you could still snap the

plank at this stage, but as the steam and heat gets into the plank it will get easier to bend. The technique is to get clamps on it as soon as they will hold, and gradually and progressively tighten them until the plank is firmly against the ribs and back rabbet. Not every rib will need clamping to, use just enough to get the plank reasonably snug on the ribs, it does not matter if there are small gaps of a couple of millimetres (1/16") on some ribs. Use wooden pads under the clamp heads where a lot of pressure is needed on the clamp because the steamed timber is soft and high clamping pressure will indent the clamp into the timber. While the first plank is heating up, put the sister plank in another plastic sleeve. When the first one is clamped up, transfer the steam hose to the second sleeve and repeat the process.

Garboard plank steamed in plastic sleeve and clamped in place.

177

If the plank is going to be scarfed to get the length, do not cut or glue the scarf before steaming, as epoxy glues cannot take that much heat and will fail. You can still steam both sections at a time, just overlap them by slightly more than the intended scarf length in the tube.

Leave them for a couple of hours to cool, then remove the clamps and take the planks out of the sleeves. Clamp the planks back up on the boat and leave them overnight to dry. You will notice that the planks will straighten out a bit when you release them but will retain most of the bend and twist and will easily bend back in place.

First Trial Fit

Once the plank is dry you can clamp it properly in place on the boat. Clamp it on at least every second rib, and tap the plank firmly down to get the tightest fit you can against the rabbet. On the first plank where you planed to the scribed line you may be lucky enough to get a dead fit first time, but it is not likely, the difference between a dead fit and a slight gap can be just one plane stroke, thinner than the pencil line you planed to. If there is a secret to well-fitting plank seams it is **evenness** and **fairness**. Wood will swell and close up small gaps but only if the gap is fairly even. A wide gap either side of a tight spot will never close up. We can get too precious about the tightness of a plank seam- many older boats have been made watertight again by recaulking even when the seam is open about 3mm (1/8")- but while it is possible it is not desirable in a new boat and you should try to get the planks to touch with just a thin sliver of light in some places. I am in awe of the Couta boat builders who do not caulk their plank seams but simply butt them up, referred to as close seams. I can always see a bit of light somewhere along my seams, but the actual gap is less than half a millimetre (say 1/32").

There are regional and personal variations in the shape of plank seams, illustrated in **Fig. 16.** The close seam mentioned above often involves "bruising" the seam by firmly rubbing a small wheel or rounded point of a burnishing tool along the seam to crush wood fibres. When water enters the seam these fibres swell up and act as caulking. In many regions the planking is first fitted as close as

possible all the way across both edges, then the caulking seam is planed for approximately two-thirds of the thickness of the plank so that the gap on the outside will be about the thickness of an old penny coin, just over 1/16" (just under 2mm). The third method is to plane the caulking bevel right across the seam. This has the benefit of a shallower angle of the bevel which holds the cotton in better, and allows the thinner wood on the inner edge to crush a little when the planking swells after launching. I tend to compromise between the last two methods. I aim to do the trial fits with the outside of the seam just visibly open, because this way it is easier to ensure that the inner edges are touching. On the last dry fit I mark where the caulking seam needs to be wider and plane it on the bench before the final fit, shading the inner third or quarter of the seam with pencil as a guide to not planing anything of that area.

On the garboard seam you cannot see light from behind, so some sort of feeler gauge comes in handy. This can be an actual mechanics' feeler gauge or a handier substitute like a 6" rule, normally a fraction under a millimetre thick. If the seam is a tiny bit open on the outside (which is desirable on the garboard seam even at this early stage), poke the ruler or gauge of just under a

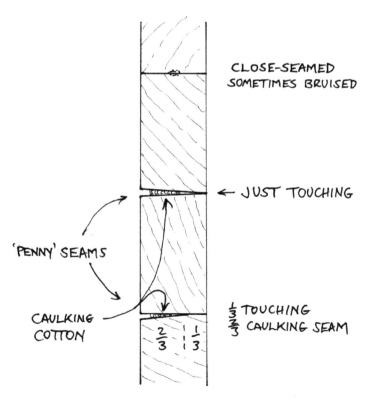

Fig. 16 Plank Seams

millimetre into the seam. If it stops about halfway in (half the plank thickness) that is ideal. If it goes the full depth to the back rabbet you need to do a bit more work. If it goes in and rattles around, you need to do a lot more work. Mark the spots where it doesn't go in far, because these are high spots that need to be planed off. If the plank touches in a few places but shows gaps larger than a couple of millimetres in other places you should treat the plank as if you hadn't planed to the spiled line, exactly as you will do for the sister plank. Such a plank needs to be re-clamped in place with a relatively even gap all the way along of about 10-12mm (3/8"-1/2"). Small spacer blocks at each end and one in the middle help make this easier. Set your compasses, if you can, so that the point will run along the inner rabbet line and the pencil will run along close to the plank edge. Set the width to your widest gap, and draw a continuous line all the way along the plank, keeping the plank vertically above the point. If you then plane to this line you will be much closer to a good fit. But wait! Before you remove the plank you need to check the fit against the ribs and the back rabbet. There is likely to be a slight concavity here in the ribs. If this is the case the top edge of your plank will be touching the ribs but the mid-section will be standing off from the lower ribs and the back rabbet. Measure this gap with your small rule or a feeler gauge and write the figure on the plank adjacent to where you measured it. Pencil either side of each rib on the

inside of the plank. Remove the plank to the bench, then place a straight edge from the inner rabbet line vertically up each rib across the intended width of the plank as in **Fig. 17** to see how much gap there is, and this is the amount you must remove from top and bottom edges of the plank. While the straight edge is there, check if the curve is even, that is whether the widest part of the gap is in the centre or closer to top or bottom. As always it is safest to remove less than you think you should and have another trial fit. A safe bet is to use the measurement of the gap at the top of the keel rabbet which will almost always be less than the widest gap under a straight edge. If there is a lot of curve and particularly if it changes quickly along the plank you should take a pattern at every second or third rib which can be as simple as bending one of those lead-lined rubber draughtsman's flexible curves and tracing it onto some pattern material like thick cardboard or thin plywood and cut out a concave pattern. Number each of these and mark the plank to locate each pattern on the bench. For all planks after the garboard or if there is substantial section of the garboard above the top of the keel there is an easier method using a scratch stock which I will go into later.

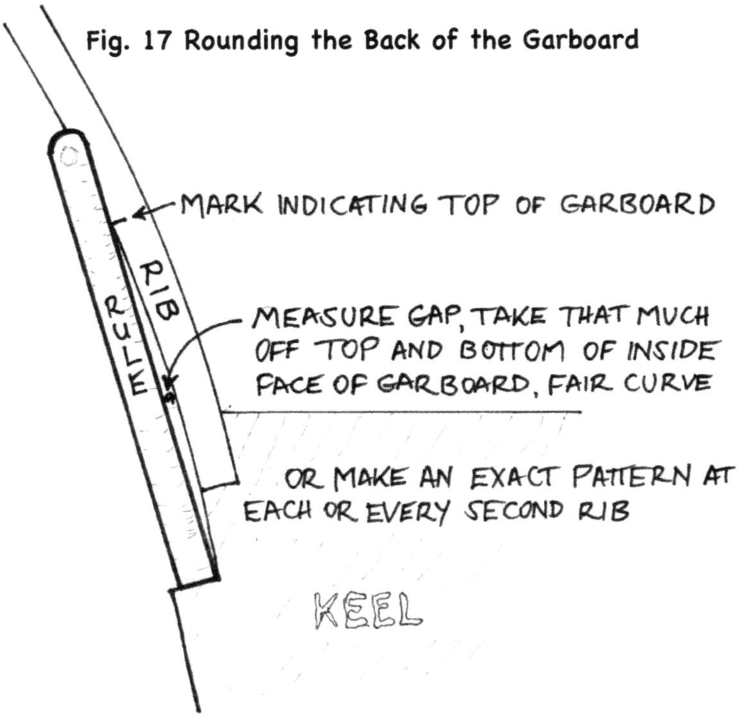

Plane to the line along the plank edge as the first job on the bench. Your planking bench should be as long as possible or use two benches, and you will need two vices or some other means of holding the plank on edge. A Number 5 plane is my choice for planing plank edges. Large boats such as trawlers with the plank curves spread out over a longer distance might benefit from using a Number 6 or 7. If there is a lot of wood to remove you could saw it off or use a power plane judiciously until closer. As you hand plane closer to the line adjust the plane for a finer cut. A thick shaving can mean the difference between a good fit and a bad one. If you have the luxury of two planes, keep one set for a deeper cut for roughing down to the line, and finish with a fine-set plane. Keep the edge square. Then plane the round into the back of the plank, but be conservative. Again, use a rougher cut to start with and finish with a fine cut.

The plank will likely have more than one trial fit. You are getting pretty good if it fits the second time you put it on the

Fig. 17 Rounding the Back of the Garboard

MARK INDICATING TOP OF GARBOARD

RIB

RULE

MEASURE GAP, TAKE THAT MUCH OFF TOP AND BOTTOM OF INSIDE FACE OF GARBOARD, FAIR CURVE

OR MAKE AN EXACT PATTERN AT EACH OR EVERY SECOND RIB

KEEL

boat. I very rarely do this. Success on the third fit is more common, but sometimes it is still not quite right. I'll tell you a secret, in commercial boatyards back in the day if you couldn't get it on the third fit you might not have a job the next day, but there were plenty of planks fitted that would have benefitted from a further adjustment.

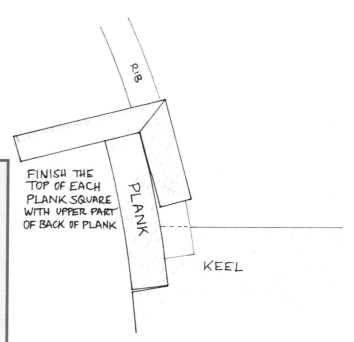

Fig. 18 Keep the Top Edge Square

> **Tip: your pencil is your best friend**
>
> You should always have a pencil with you. I generally have two, a soft wide carpenters' pencil for general work and drawing long lines, and a drawing pencil for finer marks. When you are fine tuning your work, **work to marked lines.** Don't think "I'll just take a bit off here, and a bit off there" because you will most likely get it wrong. If it's too hard to mark a line as it often is when fine tuning a plank seam, pencil in some stripes or hatching or a wavy line to your own code which exactly shows the area you want to remove wood from and gives a hint as to how many plane strokes will be necessary. And it is always safer to estimate how much to remove, then remove half of that and have another trial fit. Accuracy involves constant checking!

If your first trial fit shows that a bit more of the inside of the plank needs to be removed to get it to lay flat on the ribs and back rabbet, do that on the bench as well as trimming the edge. Once it fits, the next time it comes off will be when you hollow the outside of the plank. But first you should fair the top edge of the plank. Make sure it stays square to the inside of the plank as in **Fig. 18.** Regularly stop planing and sight along the top edge to check it is fair. **The more fair it is, the easier the next plank will be to fit to it**. If the plank has retained a fair amount of curve you may need to get creative with clamps and vices to hold it in place while you work on it.

Mark a continuous line on both edges of the plank at the designed finished planking thickness with a marking gauge or a pencil and a combination square set to that

thickness (see photo). Measure the amount of round in the inside of the plank by spanning the plank with a straight edge and measuring the gap on each side, and mark these measurements regularly along the plank. If you marked and cut out templates, use the convex side. Start with a power plane if there is much wood to remove but be careful! Finish with hand planes. A regular square-edged plane blade can still get a bit of hollow into a plank, but if your hollow is more than that you need to have a plane with a blade ground and honed to a slight radius. You will possibly need a couple of blades ground to different radii. There is no need at this stage to plane the outside of the plank to the nth degree. As

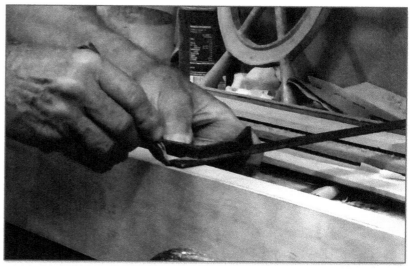

Using a combination square as a marking gauge to mark the finished plank thickness on the plank edges.

long as the edges are close to the plank thickness line (just on or over, never under) the rest will be taken care off during the hull fairing process.

Whatever number in the trial fit sequence it is, when you think you've got it you need to wedge the plank down hard into the rabbet. Sometimes you can fit clamps from under the keel to the top of the plank, and you may be lucky enough to have some plank clamps that clamp onto the rib and have another threaded piece that forces the plank down, but these are rare. The most common solution is to clamp a block of wood to the rib just above the plank and tap a wedge into the gap.

You can see how much twist there is in this garboard.

Place these on every second or third rib, with clamps holding the plank hard against the ribs on all others.

In most commercial boatyards when building carvel-planked boats was common, once the plank was a good fit it would be immediately drilled and fastened off, particularly if it was a fishing or work boat. These days most customers would expect the mating wood surfaces to be primed first, that is, the outside of the ribs and the inside of the plank. Two or three coats of your chosen primer is best. I usually drill for the fastenings during the final dry fit with the plank wedged down hard, then remove the plank to prime it. You can be working on the other side of the boat while the primer dries. In fact I usually fasten the plank at least in some places with temporary chipboard screws (which don't make the drilled holes any bigger than the nails to come) to free up some of the clamps...you can never have too many clamps.

Fastening Planks

Most carvel-planked boats are fastened with square-cut copper nails and roves. Some production builders like Herreshoff in the USA and Halvorsen in Sydney fastened the planks to the ribs with screws because it was less labour-intensive. But a through-fastening like a copper nail and rove, which is in effect a rivet, is slightly stronger. However the main problem with Halvorsens'

screwed boats was that they used brass screws and most of the boats have had to be re-fastened after 25-30 years, however some inexplicably lasted longer. Silicon Bronze screws are still used in fastening planks to stems, keels and sternpost. In the early 20th Century these areas were often fastened with blind fastenings like copper nails on smaller craft, which were sometimes twisted to help prevent loosening and bronze dumps which were simply large diameter nails on larger craft. Dumps are a good fastening, they hold really well, but the corollary of this is that they are almost impossible to remove which makes repair work harder. Monel screws are the longest-lasting but most expensive, if you can get them. In carvel work both nail and screw heads are generally countersunk and either plugged with wood plugs glued in with glue or varnish, or simply puttied over which was quite common on Australian builds.

Every plank should have two fastenings into each rib, each set in from the edge of the plank by about the same distance as the planking thickness. Whenever possible the fastenings are always reeled (staggered) so that one will be closer to the front edge of the rib and the one above it will be closer to the back edge of the rib. This helps avoid consecutive fastenings in the same line of grain of the wood. Only very wide planks require a third fastening in between the others, but planks over 5" (125mm) or so should have a third fastening in the middle into the stem and sternpost or transom.

If the landings on stem and transom are wide enough, another one or two fastenings can be set back in a second row.

Every fastening must be drilled for. I have covered this and the fastening of copper nails and roves in the Building a Traditional Clinker Dinghy Manual earlier. It is not impossible to fasten carvel planks alone, but gets more difficult the larger the boat.

Other Planks

The other planks follow the same procedures as the garboards. As long as the tops of your garboards were both cut to the same line, the next plank should fit well on both sides if the sister plank is cut to the same shape as the original spiling. However it is always advisable to leave a little extra on top of the sister plank in case you have to remove a bit of wood on the edge against the earlier plank. With many boats you will still need to steam the lower planks and it is next to impossible to mark out a sister plank back-to-back once this is done, so it is easiest to mark and cut the sister before steaming, but you should leave that extra bit of wood on top. You can transfer the plank heights from one side of the boat to monitor even progress.

Bevelling the Plank Edges

You will recall that I suggested leaving the top edge of the garboard square to the inside of the plank. The matching edge of the next plank will have to be beveled to match this. Pick up the angle at every second or third rib as in **Fig. 19** and mark it on the plank at the relevant spot. You can make up a bevel board as illustrated and write down the number of degrees, but it is simpler to mark from the bevel gauge directly on the back of the board. Constantly check your bevel angle as you plane the plank edge but remember that you don't want to plane beyond the spiled line on the inside of the plank. Err on the side of having slightly more bevel as you will have to do a bit of this anyway for the caulking seam.

Without the back rabbet behind the plank your fit can more easily be judged from the amount of light coming through than you could on the garboard/keel seam. Look on the inside of the plank as well to check you have beveled enough off the edge to close up on the inside first. Mark the high spots both inside and out if necessary.

Also on every plank except the garboard the curve of the ribs can easily be marked on cardboard or thin plywood templates. But there is a better method. Adapt a tool such as a scratch stock as in

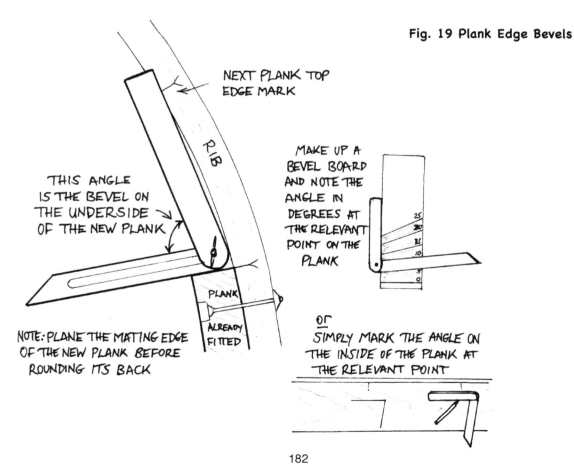

Fig. 19 Plank Edge Bevels

NEXT PLANK TOP EDGE MARK

RIB

THIS ANGLE IS THE BEVEL ON THE UNDERSIDE OF THE NEW PLANK

PLANK ALREADY FITTED

NOTE: PLANE THE MATING EDGE OF THE NEW PLANK BEFORE ROUNDING ITS BACK

MAKE UP A BEVEL BOARD AND NOTE THE ANGLE IN DEGREES AT THE RELEVANT POINT ON THE PLANK

or

SIMPLY MARK THE ANGLE ON THE INSIDE OF THE PLANK AT THE RELEVANT POINT

the photo and run it up and down the inside of the rib with the cutter set to the greatest distance to the plank, and the cutter will copy the curve of the rib. You can either do it just on the ribs which don't have clamps, or change your clamp positions to do it on every rib. On the bench, you simply plane down to these trenches and fair in the bits in between and your plank should fit perfectly on the ribs at the next trial fit.

Use the widest planks you can whenever possible. This depends on what you have in stock, but also how much extra thickness you have because in the tighter radius curves in the hollow of the reverse curve aft and the turn of the bilge (the "ridge" and "valley") narrower planks fit more easily and don't have to be as thick as wider ones to allow for the the hollow and round. Refer back to **Fig. 12**. Keep the planks running along the lines established by your ribbands, but keep them as wide as you can consistent with following the ribband lines.

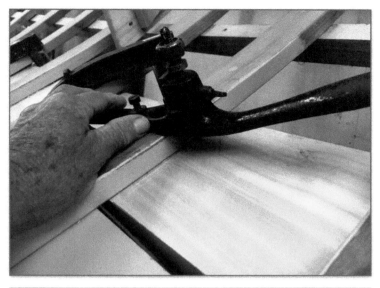

Run a tool like a scratch stock along each rib to give a guide to the amount of hollow or round in the plank to fit snugly against the ribs.

Joining Planks: Butt Joints and Scarfing

On most boats over about 16' (4.8m) you will need to join the planks to get the length. The simplest and most traditional method is to butt the planks up between a pair of ribs, tight on the inside with a caulking seam on the outside. Actually the simplest is to butt them up on a rib, but this has always been considered a bit bodgy as the plank end fastenings have to be very close to the end. Having said that, Halvorsen production boats were generally done this way to save time and they mostly seem to have gotten away with it, but there are a few sad stories so avoid this practice. The inside is covered with a butt block which laps onto the plank above and below and generally fills the space between the two ribs. See **Fig. 20**. The butt block should be shaped to fit snug against the planking if there is any curve in the planks. If it touches the ribs make sure there is a chamfer on the back so moisture can drain away. Definitely prime the mating surfaces and preferably bed it down on some compound (make sure the compound doesn't block the drainage path).

Fit the forward plank first and cut if off dead square exactly halfway between a pair of ribs. The aft plank can then simply be butted up to it and if light appears through the gap at some point you can fine tune it and tap it forward to fit. If your boat is a double-ender where the aft plank also has to fit into a rabbet, dry fit both planks individually with the other plank off the boat, then fasten off the forward plank and dry fit the aft plank overlapping the butt end and marking where to cut. Cut conservatively and plane the aft plank end down until it slides in against the forward butt end, then fasten it off, but not before planing a bevel for a caulking seam.

If scarfing, use a stepped scarf as illustrated in **Fig. 21**. The forward plank always has the scarf joint cut on the inside. It is best to plan to land the feather edge in the centre of a rib, and have the

Fig. 20 Butt Block

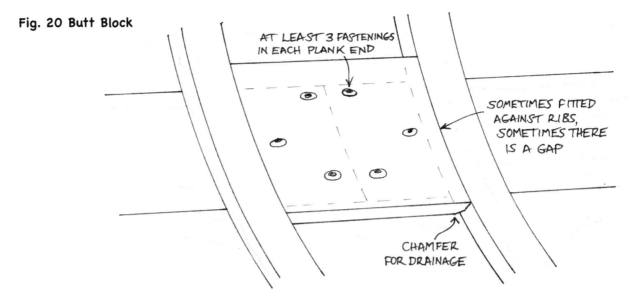

AT LEAST 3 FASTENINGS
IN EACH PLANK END

SOMETIMES FITTED
AGAINST RIBS,
SOMETIMES THERE
IS A GAP

CHAMFER
FOR DRAINAGE

scarf long enough so that the end is just beyond the next rib so that rib's fastenings will be holding down the scarf end. They are best glued up on the boat. Fit each plank individually so as to get the lower edge a good fit all the way along, then dry fit the aft plank with its scarf cut, dry fit the forward plank so that it overlaps, mark carefully for the scarf and take the forward plank to the bench to cut the scarf. Then go for a final dry fit. If all is good, fit some very thin plastic sheeting under the whole area to be glued, apply the thickened epoxy and clamp up the scarf. Once cured (usually at least 24 hours) drill for the fastenings in the scarfed area and anywhere else you haven't already drilled, remove the whole continuous plank and clean up the glue dags. Be very careful not to remove any timber from the plank edge adjoining the previous

plank. Plane along the top edge ensuring it is as fair as you can get it, as there will often be some slight unfairness as the two planks were prepared separately. Prime the plank and the outside of the ribs and fit and fasten it off.

Both butt blocks and scarf joints should be staggered over the hull so as not to be too close to each other. The rule is in adjacent strakes there should be at least three frame bays between scarfs, and if in the same frame bay there should be three planks between them. This means a fair bit of planning with your known plank stock lengths. Here's another secret, plenty of boats have got away with two plank or frame bay spacing, but if you have to do this don't concentrate them in one area. With scarfs on the first few planks I try to locate them to land on a wide structural floor for extra fastenings through the scarf.

Fig. 21 Plank Scarf

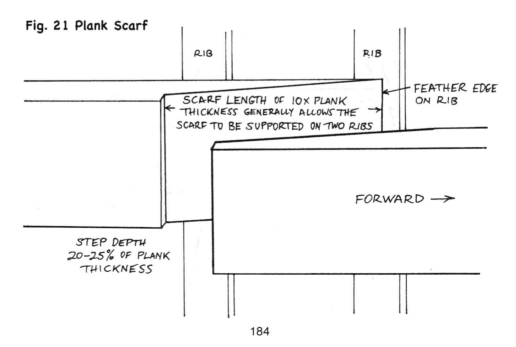

RIB

RIB

FEATHER EDGE
ON RIB

SCARF LENGTH OF 10X PLANK
THICKNESS GENERALLY ALLOWS THE
SCARF TO BE SUPPORTED ON TWO RIBS

FORWARD →

STEP DEPTH
20-25% OF PLANK
THICKNESS

184

Planking scarf ready to fit the forward plank.

Stealer Planks

Some of the boat types back in **Fig. 11** will require stealer planks to cover the territory where there is more to cover aft than forward. They can be let into the plank below in which case the line of the top of the stealer is a continuation of the line of the top of the host plank forward of the stealer, or into the upper plank in which case the stealer is normally fitted first and the host plank fitted around it. Refer back to Figure 7. The forward or nib end of each stealer needs to be backed up with a butt block as if it were any other plank butt unless like the garboard nib end it lands completely on the

back rabbet. If your structural floors are very wide it is acceptable to land the nib end of a stealer on the floor.

On boats with a tight curve under the transom in section the bend and twist in the stealer plank requires it to be carved out of a larger piece of wood as the twist would not be possible even with steam. You need to plot out the relative angles of the two ends and carve the plank out as in **Fig. 22.** Get the inside part to fit against the tuck, sternpost and ribs first, then shape the outer side. Try to carve a bit of the curve into it, but the curve is not as important as getting the twist right.

TWIST PLUS CURVE

Fig. 22 A carved stealer plank. From my book THE OPEN BOAT.

WORK OUT THE SIZE OF THE BLANK FROM WHICH YOU WILL CARVE IT

MALE AND FEMALE PLY TEMPLATES

TEMPLATING TOOL

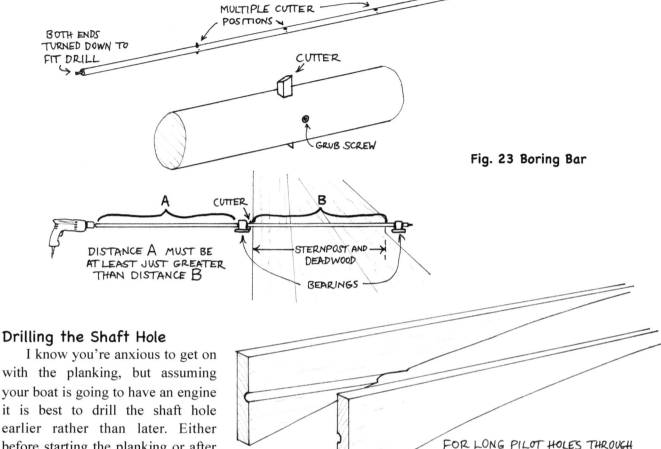

Fig. 23 Boring Bar

BOTH ENDS TURNED DOWN TO FIT DRILL

MULTIPLE CUTTER POSITIONS

CUTTER

GRUB SCREW

A   CUTTER   B

DISTANCE A MUST BE AT LEAST JUST GREATER THAN DISTANCE B

STERNPOST AND DEADWOOD

BEARINGS

FOR LONG PILOT HOLES THROUGH A SKEG YOU CAN ROUT OUT HALF AT A TIME AND GLUE HALVES TOGETHER. ONCE MOUNTED ON THE HULL, DRILL INTO THIS HOLE AND ON THROUGH THE KEEL BATTEN

Drilling the Shaft Hole

I know you're anxious to get on with the planking, but assuming your boat is going to have an engine it is best to drill the shaft hole earlier rather than later. Either before starting the planking or after just a few planks are on you will be able to clamp a supporting structure for the bearings for the boring bar across the ribs as in the photo, and you will be able to drill and bore the shaft easily alone because you can see both ends of the setup which you can't do if there are too many planks on. Start by marking where the shaft hole centre is expected to be on both the inside and the outside of the sternpost, deadwood or skeg or whichever parts it's going through. Draw a line representing the pathway of the hole on the outside of the timber and line up a drill bit of about 10-12mm diameter (3/8-1/2") at least half as long as the distance the shaft has to go through. It helps if you clamp a straight piece of wood along the pencilled line of the shaft and line up your drill bit to that, as well as making sure you are drilling along the centreline of the boat. Clear the drill often so it doesn't jam. There are lots broken drill bits acting as blind fastenings inside boat timbers but this is one you do not want to break. Drill a bit over halfway through, then go inside the boat, line it up properly and drill out towards the first hole. If you are accurate, you should find that the holes meet, but expect a little misalignment. Whether or not they meet, the next step is to incrementally increase the size of the drill bit you use until you can see light coming through. You will probably have to vacuum or blow out the drilling swarf to see through. If after the first couple of goes you still can't see through, put some dowels or long drill bits in both ends and sight up to see which way they are misaligned. Try to correct it by lining the drill bit up where you think it should go, spinning it at high speed but using very little forward pressure so that it eats into the side wall of the original hole a bit. Every time it seems to be being forced back into the original pathway, pull it out and start again. A boat with a 1" (25mm) prop shaft needs a hole about 2" (50mm) diameter for its shaft tube so you have a bit of room to play with.

To proceed much further you need to have both the shaft tube (traditionally copper or bronze with the bearing and stern gland threaded onto them, but now there are also fibreglass tubes that the bearings are simply bedded into) so you know the final diameter, and the <u>boring bar</u> which has to be long

A string line represents the centreline of the shaft.

enough to be greater than the distance between the bearings by at least the distance the cutter has to travel as illustrated in **Fig. 23.**

Keep drilling through your pilot hole until there is a clear line of sight along the line of the shaft. In fact it needs to be a big enough hole for the boring bar which is usually 1" (25mm) diameter or bigger to easily slide through on the shaft line without cutters. The other reason for drilling the shaft hole early in the piece is that it helps if one of the vertical centreline posts that supported the moulds is still in the boat (if not you have to put it back!) and you mark the projected height of the centreline of the shaft taken from the lofting. Be sure that the boring bar will have plenty of room to line up in the right spot, without touching the walls of the hole at all. Drill from both ends with a bigger drill bit if in doubt. Run a tight string line between the mark on the post through the pilot hole to a cleat tacked across where the hole emerges from the sternpost so that it is exactly on the centreline of the shaft all the way as in the photos. Take measurements so that you can mount the bearings for the boring bar outside and inside the boat. Remove the string line, mount the bearings and replace the string line through the bearings and tighten it again. Adjust the bearings so that the string line runs exactly through their centres. Fix the bearings solidly in place. Remove the string line and insert the boring bar and attach the cutter so that it barely protrudes above the surface of

Bearings for the boring bar are set up on the outside and the inside of the boat.

the boring bar. You will need a fairly powerful drill to drive it. Spin it at high speed but push it only slowly through the hole. To ensure the final hole is straight you must only take off a very little cut from the walls of the pilot hole at a time. If you force a deep cut the bar may bend away from the harder (closer) side of the pilot hole and the hole will take a curve. Keep increasing the height of the cutter until you have reached the final diameter. You want a slide-in but not a rattling fit for the shaft tube, so

this means you should stop just before you think the hole is big enough and try to fit the tube. Unfortunately you have to remove one of the bearings to do this and replace it again for the next cut, so it pays to have the bearing easy to remove and replace exactly in the same spot.

For really long shaft holes such as in the skeg of a motor launch it is possible these days to make up the skeg in two lateral halves in which half the pilot hole is routed out on either side. The block to which the stern gland attaches inside the boat can also be done this way. You still have to drill through the hog or keel batten, and then run a very long boring bar through the whole setup. The two halves are epoxied together, and I would probably bury a couple of fastenings in there too. Refer to **Fig. 23**. Most small launches were not fitted with shaft tubes so the inner fairing block must be well bedded down.

Similar techniques are used if your boat has an inboard rudder for the hole through the hog but this usually happens after the deck framing is on.

Now you can get back into planking.

The Upper Planks

Every plank that is spiled should have the spiling batten lie as naturally as it can on the boat and on the plank stock, without any edge set. This is vital where the planks are wide. But once you get down to the narrower planks at the turn of the bilge there is usually considerable curve upward in the middle   of these planks (this is counter-intuitive because when viewed from a distance out to the side of the boat they appear to curve down in the middle and up at the ends). This means that some would have to be cut from very wide planks which you may not have. But once your planks are down to 5" (125mm) or so amidships, and narrower at the ends, they will be able to be bent a bit on edge and so be cut from narrower stock. Lay your spiling batten on the boat and bend it to fit where the plank will lay rather than let the batten lie naturally, that is, edge-set the batten ends down. As long as too much force was not needed, this should work. Lay the spiling batten naturally on the plank stock, mark and cut it out, and it should bend where you want it to go, especially if steamed.

Planking proceeded up from the keel and down from the sheer in professional yards. Workboat Jackpot, Brown Bros Balmain 1958. PHOTO BILL BOLLARD.

Plank Seam Bevels

If you are planking continuously from the keel up to the sheer you should continue to finish the top of every plank square and bevel the underside of the next plank to match. If you are starting at the sheer to work down to a shutter plank you should reverse this, plane the bottom edge square and bevel the top of the new plank. The principal is the same in both cases, you are bevelling the edge you are trying to match to the previous plank, and you are leaving the other side square. The shutter plank should be at the turn of the bilge, i.e on the "ridge" and there will be a diminishing fit. Do an accurate spile of both sides of the gap and cut your shutter plank and plane to those lines conservatively. You will have to get creative to hold the plank in position while trial fitting it (shores from walls, floors and benches and cleats screwed to stem, stern and other planks). Mark the tight spots and whittle the plank down conservatively. A bit of judicious pounding is acceptable to force it home for the final fit. On the whole it is a process better avoided which you can do easily if working alone by starting at the garboard and working up.

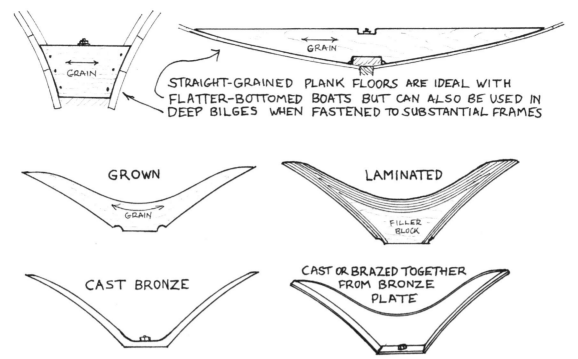

STRAIGHT-GRAINED PLANK FLOORS ARE IDEAL WITH FLATTER-BOTTOMED BOATS BUT CAN ALSO BE USED IN DEEP BILGES WHEN FASTENED TO SUBSTANTIAL FRAMES

GROWN

GRAIN

LAMINATED

FILLER BLOCK

CAST BRONZE

CAST OR BRAZED TOGETHER FROM BRONZE PLATE

Fig. 24 Structural Floors

Structural Floors

You may wait until the planking is finished to start on the internal structure of structural floors, stringers and clamp/beam shelf etc, but I would advise fitting each of these bits earlier in the process, in fact as soon as it becomes possible. For the floor timbers, this is once the planking has reached the point where the longest arms of the floors will reach. The main reason is that it allows a single person to drill and fasten the floors alone.

Boats with sawn frames always have the floors bolted or riveted to the frames or as a continuation of the frame itself. The European and American tradition of square bent ribs also has the floors fastened fore and aft to the frames in most cases with the floors worked to fit against the ribs. Aussie flat ribs do not allow this, so structural floors here are generally set between a pair of ribs and fastened only through the keel and planking. The thickness of the floors (their fore and aft dimension) is usually greater than European or American counterparts. Many local boats did not have enough floors and leaking garboards is a common problem for local boatyards to fix. My Ranger has more floors than the original boats in the class did, as most of them have required the fitting of extra floors later in their life.

Fig. 24 illustrates the main varieties of floors possible. If the boat design has very deep bilges or conversely very shallow bilges ("flat floors") the

A curved-grain natural crook being fitted as a floor timber. Note three laminated floors forward of this one.

Mark and cut the top of the floor timber only after the final dry fit. Note the template at the top of shot.

floors can be cut from wide and thick straight-grained planks. Prepare the areas where the floors will land, smoothing out any plank edge misalignments. Make a plywood or thick cardboard template for each floor, except for very flat floors which can be scribed directly onto the stock. It is easiest to build up the template from smaller pieces. This allows you to scribe each side and fit them individually before joining them with a piece across the bottom. To mark where they fit pencil the line of the biggest side of the floor which will be the aft face on forward floors, and the forward face on the aft floors (hint: a laser level that can project a vertical line is great for this). Hold the completed templates in place dead vertical or square with the keel if that's what the designer called for, vertical is by far the most common. With a bevel gauge measure the angle of the under bevel you will need at a number of points. Either write down the angle from a bevel board or draw each angle on the straight edge of a board annotated so you can locate it to use it in the right spot. Some angles may be the same but they will generally change a few degrees over the length of the arm of a floor. Be aware that in the after part of the ship where you need to template the forward face of the floor, the keel side will become a standing bevel, the opposite way from the bevels on each arm, so remember to allow for this when marking out from the template.

Use the templates to select your stock from either straight-grained stock or from grown crooks or knees. Pencil around the template, then cut close to the line. If you have a bandsaw that will cut to an angle this is best (if you don't have one, go and buy one!). If the bevel angle on the arms changes, cut to the largest angle you have marked, i.e a square cut is 90 degrees, a slight angled bevel might be 87 degrees and if any part is a sharper angle than that with more bevel, cut the least bevel and plane the greater bevel. Leave plenty of extra wood on the upper surface of the floor, this is not trimmed off until the floor fits perfectly.

Offer it up to the boat for a trial fit. It should be close enough for you to scribe a line with a set of compasses on both faces. Make sure the pencil is dead vertical over the point at all times, not square with the planking. Plane to this line and try again. By this stage the blue chalk method comes into play. Rub the hull with blue chalk, place the floor in position and wiggle it a bit. The blue chalk will mark where it is touching. Plane off those high

A bit of caulking

Before the floors are bedded down you need to prime the hull where you probably removed a bit of paint while smoothing out the plank edges where the floor will land. It is best to roll a strand or two of cotton into all of the seams to prevent the priming paint dribbling into the seams and through to the outside of the boat. Dribbles of paint in the seams will hinder caulking properly and the important evenness of the seam.

Rolling a couple of strands of cotton into the seams before priming inside. The roller here is a blunt pizza cutter.

spots and try again. Repeat until the blue chalk is found fairly evenly over the whole of the mating surfaces. Then, and only then trim the upper part of the floors to the finished shape. Drill for the fastenings with the floor clamped or temporarily held firmly in place. These are usually one central bolt through the keel and at least three long copper nails, or bolts on bigger craft through each arm, each one located preferably in the middle of a plank, or at least not close to the edges. Prime the mating surfaces and bed the floor in on bedding compound and fasten off. Floors that will be under the mast step if there is one are fastened to the keel with temporary bolts which can be just hardware store threaded rod.

Laminated Floors

There are two ways of tackling this. You can simply make up your template and laminate a floor together on the bench to make one solid block which you then fit as described above for one-piece floors. Or you can build them up on the boat. In either case the laminates can be made up of thin enough pieces to take the curves cold, or thicker pieces which are steam bent to the hull or a jig, then dried before gluing. On the Ranger project as pictured, I chose to build them up on the boat from steam-bent laminates.

Stringers

The purpose of stringers is to support the flatter areas of the hull. The European and American tradition is to have just one stringer more or less central to the flat area of the bilge aft and through the relatively flat lower topsides forward. They are fitted on top of the ribs and fastened right through the planking, so in engineering terms they are like an I-beam, two load-bearing fore and aft members (planking and stringer) separated by the ribs but fastened together so that the combined strength of the "beam" is much greater than its individual components. Carvel-planked ships generally had almost a full set of planks of various thicknesses on the inside of the frames known as ceiling which increased the hull strength in the same way as stringers do (in fact analogous to foam-cored fibreglass in modern boats.....two load-bearing skins separated to greatly increase the combined strength).

Boats built around Sydney and some other places in Australia generally had at least two sets of stringers. The upper one often came to be placed along the "ridge" line of the turn of the bilge, and I'm not sure why. The turn of the bilge area is a compound curve and has massive strength because of this...the flat areas of the bilge are likely to flex or "oil-can" if unsupported, the compound curve at the turn of the bilge is not. It's possible that the stringers were placed there due to the common building method mentioned earlier of setting a number of stringers and temporary battens around relatively few moulds and bending the ribs around the outside of these. The hardwood stringers would be the best to take the stronger pressures at the turn of the bilge so it

was tempting to place them there. Unfortunately this has resulted in the large majority of boats done this way having many, sometimes all of their ribs crack through exactly behind the stringers. So if you have two stringers they both should be on the flatter areas. But wherever they are to be located, it is best to steam bend them in before the planking quite reaches where they will live so they can easily be clamped to the ribs, and finally fastened in as soon as the planks outside them are fitted so that they can still be reached by clamps as well as being fastened through the lot.

Ranger 24 with stringers landing on all floors, not often done traditionally.

A locked stepped scarf on a stringer was traditionally just fastened, but these days can be glued as well.

191

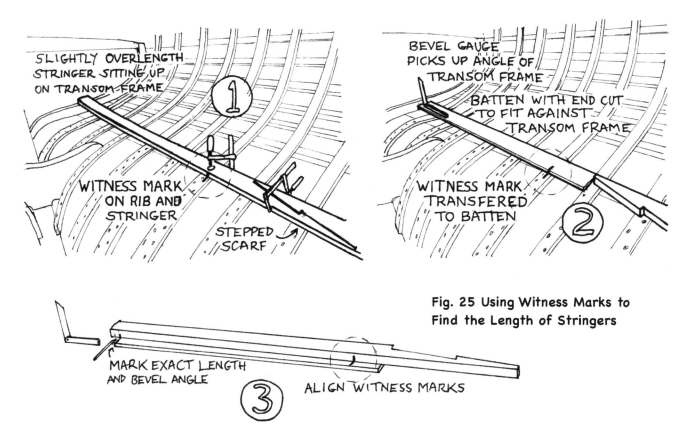

1 - SLIGHTLY OVERLENGTH STRINGER SITTING UP ON TRANSOM FRAME. WITNESS MARK ON RIB AND STRINGER. STEPPED SCARF

2 - BEVEL GAUGE PICKS UP ANGLE OF TRANSOM FRAME. BATTEN WITH END CUT TO FIT AGAINST TRANSOM FRAME. WITNESS MARK TRANSFERED TO BATTEN

3 - MARK EXACT LENGTH AND BEVEL ANGLE. ALIGN WITNESS MARKS

Fig. 25 Using Witness Marks to Find the Length of Stringers

On the Ranger project I made the lower stringers land on the arms of all of the floors as in the photo, a technique usually only done in laminated boats. This gives the area massive strength, probably far more than it needs and is considerably more work, but hey, I'm retired and I enjoy the work. The upper stringers are just below the turn of the bilge where it begins to flatten out.

Victorian Couta boats are lined with ceiling planks rather than individual stringers. This provides plenty of strength and also gives a smooth surface to work on and chuck fish around on. If you are building with the ribs on the outside of the ribbands you will have been able to fit the stringers into the setup at the same time as fitting the ribbands.

Stringers do not always reach the stem and the transom particularly on smaller boats, but where they do the forward ends are sometimes joined to the stem and each other with a breasthook (see below in the clamp/shelf discussion). The aft end is not often fastened to the transom.

Wouldn't it be wonderful if we could all have timber long enough to have full-length stringers! Most of us will have to join them with scarfs. You will almost definitely have to steam the stringers to bend them in. Same as for the planks, I didn't have a huge steam box and a lot of helpers so I steamed

the parts of the stringers inside the hull in a plastic sleeve, pretty close to where they will live and with the areas to be scarfed overlapping. Usually made from hardwood and of thicker dimension than the planking they will need longer steaming times. The same technique applies, clamp them close to their final location at the ends and gradually force the middle down to the ribs as the steam takes effect. The scarf joint is best located aft on the flatter areas, but if you have multiple stringers stagger the scarfs. Before glues a locked step scarf as in the photo was used but this is not strictly necessary, a feather-edge scarf will do, but sometimes these scarfs will be visible and they are an interesting exercise and a chance to show off. Cut the first one on the bench on the forward section and clamp it in position on the boat, making sure it fits well against the stem. Lay the aft section so that it overlaps the cut scarf and trim the aft end to fit against the transom. Mark where you expect to cut the new scarf joint exactly where it overlaps the other.....but you are not going to cut it here, you are going to cut it exactly 1" (25mm) forward of that position so you have a safety margin. Take both pieces to the bench and mark and cut a matching scarf. Take your time and get a good fit. Take both parts back to the boat and clamp them in place, starting with the forward section, then clamping the scarf

Fig. 26 Sheer Clamp and Beam Shelf

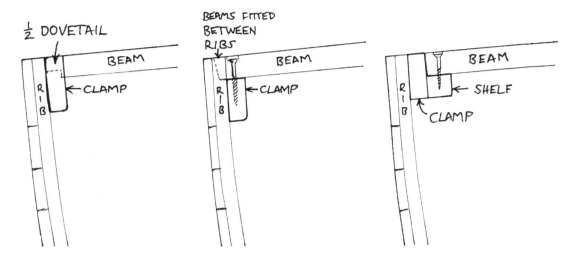

together and clamping the aft section down to the ribs from forward, with the aft end sitting higher on the transom or sticking out through the transom frame if that's what you have. Keep adding clamps as you go aft until you can't get the stringer to sit down on the ribs. Mark the last rib that the stringer touches and the stringer as well with witness marks as in **Fig. 25**. Unclamp and put aside that part of the stringer, and get a batten about as wide as the stringer but thinner, fitting its aft end exactly to the transom, clamp it where the stringer will go and mark your witness mark onto the batten. Get a bevel gauge and note the angle that the end of the stringer needs to be flush on the transom. Back to the bench, and you can line up the witness marks on stringer and batten, and the aft end of the batten is where you need to mark for cutting the transom end of the stringer. This line will represent the underside of the stringer. Remember the bevel angle and mark and cut. For your first few, I suggest you still leave a little bit of extra wood on, and worry it down through a series of trial fits. Before joining the pieces again on the boat, plane some taper. Stringers are usually tapered for the last 20-25% of length at both ends, always on width and usually on thickness as well.

The back and ends of the stringers should be primed before final fitting and fastening. The inner face generally has a chamfer along both edges. Leave the area near the scarfs to be done after the scarf joint is completely fitted into the boat. Traditionally scarfs were just fastened, these days there is no reason why you wouldn't glue it as well, naturally before fastening off the stringer so you can have plastic sheeting to prevent the scarf from

being glued to the ribs. The fastenings are large diameter copper nails with roves, staggered or "reeled" along the stringer, right through the planking, rib and stringer.

Beam Shelves and Clamps

In some open launches and day sailers there may be a higher stringer found on most small traditional boats called a riser on which the thwarts and other seating rests. These rarely go all the way to the stem and stern, usually terminating a frame bay or two beyond the seating. Other than than that the only other longitudinal item is the beam shelf and/or clamp set at a height to have the top of the deck beams flush with the top of the planking. Several different possibilities are shown in **Fig. 26.** Clamp and shelf arrangements become more common the bigger the boat. Dovetailed deck beams are are strong feature but having the deck beam sit on top of the shelf does allow air movement an area where rot sometimes starts. Fitting shelves and clamps uses the same techniques as for stringers. Often they are softwood and are a bit easier to work for scarfs and for bending them in. Make sure they are set high enough to allow for the deck camber.

They are joined at the stem by a breasthook fastened to both longitudinal sand to the stem. The breasthook can be a natural crook or laminated, or sometimes just a sold block of wood.

You'll be anxious to start fitting deck beams, but wait a minute, there are a few more items to go into the hull and it is easier to work there before the beams go in. These are the engine beds and the mast step if the boat will have a mast.

Engine Beds

Whether it's a motor boat or an auxiliary-powered yacht, the engine needs to sit on a solid foundation. These are almost always solid fore and aft timbers notched over at least two and sometimes more structural floors. Some variations are shown in **Fig. 27.** You need to know the details and dimensions of the engine you plan to use before building the engine beds as every brand and size of engine is different. You need to know:

A. The distance between centres of the four mounting points from each other both fore and aft and athwartships.

B. The height of the plane of the bottom of the engine's mounting feet relative to the centreline of the shaft. There will usually be a bit of play designed into this measurement, pick the middle of the range.

C. The clearance you need under the sump.

Of course you should have checked all these things as well as the height and width of the engine to ensure it will fit in the boat as designed _before_ you bought the engine.

Set up the string line representing the shaft centreline again. The distance B gives you the height of the top of the engine beds. The timber for the engine beds should be wider than the mounts and long enough to land on two or more structural floors. They should be notched over the floors with approximately half of each notch coming out of the beds and half out of the floor. They must be firmly fixed to the floors, in most cases this means being bolted right through the hull.

Mast Step

A mast and its rigging are like a giant crossbow trying to fire the mast through the bottom of the boat. So the base of the mast needs to be very strongly supported. This is done with a big chunk of hardwood notched over several structural floors as in **Fig. 28.** The notching does not have to be deep, and you should take half out of the floors and half out of the underside of the mast step. A mortise in the top takes the tenon in the heel of the mast. The mortise is usually made longer so that the rake of the mast can be adjusted, then locked off with chocks. The floors are fastened with permanent centreline bolts right through the mast step, floors and keel, replacing the temporary centreline bolts.

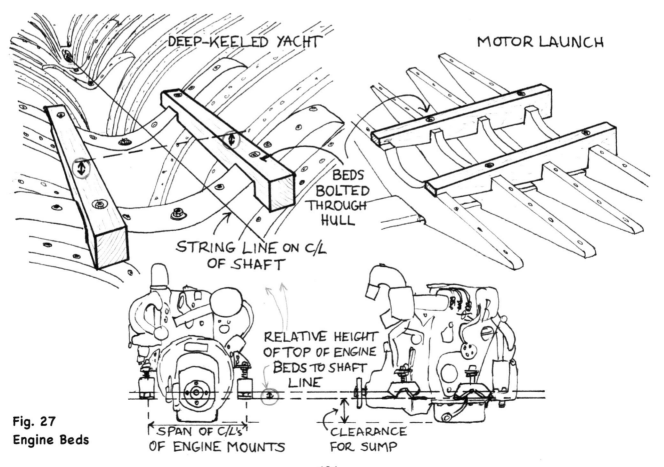

DEEP-KEELED YACHT

MOTOR LAUNCH

BEDS BOLTED THROUGH HULL

STRING LINE ON C/L OF SHAFT

RELATIVE HEIGHT OF TOP OF ENGINE BEDS TO SHAFT LINE

Fig. 27 Engine Beds

SPAN OF C/L's OF ENGINE MOUNTS

CLEARANCE FOR SUMP

Fig. 28 Mast Step

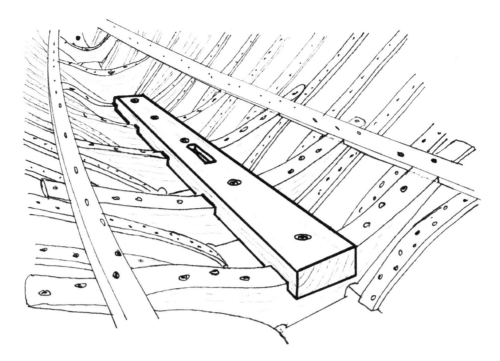

Fairing the Hull

The outside of the hull planking needs to be faired and this could be done now or a bit later. It can be quite an aerobic exercise, so around Sydney you may choose not to do it in the Summer. Assuming that you made sure the edges of each plank were close to the designed planking thickness, I would suggest getting a pencil and hatching along the plank seams. When you are planing off all the high spots this hatched area will serve as a guide to where you should not plane beyond. The upper planking will be easy to plane with regular flat-based planes, I usually use a Number 3 or 4. A wooden plane or transitional plane can be lighter and less tiring. Plane mostly diagonally, keeping moving over the surface and changing the diagonal angle. Do not try to get one small area perfect before moving on, it is far better to take a little off a large area and keep coming back to take a bit more. Flexible timber battens are useful to bend around the hull at various angles to show high and low spots. You can rub chalk on the edge of a flexible batten and rub it on the hull to highlight the high spots in chalk. Go as far as you can with the plane. For hollow areas you will need some rounded-sole planes, easily made from old wooden planes which are generally quite cheap, or build up your own..

Eventually you will have to resort to the aptly-named torture boards to get a fair surface. These and the techniques to use them are described in the Strip Planking Manual. If you want a fair surface on the topsides that will show up well under gloss paint you cannot avoid this step. Random orbital sanders do not fair out the surface as well....there is a big difference between fair and smooth. They are adequate for underwater areas if you planed those areas quite fair. You can do the finish grades of paper with a random orbital sander though before priming.

Caulking and Paying the Hull

As mentioned earlier you may have rolled a couple of strands of cotton into the seams to prevent the inside paint from bleeding through the seams. But at some stage before launching you have to caulk the whole hull. Caulking is simply hammering soft cotton (or oakum) strands into the seams. There are several over-riding rules:

1. Do not caulk one long seam by itself and then move onto the next. Hardening up the caulking exerts considerable sideways pressure on the planks, so it is better to tap the caulking into several adjacent seams at a time. Have a look closely at each of the seams before you start and mark which ones seem tight (no light coming through) and which ones seem open (or have a look inside the boat closely at each seam if you have already rolled some cotton in). After tapping the cotton in to all seams, harden up the tight ones first. Don't harden up the seam closest to an uncaulked area at this point.

195

2. Do not hammer it in too tight. Larry Pardey gives a great guide to the amount of power in each hit by likening it to the the amount of force needed to hammer in different sized nails and I strongly suggest that first-timers get his book, listed in the Appendix.

3. Hammer it in evenly. If a spot where you have not had to hammer it in hard is next to a spot where you have hammered it **very** hard, the soft area is guaranteed to leak. If you come across a spot where you have to hit very hard to get the cotton below the surface, you have too much cotton at that point. Pull it out and start again with less strands. You can either add in or take out strands to get the right amount as you move along the seam, or vary the amount of twist in the cotton: more twist will make the strands thicker. If your seams are fairly even, and they should be on new work you should not have much trouble. Repair work can be a bit more tricky.

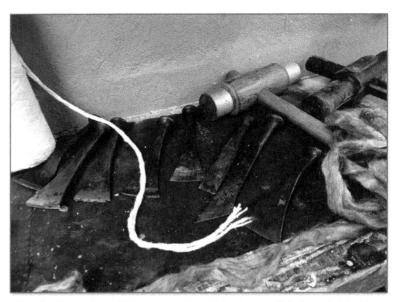

A selection of caulking gear. The full-size mallet top right, the oakum (Brown fibres) and the two double-crease irons second and third from the left are all rarely used on boats under about 35-40 feet. Cotton, thin irons and the newer "yacht" mallet are the rule for smaller boats.

Oakum is used on larger boats with wider seams and especially if the planking is hardwood. I usually run a couple of strands of cotton and then add oakum to the stem and the garboard seam where one side is hardwood and the other is softwood planking. Caulk plank butt seams first in any area that has them with a few strands of cotton with a couple of inches of cotton above and below the butt seam. Separate these into two like a moustache and lay them in separate directions in the plank seam above and below the butt seam. Caulk over these when doing the main horizontal seams. You do a similar thing at the stem. Separate the strands and run half up the stem seam and half down it and caulk the stem seam in one long go over each moustache.

The seam is primed over the caulking before applying the chosen compound for paying the seam.

On new work you may choose a polyurethane compound squeezed out of a tube or sausage. I generally choose to use traditional linseed oil putty. The technique is to knead it to get it at an even consistency, then knife it into the seam with a bit of a rolling action so that the air of the seam is not trapped but is continuously forced out. Rub the knife along the overfilled seam under pressure and the. Scrape off the excess. Rubbing the seam with a finger will often also help to smooth it, but you can also use a rag dipped in turps. This will generally slightly indent the putty. This is not a problem because after it dries (sometimes several weeks) you will be going over all of the seams with a proprietary stopping or simply make up a paste of whiting powder in linseed oil. Once dry this will sand very well before priming. And I'll tell you a secret, once or twice I've used epoxy filler as this final stopping coat (but never in the seams proper).

Some underwater critters like to eat linseed oil putty, so for areas below the waterline add a little anti-fouling paint to the putty. Wear gloves while working with this, anti-fouling paint is designed to be poisonous.

Deck Beams

General deck beam principles have been covered in the section on Strip Planking, but in carvel-planked boats it is better not to glue them in. The simplest system is to rest them on top of the beam shelf as in **Fig. 27** and fasten them to or through the shelf. This also has the advantage of air movement in an otherwise damp area. If you use dovetails they do help lock everything together, and the technique for marking and cutting them out is illustrated in **Fig. 29**. There is a lot of work in these, though you will get quicker as you gain experience, but you may wish to consider one of the simpler, non-dovetail methods in **Fig. 26**. Beams that link to bulkheads and furniture need to be fitted plumb, dead vertical in the fore and aft dimension. Otherwise they can be fitted square to the sheer clamp.

Carlins

Carlins are the fore and aft members that edge any breaks in the deck beams, for cabins, hatches and cockpits. Use temporary beams to support these in place, remembering that the longer ones on cabin and cockpit will probably have some sheer curve in them. Their ends should be dovetailed into the deck beams at both ends. These beams are often wider than the others to allow for this. The dovetails are done as in **Fig. 29** or as in **Fig. 30** so as not to take too much meat out of the deck beams. The short beams between clamps and carlins are also dovetailed into the clamp and carlins.

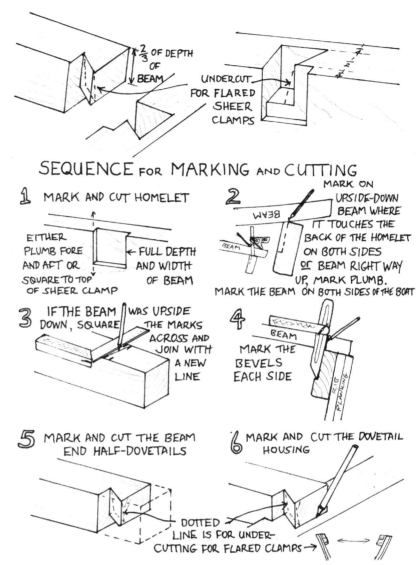

Fig. 29 Beam to Sheer Clamp Half-Dovetails

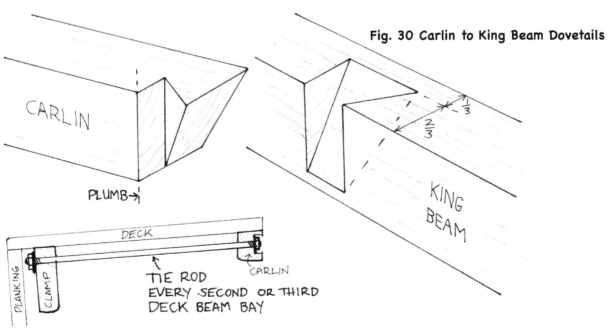

Fig. 30 Carlin to King Beam Dovetails

Most carvel-planked boats are fitted with plywood decks these days and the considerable number of fastenings used into the beams and carlins tends to lock all this together. If you are planking your deck traditionally, either with tongue-and-groove planks laid fore and aft, or a full caulked and payed laid deck you need to fit metal tie rods between the clamp and the carlins to prevent expansion here when the boat works in a seaway, and especially if you did not use dovetails. In fact I suggest they should be fitted even when you have plywood decks, between every second or third deck beam. Make your own tie rods from copper or bronze cut to length with a thread on each end for nuts.

Deck beam on a Clem Masters-built Dragon class yacht shows a simpler full-depth half-dovetail.

Knees

The designer should have drawn where he requires knees. **Fig. 31** shows the main types, hanging knees, lodging knees and breasthooks. These can be cut from solid crooks or laminated, and fastened with at least two and probably three fastenings in each arm (or is it leg seeing it's a knee?). As I said earlier, the secret to fitting knees is to get one side (the straightest side) dead right first, then work on the other side.

Bulkheads

Traditional bulkheads were diagonally planked and fastened through or vertically planked in one layer on a substantial framing structure, and fastened to a frame or rib or an added frame or grounds on the hull sides and a deck beam across the top. Plywood is probably used more often here these days but many builders will still panel at least one side of the plywood with a feature timber. Whichever method you choose make sure the end grain of all timber and plywood is well sealed before installation.

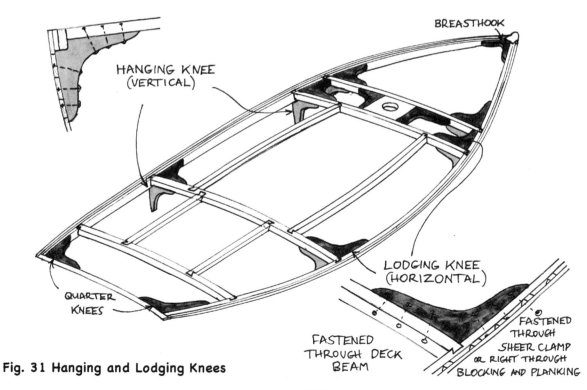

HANGING KNEE (VERTICAL)

BREASTHOOK

QUARTER KNEES

LODGING KNEE (HORIZONTAL)

FASTENED THROUGH DECK BEAM

FASTENED THROUGH SHEER CLAMP OR RIGHT THROUGH BLOCKING AND PLANKING

Fig. 31 Hanging and Lodging Knees

Bulkheads and internal furniture parts are much easier to fit before the deck goes on seeing you will have more air and light. I would even suggest doing all the painting and varnishing on the interior before the deck goes on. I would also suggest planning and installing all of your systems, electrics, plumbing and fuel before finalising the internal furniture and well before the deck goes on. There is such a variety of these installations that I cannot go into it here, other than to emphasise <u>prior planning</u>.

The Deck

Fairing the deck beams and carlins and scarfing the plywood has been covered in the Strip Planking Manual. The underside of the deck (and cabin top) on a traditional boat always looks better with the traditional v-joint or moulded edge and there are three ways to do this. The first is of course to lay the deck with traditional fore and aft planks. The second is to lay thin boards with the moulded joint facing into the cabin, and glue and fasten plywood over the top. The third, and this is cheating, you can rout a v-groove pattern into the underside of the deck plywood before fitting it. Whichever method you choose it is always best to paint the underside fully before fitting. If you are going to glue the deck to the beams which I don't like on a traditional boat but really is a matter of personal preference, you should mask off the

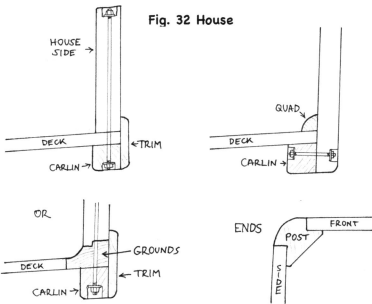

Fig. 32 House

A carvel-planked boat needs traditional hatches. A sliding companionway hatch in Teak sets the boat off. A skylight can be built as a one-piece hatch, rather than the more traditional butterfly hatches which are beautiful but notorious for leaking.

landing areas for the deck beams while painting. Of course you will paint in with white or pale gloss or semi-gloss paint.

Deck Structures– The House and Cockpits

Some of the alternatives for house construction are illustrated in **Fig. 32.** House (cabin) tops are built with deck beams and carlins at hatches the same as main deck structures, usually of slightly smaller dimensions.

Cockpits are either suspended from the cockpit carlins or resting on beams under the cockpit sole which span the ship and are fastened to ribs or stringers.

Hatch structures are also so varied that I will not go into them other than to suggest that a double coaming is usually a good idea for hindering water access.

This section on Carvel Planking has been designed to get you through the main woodworking parts of constructing the hull and deck, just like the earlier Manuals did for their method of construction. There is a lot more than this to launching a boat. Installing the systems and the detailed joinery of the interior will take a big slice of time, not to mention the rig if there is one. Please check the references in the Appendix on Recommended Books for further reading on the bits I've already covered as well as those on the other aspects I have not covered.

But I hope I've got you off to a good start.

Restoring a Putt-Putt Launch

I have had many enquiries over the years from people who want to restore an old putt-putt launch, and many of them don't even have the boat yet. I have outlined some of the issues and practical points to consider in deciding to restore a putt-putt.

Are you sure you want to do it?

It will not necessarily take huge amounts of money to restore an old launch, certainly not enough to be a strain on anyone in regular employment, but it will definitely take a large amount of time! So the first decision is, do you want to spend most of your spare time for at least months, and possibly a year or more working on a boat?

If you plan to sell the boat at some stage in the future, you might expect to get back the money you spend on materials, but realistically you cannot expect to get any money for the time you put into it.

I have listed some of the common problems you'll find in a restoration project, and suggested a few of the techniques that you might employ to fix the problems in just enough detail for you to make an informed decision as to whether you want to get involved with a particular boat.

What price should you pay?

The price should be dependent on two things: the equipment that comes with it, and the amount of work it will need to restore it. A working engine is worth something, especially if it is a Chapman or a Simplex, parts for which are still available. A non-working engine is not worth very much at all. A trailer is worth something, though considerably less if is not registered, as there may be a lot to spend to get it to pass registration. However, the trailer's most important role will be to take it to where you are going to work on it, and eventually to take it to the water, traditional wooden launches will dry out and open up if left on an exposed trailer and driven long distances on highways in the summer. Consider trailing the boat only if you have a sheltered, cool place in which to store it, you plan to use it regularly, and do not intend to travel very far to launch it.

Be cautious if the boat has been stored where leaf litter or other decaying organic matter has collected, or if rainwater has pooled, or worse, where muddy tide marks show fresh water has pooled and then leaked out!

I can't come up with any dollar figures, it's a bit like saying how long is a piece of string, but the only time you should have to outlay much money for a putt-putt is if it has a working engine and

There were hundreds of hire boats like these up and down the East Coast until the 1980's. This is at Taylor's Boatshed Narooma.

needs only cosmetic work to have it looking good. If there are repairs to be done, the price should drop accordingly, to a point where if the majority of planks need replacing and most ribs are broken and the planking is coming away from the stem and the tuck, they should be paying you to take it away. Most boats will be somewhere in between, and I'll try to show you what to look for.

The Planking

If the boat appears to be in reasonably good condition, but is leaking through the plank seams, this may well be a relatively simple problem to fix. Most launches under say 20 feet (6 metres) will have been built either clinker style or seam-batten carvel. (See **Fig.1**). You can ream out the seams with a bent file sharpened as shown, and apply a low-modulus (easy-stretch) polyurethane sealant such as Sikaflex LM15 (sold in the building game), or a low-modulus polysulphide. A difficult problem is if the bilge is oily and the oil has been leaking through the seam because the modern sealants will not stick to oily timber. If it's clinker, and the planking is otherwise in good condition, you could fit a small piece of quad on a bed of sealant on the plank edge covering the seam, with some very small gauge fastenings; but expect some leaking here at some stage. Pitch referred to as *blackjack* by boatbuilders, and available as knifing grade roofing

Wal and Chris MacAdams are serial restorers of old putt-putts.

tar is a better sealant where oil is present, but it too is incompatible with modern sealants.

It is common to find some, or all of the planks cracked. Some short cracks can simply be reamed out with the bent file a little and have the sealant applied, but you should monitor this over time. Traditionally, short cracks, say under 400mm long could be covered with a tingle, which was a piece of sheet copper talked with copper tacks over the crack on the outside on a bed of blackjack. You could still do this using roofing tar , or even the same sealant as you use in the seams. Don't forget that the modern sealants and the old pitch-based products are incompatible, so you should keep pitch away from any part you may wish to make a more permanent repair on later.

Fig. 1 Sealing Seams

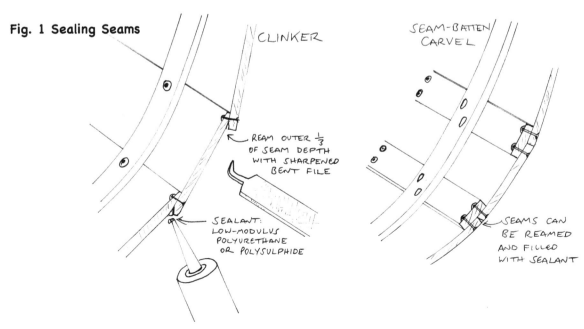

CLINKER

SEAM-BATTEN CARVEL

REAM OUTER ⅓ OF SEAM DEPTH WITH SHARPENED BENT FILE

SEALANT: LOW-MODULUS POLYURETHANE OR POLYSULPHIDE

SEAMS CAN BE REAMED AND FILLED WITH SEALANT

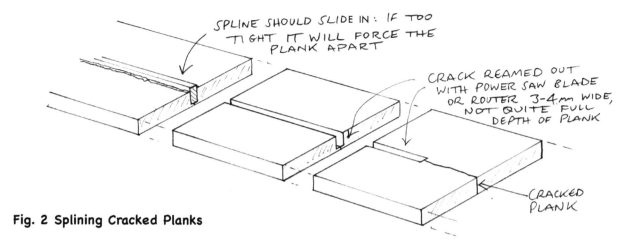

Fig. 2 Splining Cracked Planks

If a plank is split along the nail line over more than 4 or 5 nails, which is common, it should be replaced. If a crack is not on the nail line, it should be splined, which means widening the crack with a thin power saw blade or router, and epoxy gluing in a spline of the same or similar species of timber (see **Fig. 2**).

Another common problem is that the plank ends at stem and stern may be coming away from the stem and tuck, or may be split at the hood-end nails enough to suggest they would come away easily if tested. New nails or screws may work, but only if there is enough wood left to fasten through. Generally they will need to have new end sections scarfed in, as in **Fig. 3**. You may be able to get away with adding an additional apron behind the stem, or fashion pieces inside the tuck as extra fastening wood as in **Fig. 4**.

Scarfing can also be used when part of a plank must be replaced but another part is fine. Butts are another possibility, as in **Fig. 5**, but butts in adjacent planks should be at least three frame bays apart, and butts in planks in the same frame bay should have at least two continuous planks passing between them.

There gets to be a point at which it is easier to replace a whole plank than to do a series of scarfs, splines and butts.

Replacing Fastenings

Roved nails are quite quick and easy to remove by grinding the peened area with a 100mm grinder, being careful not to overheat it so much that the wood catches fire! In seconds the square section of the nail will be able to be seen if you look closely, and the rove may even fall off. The nail can be punched out with a fine nail punch, at least enough to get a claw hammer under the head. Back up with a dolly on the outside of the hull when punching out the nail.

Boat repairers used to use a seam knife to cut through fastenings, which was a sharp blade with a cranked handle resembling a narrow trowel, but even if you find one, it has its limitations, chiefly that in some softer woods (and most planking timbers are soft), a reasonably sound nail will bend sideways and tear into the wood before being cut through. This is a serious problem if one plank of the two being separated is to stay on the boat.

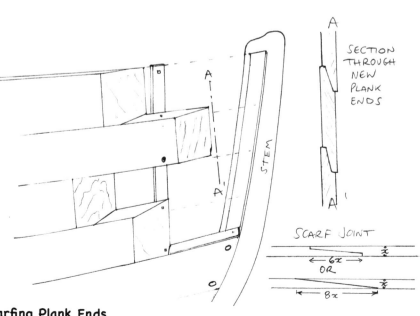

Fig. 3 Scarfing Plank Ends

Fig.4 Plank End Support

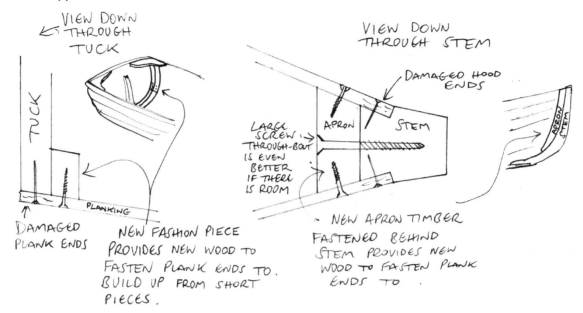

A miniature hole saw with teeth filed on the end of a small metal tube, using it in a drill to cut a circle around the head of the fastening is a good means of freeing planks from nails or stubborn screws in the hood ends at stem and stern. Planks to be scarfed can be cut through with a series of holes and finished with a keyhole saw or hacksaw blade. Once all fastenings are out, the plank or part plank should slide out by pushing aft and down (if the boat is right way up). Accumulated paint in seams may make it hard to start moving, and a fine knife or hacksaw blade could help here. If it refuses to budge, and as I mentioned before, it <u>will not</u> budge if the plank has been fitted with a modern sealant, you will need to destroy the plank to remove it. Naturally it is better not to have to destroy it as it could be used as a template if it is essentially whole. I won't go into spiling and shaping a new plank here as it is covered in the Traditional Clinker section on page 44.

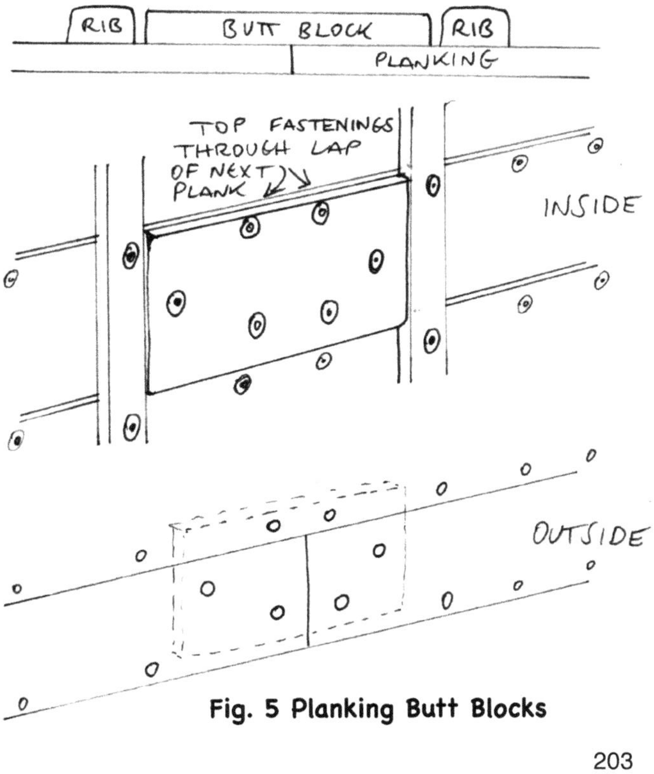

Broken Ribs

An occasional broken rib may not be a problem (at least in a boat!) but if the nearest plank seam is forming a hard spot by forming an outward-facing "V", or if three or more ribs are broken in a row along a plank seam, something will have to be done. The best solution is to replace the ribs with new ones steamed in. This is only possible if the deck is off in the vicinity, but this is often the case anyway. If the deck is in place and sound, "sistering" the rib by adding another section alongside the broken part, either by steam-bending or by glued lamination is the only solution. See **Fig. 6**. There are several ways to laminate ribs, and the position in the boat and other factors such as the presence or absence of longitudinal stringers or other stretchers in the boat will influence the method chosen. Remember if laminated in situ, the lamination is significantly harder to clean up, but sometimes it is the only way.

Fig. 5 Planking Butt Blocks

Fig. 6 Broken Rib Repairs

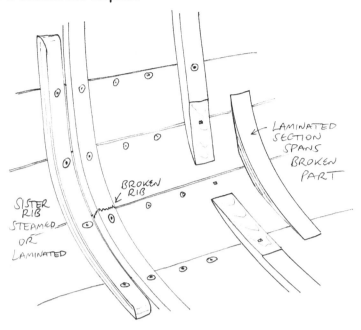

LAMINATED SECTION SPANS BROKEN PART

SISTER RIB STEAMED OR LAMINATED

BROKEN RIB

The Tuck

Cracks in the tuck are common, and if isolated, can be splined as for planks or simply backed up with a plywood patch on the inside. But rot is often the biggest problem, and is found either travelling downward from the deck or around the edge under the plank ends or possibly around the fastenings of the knees. You must face it: rot is like cancer, you have to completely remove affected areas, and a little more was well, otherwise it <u>will</u> return. You can scarf in small sections, but if much rot is present it is easier to replace the whole tuck.

Decks and Cabins

Though I've spent more time here on the hull, decks and cabins generally show more signs of deterioration. Edges and joints, and around fittings are the problem areas on decks, and joints and particularly the area around windows are the problem areas on cabins. As I said in the case of the tuck, all rot must be completely removed. You can scarf in patches, but there gets to a point quite early on where it would actually be less work to renew the whole area that coincide with the size of a sheet of plywood, with the added benefit that by removing more of the deck you expose more of the deck beams and other structure and can find possible problems (like rot) before they spread.

Floors

The garboard, the first plank next to the keel is often one of the problem planks in an older boat where everything has worked a little loose. If the rib fastenings to the keel have deteriorated, the garboard will be taking a lot of the strain of connecting both sides of the boat to the middle. Most boats will benefit by the addition of several floors through the centre of the boat for long term strength as in **Fig. 7**.

There are a number of annual and bi-annual gatherings for wooden launches, like these at Narooma Boats Afloat.

Fig. 7 Floors

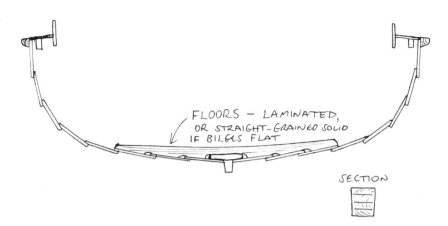

FLOORS — LAMINATED, OR STRAIGHT-GRAINED SOLID IF BILGES FLAT

SECTION

Two Things You Shouldn't Do

Don't be tempted to sheathe a traditional hull with fibreglass. It may be a way of extending the life of a boat for a few more years, but in almost every case I've come across, it has meant a rapid deterioration of the wooden structure of the boat.

Don't be tempted to fill the seams with hard epoxy. A traditional hull needs to allow for slight movement, and if the movement cannot occur in the seams, it will occur in the planks, and I have not yet come across a hull treated this way more than a couple of seasons old that has not split at least one plank on each side, and in most cases, every plank has split. This applies to both clinker and seam-batten carvel hulls.

Enjoy Your Project

Putting along in a boat you restored yourself is a fantastic feeling, but make sure you enjoy the experience of restoring it as well. Look forward to the process: if you are not looking forward to it, it would be better not to start. There are easier ways to get afloat, if that is your only aim. But for those who can enjoy restoration, and can look forward to using the boat as well, it's a double pleasure.

Final Word

If you can't find a suitable boat to restore you can always build a new one. Plans for the Chapman 16' launch will soon be available on the website.

Narooma is still a haven for putt-putts like these restored launches.

Plans of Boats You Can Build

We have gathered a selection of plans from several different designers including rowing boats, sailing boats and motor boats. All have been built multiple times in the School. Some can be built by more than one method. All plans contain full-size paper patterns which eliminate lofting. Please go to our website www.sydneywoodenboatschool.com.au for more information on each boat and to order plans.

Clamping the rub rails on Pee Wee.

Pee-Wee and Petrel

Pee Wee and *Petrel* are the two dinghies that feature in the **Building a Traditional Clinker Dinghy** section. *Pee Wee* designed by Ian Smith is the smaller at 2.1 metres (6'11"), with *Petrel* designed by Nigel Shannon at 2.3 metres (7'6"). Both make ideal yacht tenders, and also serve as a proven great introduction to traditional clinker building. Both can be built with traditional clinker planking, with ply clinker planking and with strip planking.

Huon Pine Petrel planked up.

Pee Wee being towed.

Pippy 2.2 metre (7'3") Stem Dinghy

We were looking for a design for a stem dinghy that was only 2.2m long but could still be relatively stable, as well as attractive. My son Jordan Smith drew up the lines, and we built the first boat in a regional class in Newcastle in 1994. The boat proved to be what we wanted, attractive and stable for its size.

After that we built Pippies by four different methods, strip-planked, ply clinker, traditional clinker and diagonally-planked. Each method can produce a fine vessel. The three modern construction methods weigh in at about 25kg, the traditional Huon Pine at about 30kg, but would be lighter in Cedar. The plans show construction details for each method (other than diagonally planked).

Designer Jordan Smith rows the first Strip-planked Pippy.

Pippy is built upside down in all methods, but the traditional clinker planked boat can also be built right way up.

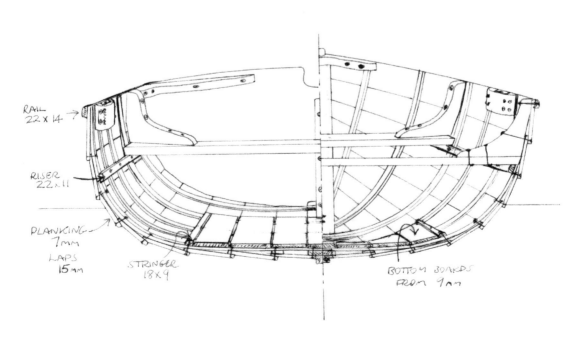

RAIL 22 X 14

RISER 22 X 11

PLANKING 7mm

LAPS 15mm

STRINGER 18 X 9

BOTTOM BOARDS FROM 7mm

207

The Fisher Skiff
13'9" (4.2m) of Rowing Pleasure

Bill Fisher of Drummoyne and then Putney, from the famous boatbuilding family, built the original of this boat, *Eva Seabird*, in 1947 for his own use, when in his 70's. He built it like the Watermen's skiffs that were common before the turn of the 20th century when he began to learn his trade. Bill Fisher was well known in the 1950's for rowing everywhere around Sydney Harbour and even offshore to catch a snapper for lunch. In fact in the early 1950's he raced another veteran, Tom Hall from Palm Beach to Manly and won. He was by then in his eighties. Unlike most exercise rowing craft, the Fisher Skiff can handle chopped water.

I took the lines off *Eva Seabird* in 1992, and several boats have been built to this design since. At the School we used three different methods as described in this manual to build several Fisher Skiffs. They have been constructed in traditional clinker, ply clinker and strip planking. The Fisher Skiff is an excellent rowing craft for one or two people and so far is the only authentic Sydney Harbour Waterman's Skiff design available.

Eva Seabird, the original Fisher Skiff as she was in 1992.

The Fisher Skiff can be built strip-planked like this one in Surian Red Cedar

The Fisher Skiff is a pleasure to row.

The Whiting Skiff 11' (3.3m)

The step by step manual on how to build the *Whiting Skiff* is reproduced in this volume, but you will need the plans to build it. Designed as a good learning project it also turned out to be a great boat in the water and with only 4 planks a side it can be built relatively quickly. The *Whiting Skiff* can be rowed, sailed or powered with a small outboard.

A Whiting Skiff nears completion at the Rathmines Men's Shed.

Just after coming off the moulds and being turned over, the hull reveals its simple construction.

The author sails the family's Whiting Skiff on Blackwattle Bay.

The Snapper Boat
17' (5.2m)

The Snapper Boat was drawn up for us by David Payne along the lines of the Snapper fishing boats of either side of the turn of the 20th Century. We were looking for a local working boat type that would be suitable as a half-decked family trailer sailer with the option of an inboard engine and the Snapper boat fits the bill admirably. The plans were drawn up for strip-planked construction, but after a number of enquiries David and I worked up a clinker planking lineup and David drew a construction plan for plywood clinker construction. A number of other people admired the design as a motor boat without sailing rig, and a number of these have been built with larger motors than the sailing version. Some of the sailing versions have been built with an outboard under the aft deck working through a well built into the hull.

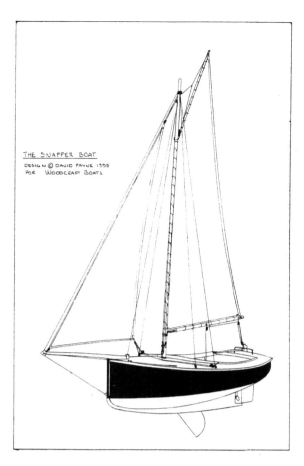

THE SNAPPER BOAT
DESIGN © DAVID PAYNE 1995
FOR WOODCRAFT BOATS

A Snapper boat built with Ply Clinker planking.

The first Snapper Boat Lavinia of Struan.

16'5" (5m) Ski Boat

We asked David Payne to draw up this Aussie-style Clinker ski boat when increasing interest in this type of boat was becoming apparent. With the number of restorable boats decreasing, building from scratch is an option, especially now that the use of plywood clinker construction means that the boats will be stronger than they ever were, and leakproof, both of which are very important seeing these were the two main problems in the original traditionally-built boats. The hull will take up to a 350 V8 Chevy or Ford, and skiers would probably go for these, but a 179 Holden would still drive it along quite nicely as a runabout.

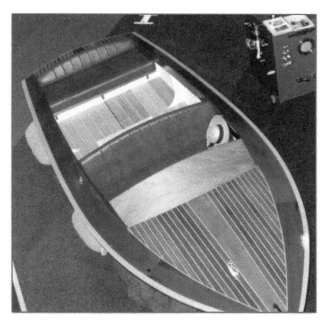

Varnished Cedar and Ash hull and deck really set this boat off. We exhibited the first hull at the Sydney Boat Show in 1995.

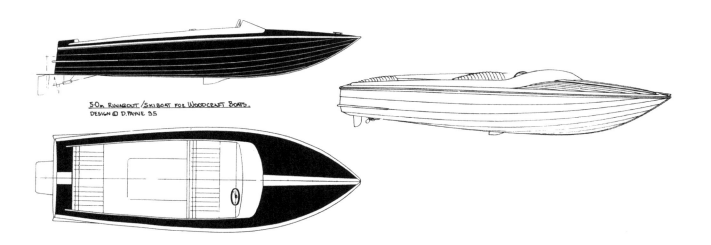

5·0m Runabout/Skiboat for Woodcraft Boats.
Design © D.Payne 95

Ply Clinker construction over ply frames on edge give this hull a strength that the original boats never had.

The Sydney Wooden Boat School

The Sydney Wooden Boat School ran classes from 1989 to the early 2000's. The School was set up at River Quays Marina, Mortlake in July 1989 with the encouragement of Adhesive Technologies the promoters of WEST System Epoxy Resins and the encouragement and financial backing of Marina owner John Wood. I was the Shipwright Manager at the Marina at the time and ran the first class in WEST System Strip Planking, and more applicants than we could handle meant we ran over two nights per week for 20 weeks, and then ran another soon after the first classes had finished. These classes remained the most popular for the whole period in which the School operated. Other classes such as Traditional Clinker Construction, Plywood Clinker Construction, Repair and Restoration were also regularly featured, and other instructors included Rick Wood, Nigel Shannon, Gary Ferres, Michael Staples and Larry Pardey.

In 1992 River Quays Marina changed hands and in 1993 I moved the School up the road to the old Mortlake Post Office and factory building behind. This was the most productive period in the School's history, with weekend, weeknight and Summer School classes in which more than fifty boats were produced over a three and a half year period. With plenty of space we had a number of

The School occupied the old Mortlake Post Office and factory in the mid-1990's.

people building their own boats in the shed as well resulting in another twelve boats from a small nesting dinghy to a 25' Vertue Yacht.

Real Estate costs meant that the School had to relocate to the Blackwattle Studios in Glebe in 1996, and discontinue all but the Summer School classes which ran until 2000 when that complex was demolished. In the meantime I had been involved in daytime and weekend classes for at-risk teenagers in the outer suburban areas of Sydney, and at the inner-city South Sydney Police and Community Youth Club. Also in the late 1990's the Federal Government started the Work-for-the-dole scheme and I became involved with the Salvation Army's Oasis Youth Centre and helped teams of young unemployed folk build two 24' yachts (the Salvo class) for Sailability the organisation that helps disabled folk go sailing, then two lifeboats for the square rigger James Craig as well as other projects for the Sydney Heritage Fleet on the steamship John Oxley, and the restoration of the 45802, the Captain's launch from the HMAS Sydney.

Only a few classes have been run since 2000, mostly for youth groups and at-risk kids, except for a period in 2013-14 when Larry Eastwood set up the Pittwater Wooden Boat School which ran for about 13 months in which I ran clinker dinghy classes. Larry hopes to revive that School, and it appears to be the only hope for boatbuilding classes in Sydney in the future.

After the first few years of running classes I produced the manuals which are combined here. The Sydney Wooden Boat School exists only as an online presence to sell my books and a small selection of plans.

www.sydneywoodenboatschool.com.au

The Summer School ran out of a shed at Blackwattle Studios in the late 1990's

Glossary

Amas: The floats on a trimaran.

Apron: a piece of timber fastened to the inside of the stem so as to provide a bigger landing for the planks ends; or an item of apparel worn by cooks and some woodworkers but rarely by boatbuilders.

Athwartships: in a direction at right angles to the centreline of the ship, as opposed to **fore and aft** which is in line with the centreline of the ship.

Back rabbet: the surface on which the inside of the plank lies on the keel, stem and sternpost.

Ballast: heavy materiel such as iron or lead low in a boat to resist the pressure of wind in the sails trying to heel the boat over.

Batten-seam carvel: planking method where the planks butt up together in section and the seam is backed up on the inside by a batten to which the planks are fastened. It originated in whaleboats.

Beam: the widest point on the deck of a boat; **abeam** or **beam-on** refers to something the position of which is on a line at ninety degrees to the fore and aft centreline of the boat; a **deck beam** is an athwartship structural member supporting the deck.

Bevel: the angle on a surface relative to the other surfaces of the item. A **sliding bevel or bevel gauge** is a tool for finding these angles. A **bevel board** is a board with angles in degrees marked on it accurately.

Breasthook: a bracing knee or gusset joining the two sides of the boat at the sheer to the stem, usually cut from a crook where the grain follows the required curve.

Browing off: planing or chiselling off excess timber to make a good landing for a plank on the stem, keel batten, sternpost or plank lap.

Bruised-seam: when carvel planks are not caulked the seam is bruised with pressure from a hard tool that compresses wood fibres which means they will swell up when they get wet and resist further water penetration.

Built-heel: a boat where the planking in section takes a reverse curve down onto the keel at the stern.

Buttock: in three dimensions a buttock is a plane vertical surface parallel with the centreline of the boat at a set distance from that centreline. Where it intersects with the hull will therefore be a straight line in plan view, a straight line in end elevation (body plan) and a curved line in elevation (profile).

Butt block: A block of wood used to back up and connect two plank ends that don't overlap but butt up (touch each other).

Carlins: part of the deck structure, the fore-and-aft perimeter of a hatch or other deck opening and member housing the inboard end of the side-deck beams.

Carvel planking: planking method where the planks are butted together in section. If the seams are not backed up with a batten (see **batten-seam carvel**) the seam is caulked with cotton or oakum.

Caulked seams: carvel planking has its seams caulked with cotton or oakum and payed (filled flush) with pitch or putty.

Clinker planking: planking method where the planks overlap and are fastened to each other.

Close seam: when carvel planks are fitted tight against each other right across the seam, with no allowance for a caulking bevel.

Coaming: wooden member covering the inboard ends of the deck beams at a deck opening, generally standing proud above the deck to deflect water trying to enter the opening.

Couta boats: half-decked fishing boats from the state of Victoria, Australia. They survive as a large racing fleet.

Crooks: grown timber, that is timber with curved grain to give strength to a knee or gusset, generally cut from trees where breaches or roots join the trunk.

Cross spalls: athwartship timbers supporting the sheer ends of the building moulds, usually set up at exactly the same height.

Deadrise: the angle of deadrise is the angle between the planking in section out from the keel and horizontal. A large angle means the hull has steep deadrise.

Diagonal: in lofting, a diagonal is a line or in three dimension a plane surface from the centreline of the boat which crosses the hull surface approximately at a right angle. When plotted out two-dimensionally is is the best indicator of whether the planking will lie in a fair curve, i.e one without bumps and hollows.

Double-ender: a boat with a pointy stern as well as bow. Boats with a snub or pram bow as well as a square transom, in

Australia the **tuck**, were known as **double-tuckers.**

Edge-set: when a plank is bent on edge, that is on its larger sectional dimension.

Floors: Large knees or crooks fastened to the keel and the first few bottom planks, tying both sides of the boat together as well as spreading the load of the mast step.

Forefoot: the lowest section of a built-up stem, also known as the **gripe.**

Futtocks: individual parts that are fastened together to build up a frame.

Gaff: a spar on the head of a four-sided gaff sail, the lower end of which pivots on the mast.

Gaff cutter: a boat with a gaff-rigged mains'l and more than one headsail.

Garboard: the plank closest to, and fastened to the keel.

Grounds: a structural member fastened into a boat to which other items are fastened, for example centreboard cases will sometimes have grounds between the bottom of the case and the keel, and bulkheads may be attached to grounds that are attached to the hull.

Grown frames: curved boat frames made from naturally curved timber, either one piece or built up from smaller curved sections.

Gunl's: gunwales, the sponsons or rub rails added at the sheer line outside the planking on small craft. Also used to refer generally to that area of the hull.

Half-decker: a boat with a foredeck, usually not as far back as the mast, mostly a side deck, and occasionally a narrow back deck.

Hog: a timber along the centreline that planking on both sides of the boat fixes to, and which joins the stem to the stern structure. Sometimes called the keel batten or even just the keel. On boats with counter sterns, the hog is the central fore and aft member of that part of the boat.

Homelet: a shallow recess in a piece of timber to house another piece. Often used as part of the housing of a half-dovetailed deck beam.

Inwales: a fore and aft timber fastened through the frame heads.

Jerralds: the gains or rebates that let plank ends into each other to end flush at stem and stern.

King beam: the full breadths deck beams that are at both ends of a deck opening. Usually a bit wider than the other deck beams.

Knees: timber crooks, cut with the grain curved, usually from where branches or roots joined the main trunk.

Lapstrake: synonym for **clinker** planking.

Lining-out: the process of working out where the planking will lay on the hull.

Lofting: the process of drawing out the lines plan of the boat full size to get the full and fair shapes of the moulds around which the planking will be bent.

Oakum: fibrous material usually hemp, soaked in Stockholm Tar (Pine Tar) and used to caulk wider seams on carvel-planked boats and especially in Australia when hardwood (generally Eucalypt species) is used for planking, .

Offsets: measurements from a base line, waterline or centreline to a position on the hull for lofting purposes.

Paying the seam: filling over the cotton or oakum caulking with some variety of putty.

Peening: the process of riveting, spreading the end of a metal rod or nail to prevent it from being pulled through a hole you don't want it to be pulled through.

Rabbet: the rebate in the stem, keel and stern knee to house the planking.

Rake: the angle of of a mast from vertical, or of a keel from horizontal. Or as in **rake the seams** which is to scrape paying and caulking out of hull or deck seams.

Reeling: Staggering nail positions alternately.

Ribbands: timber battens fastened around the moulds when setting up to construct a boat around which steam-bent frames or ribs will be bent, either inside the ribbands or outside.

Riser: a fore and aft timber fastened through the ribs and planking at the correct height to support the thwarts.

Rocker: curve in the keel or the bottom of the boat when viewed in profile, also referred to as **spring.**

Sawn frames: curved frames built up from pieces (futtocks) cut from straight-grained stock, usually doubled with joints staggered.

Saxboard or Sackboard: a light timber on the inside upper edge of the **sheer plank** made to the same thickness as the seam battens, acting as a continuous packer under the rib heads.

Scarfing: joining two pieces of timber with matching angled cuts called **scarfs.**

Scribing: drawing a line exactly parallel to an edge, generally using a set of compasses or a block of wood of the correct size.

Sheer plank: the uppermost plank.

Sheerline: the top of the outermost edge of the deck as seen from the side.

Sistering: adding extra frames or sections of frames (**sisters**) next to broken frames.

Sole boards: boards fastened on top of the ribs to protect the planking from boofy feet, also known as **bottom boards** or just **floorboards**.

Spiling: A technique for establishing the exact shape of a plank.

Spring in the keel: curve in the keel when viewed in profile, otherwise known as rocker.

Stealer plank: a plank let into a host plank to mimic a wider plank.

Stemhead: the top of the stem at deck level.

Stopping: very fine putty used to fill the smallest of holes and seams in planking.

Stopwaters: small dowels of softwood rammed into hole through joints in the backbone structure of a boat to stop water migrating along the joint.

Stringers: longitudinal members fastened to the ribs and planking to reinforce flatter areas of the hull.

Swarf: the waste produced by drilling, or sawdust from a saw.

Thwart: a plank fitted across the hull, fastened on top of the **riser.**

Tie rods: bolts from sheer clamp to carlins to prevent the deck spreading in these areas. Also for connecting the deck to the mast step near the mast to prevent the deck lifting at that point.

Tom: (verb, as in to **tom off** or **tom down**) to brace or shore, for example boatbuilding moulds may be tommed out to the walls or tome down from the rafters.

Transitional plane: a hand plane with metal blade adjustment mechanism but a wooden sole.

Tuck: local term for the transom. **Turn of the bilge**: the area of hull planking between the bottom, more horizontal planks in section, and the topsides or upper, more vertical planks. A boat with a sharp turn here is referred to as **hard-bilged**, one with a more gradual transition has **easy bilges.**

Waterline: a plane horizontal surface parallel with the floating waterline of a boat. In **lofting**, a waterline represents the intersection of this plane with the hull surface, so will therefore be a straight line in the body plan (end elevation) and profile, and a curved line in plan view.

Worked frames: frames for ships and small craft that are built up out of smaller sections of generally curved, but sometimes straight-grained timber.

Recommended Books

This list is not exhaustive, there are plenty more books and you will learn something from every one you pick up. These are just my favourites.

Traditional Clinker Construction
- Leather, John, *Clinker Boatbuilding*, Adlard Coles Nautical, London 1973. A classic text heavily slanted towards a study of English types and fascinating, but most people would not be able to learn how to build a boat from this.

- Seymour, Martin *Clinker Boat Building*, Crowood Press, Marlborough 2012. Martin's book is thorough and well-illustrated.

Strip Planking
- There are several books on Strip Planking of small craft, but none I am aware of that cover bigger boats. You're stuck with this volume.

Plywood Clinker Construction
- Oughtred, Iain. *Clinker Plywood Boatbuilding Manual*, Scotland 1998. Iain's Manual is a must-have for those building his boats, and worth it alone for his fabulous drawings. Now published by WoodenBoat.

Carvel Planking
- Birmingham, Richard. *Boat Building Techniques* Illustrated, Adlard Coles Nautical, London 1984. Exactly what it says, Richard's book focuses on techniques and illustrates them mostly with photographs. This book was a definite success as one of my recommendations, a friend bought the book on my advice and has built a Folkboat similar to one illustrated in the book and has made a terrific job of it.

- McIntosh, David C.'Bud' *How to Build a Wooden Boat*, WoodenBoat Publications, Brooklin ME 1987. You need this one if you are building a carvel-planked yacht. Bud writes in an entertaining manner and goes through the process step by step. Sam Manning's drawings are the best in the business.

- Pardey, Larry. *Details of Classic Boat Construction* W.W.Norton & Co New York 1991. Another must-have if you are building a Carvel-planked boat. Larry photographed the whole process and included a myriad of details and professional tips.

- Powell, Luke *Working Sail*, The Dovecote Press, Stanbridge, Dorset 2012. Not a Boatbuilding text as such, but contains lots of fascinating photographs of Luke's heavy pilot cutters under construction.

- Smith, Ian Hugh, *The Open Boat*, Sydney Wooden Boat School 2017.
As well as discussing the origin and evolution of Aussie 18-footers, *The Open Boat* has the only extensive coverage I have seen on batten-seam carvel construction.

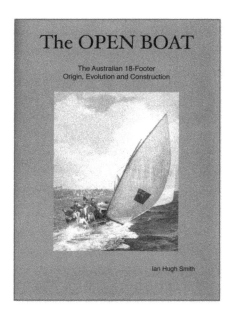

- Steward, Robert M. *Boatbuilding Manual*, International Marine, Camden ME 1970. A thorough textbook which has recently been revised and extended.

Conventional Plywood Construction

- Witt, Glen L. *Boatbuilding With Plywood*, Glen-L Marine Designs, Bellflower CA 1989. Glen covers all aspects of plywood construction in a thorough manner. You will not need another book.

Cold Moulding

- If you can find John Guzzwell's *Modern Wooden Yacht Construction* (it's almost at rare-book status) you'll be well-armed to build a cold-moulded yacht.

- Hub Miller's *The Laminated Wood Boatbuilder*, International Marine, Camden ME 1993 is more readily available and particularly well-illustrated.

Stitch and Tape

- Devlin, Samual Devlin's *Boat Building*, International Marine, Camden ME 1996. Sam's book is the Bible for stitch and tape builders.

History and General

- Frost, Ted *From Tree to Sea*, Terence Dalton Ltd, Lavenham Suffolk, 1985. A fascinating look at how large fishing trawlers were built in England in the early 20th Century written and well-illustrated by a man who was there.

- Svensen, Randi *Wooden Boats, Iron Men The Halvorsen Story*, Halstead Press Sydney 2004. Randi's great history of the Halvorsen boatbuilding family is proudly displayed by every Halvorsen owner, and most of them have read it!

Videos

- Any boatbuilder needs to become a subscriber to Off-Center Harbor at **www.offcenterharbor.com** for access to a huge number of boating and boatbuilding videos, professionally filmed.

- There is a lot of stuff on YouTube. The best is Leo Sampson Goolden's series on his restoration of the Albert Strange designed yacht *Tally Ho*. Leo is only young but has already built up a lot of experience and obviously learned from people who knew what they were doing, and is good at explaining what he does.

- Louis Sauzedde's *Tips from a Shipwright* website and YouTube channel is another must-watch.

- *From Acorn to Arabella* is a YouTube series where a couple of young fellas are building an Atkin Ingrid design traditionally. They had very little experience when they started but they have obviously researched it all and are doing a sound job in a proper manner and filming every step of the process.

- And while you're on YouTube have a look at my *Ian Smith Boats* channel with a growing list of short boatbuilding and sailing videos or see them on the Sydney Wooden Boat School website.

Building Britannia

I dug up the footage of the Britannia replica being built in 2001-02 and her launch day. It's not quite a how-to video but there are lots of tips to go along with The Open Boat book.

Can't stop building boats!

In a forty-plus year career in boatbuilding and boatbuilding education Ian Hugh Smith built upwards of 80 boats and helped hundreds of first-time builders to learn how to build their own. Now retired from commercial work Ian is concentrating on putting his experience down on paper, but still finds time to build a 24' Ranger class gaffer and race his Historical 18-Footer replica *Britannia* on Sydney Harbour. He is the author of *The Open Boat, the Origin Evolution and Construction of the Australian 18-Footer 1850-1950* and is working on a volume on traditional clinker boatbuilding.

CPSIA information can be obtained
at www.ICGtesting.com
Printed in the USA
BVHW020935120620
581244BV00010B/455